INDUSTRIAL ARTS for the GENERAL SHOP

DELMAR W. OLSON

PROFESSOR OF INDUSTRIAL ARTS
KENT STATE UNIVERSITY, OHIO

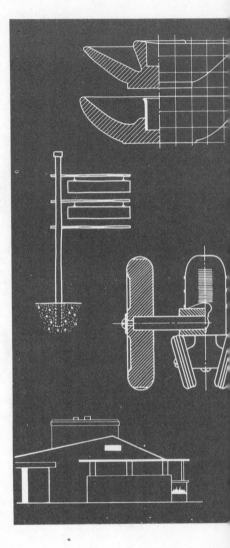

ASSISTED BY THE FOLLOWING INDUSTRIAL ARTS TEACHERS:

Russell J. Adams, Jr.
HUDSON HIGH SCHOOL, HUDSON, OHIO

J. Sam Biedler
LABORATORY SCHOOL, KENT STATE UNIVERSITY, OHIO

Kenneth J. Field
TALLMADGE HIGH SCHOOL, TALLMADGE, OHIO

Duane E. Work
CUYAHOGA FALLS HIGH SCHOOL, CUYAHOGA FALLS, OHIO

Englewood Cliffs, N. J.

INDUSTRIAL ARTS for the GENERAL SHOP

PRENTICE-HALL, INC.

First printing .... June, 1955
Second printing .... March, 1956

PRINTED IN THE UNITED STATES OF AMERICA
45916

DEDICATION

To my own junior high school youngsters, Jonny and Marene, and to every industrial arts teacher who believes as I do that what the chunk of clay and piece of wood do to the child is more important than what the child does to them.

D. W. O.

ACKNOWLEDGMENTS

This is to express my appreciation to my many students and colleagues who in one way or another assisted in the preparation of this book.

Cooperation by the many industries and organizations which furnished illustrations and technical assistance was most gratifying.

Special acknowledgment is due Irene, Jonny, and Marene, who understandingly did without the father in their family for the many months during which this book was being written.

Work of the following students is included among the illustrations. May this inspire them to authorship!

Patricia Adams
Sister M. Augustine,
   O.P.
Gilda Bonvissuto
Anne Browne
Ronald Chambers
John Fabjancic
Richard Farrell
Frederick Felton
Arthur Gorman
Donald Gray
William Heasley
James Higgins

Alice Jones
John Lacsko
Raymond Lisowski
Robert Locke
Emory Lynch
Robert McFerren
Joseph Mullane
Henry Paulin
Eleen Plevny
Richard Raidel
Norman Rodatt
Vivian Saccone
Julius Sirilo
Adrien Smith

Stanley Spring
Allan Sveda
Lloyd Swan
Glen Swindler
Ronald Todd
James Vlach
Frederick Vollman
Gene White
Charles Wink
Edward Yursky
William Zinz
Joseph Zsiga
William Zuschin

TO THE TEACHER

My intent in this book is threefold. First, I wish to open the eyes of students to the breadth of possible activity in industrial arts stemming from an even broader and more diversified American industry. Second, I want to acquaint the students with the basic materials, tools, machines, processes, occupations, and industries upon which the American economy depends, with special attention to the six areas of industrial arts subject matter deemed most important by teachers from coast to coast. And third, I hope to stimulate their desire for learning, so that they will not be limited by the covers of this book.

The book is designed to supplement the work of the teacher, not to replace him. When it seemed best, I avoided setting up fixed procedures for manipulating materials, realizing that there are many ways to solve the same problem. Detailed instructions are given for the activities the student can learn through words and pictures, but the more complex activities are described only in a general way, since such instruction is most effectively handled by the teacher.

As teachers, we have a responsibility to urge students to search for facts. Therefore answers are not provided for all of the questions in this book. The lists entitled "Some Things to Find Out" point to information that boys and girls should be encouraged to acquire.

As teachers, we also are often concerned about whether we are accomplishing the aims of industrial arts. I have tried to keep these functions in mind throughout the book. If the student has the opportunity to take industrial arts in the seventh, eighth, and ninth grades, he should receive considerable *orientation*. If he can work and study in all of the areas covered in this book, he will gain a broad *technical* background. When he finds industrial arts interesting and useful, he will explore the subject further in his spare time as an *avocation*. The experience he gets in group thinking, planning, and problem-solving, and in organizing and carrying on group projects, assists in his *social* growth. The more he understands the workings of American industry, the more appreciation he has for American *culture*. The more he knows about materials and processes used by industry, the better he understands the manufactured products, and the better he can exercise *consumer judgment*. Experience with the materials, processes, products, and occupations of industry helps him to know his own strengths and weaknesses as they affect the selection of an *occupation*. In these ways, industrial arts both directly and indirectly fulfills its purposes; this book was written to promote these functions.

The projects are intended to encourage the student to learn, and to challenge him to work to capacity. Some are presented in full detail and others with none, except as apparent in the illustrations. To keep these projects from becoming "cut and dried," the teacher should invite every student to improve on the design and construction. Thus more individuality will appear in the projects.

DELMAR W. OLSON

TABLE OF CONTENTS

CRAFTSMANSHIP

"Craftsmanship" is a word widely used these days. We often think that it applies only to those who work in such trades as cabinetmaking, tile setting, tool and die making, and the like. As a matter of fact, the word "craftsmanship" has a much broader application. I like the definition, "a craftsman is one skilled in the mechanics of a craft," for this meaning can be applied to writers, speakers, dentists, surgeons, and musicians. It even includes cooks and seamstresses.

To say that a person is a craftsman is to pay him a very high compliment, which he has earned through his own efforts. Such a title is not one that a person can acquire by simply reading a book or watching someone else perform, although reading and observing do help in acquiring the skill necessary to good craftsmanship. Being a craftsman means that a person has high standards of workmanship and an appreciation of quality work. It means, too, that he plans his work carefully and methodically and that, where appropriate, he is aware of the need for good housekeeping and understands and practices safety.

When we think about great American craftsmen, we remember Paul Revere, the coppersmith and silversmith; Benjamin Franklin, the writer and printer; Daniel Webster, the orator— a craftsman in speechmaking; Longfellow, the poet; Thomas Edison, the wizard of electricity; Henry Ford, the automobile mechanic and manufacturing genius.

Whatever your aim in the world of work, be a craftsman!

DEWEY F. BARICH

Man makes machines that make other machines that make the products that he uses in living. This particular machine is a radial drill. (Courtesy: The American Tool Works Co.)

1 INDUSTRIAL ARTS and YOU

Now that you are taking industrial arts it seems that you should know what it is, so that you can get the most good out of it. Industrial arts is a study about industry, its materials, tools, machines, processes, products, and occupations. This study includes work and experience with materials, tools, and machines. In industrial arts you learn by doing, as you plan, design, and construct *projects*. These projects, in industry, are *products*. The purposes of industrial arts for you are:

1. To show you how important industry is in the American way of living.

2. To show you how millions of Americans earn their livings in industry and to help you find and actually try out occupations you would like to follow.

3. To give you opportunities to do some exploring among things industrial—some inventing, experimenting, engineering, designing, and constructing with materials, tools, and machines as is done in industry.

4. To show you how to make and do things well and safely so that you may become a fine craftsman. This may help you to earn money in your spare time.

5. To show you how to fix things so that you may be handier around home.

6. To help you find and develop a good hobby.

7. To help you to better select, use, and judge the products used in day-to-day living.

Why there is an industrial laboratory. The industrial arts laboratory (often called a shop) provides an industrial atmosphere which is the ap-

1

propriate setting for studying about industries. It has many types of industrial tools and machines for you to learn to use.

How you can get the most good from industrial arts. The more you follow these suggestions, the more enjoyable and worth while will be your work in industrial arts:

1. Be always curious and eager to find out new things and to get new experiences.

2. Plan to learn to use every tool and machine in the laboratory.

3. Get acquainted with every available material by using it in some form of construction and manufacturing.

4. Work accurately and safely at all times.

5. Be as inventive and creative as possible.

6. Try to find out what your talents are so that you can develop them.

7. Work cooperatively with others and assume your full share of responsibility for making the laboratory operate smoothly and efficiently.

American Industry, Occupations, and Your Future

When the first pioneers came to this country they saw only forests and wilderness. There were no roads, cities, machines, or industries. In only three and a half centuries we Americans have covered the nation with highways and have planted towns and cities so thickly that they are growing together. We produce approximately six million autos and trucks a year, fly twice as fast as the speed of sound, and have about sixty million people

Fig. 1.1. Looking into the world's largest aircraft hangar at Akron, Ohio. The nose of a blimp can be seen inside. This steel-framed structure is so large that it has its own weather problems. Clouds are formed and rain falls inside. This hangar is another product of American industrial know-how. (*Courtesy: The Goodyear Tire and Rubber Co.*)

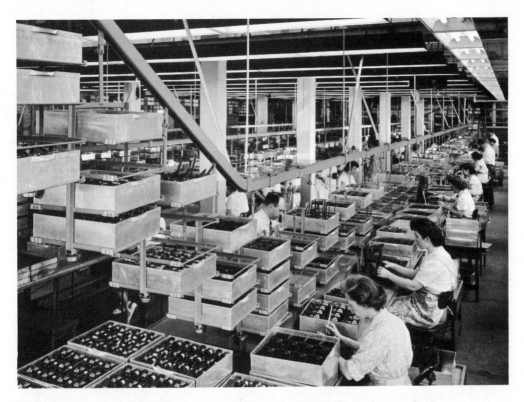

Fig. 1.2. A modern assembly line, where various parts are brought together and assembled into products. Note the conveyor delivering parts for cameras.

employed, most of them in industries producing the goods that all of us use in living. Scientists have sent rockets hundreds of miles into space; industries are pushing rapidly toward "automation" (this word may be so new that it is not in your dictionary), which means the production of goods entirely by automatic machines.

Had you been in school fifty years ago you could not have gone to a store or a dealer and bought an automobile, an airplane, a radio, a television set, fluorescent lights, a miniature camera, a model airplane kit, a motor scooter, pneumatic tires, a bulldozer, comic books, sliced bread, or thousands of other products which today we take for granted.

It is impossible to predict accurately what industrial products we will be using in the year 2000. Experts tell us today that we will be traveling through space among the planets before long. At the middle of this century such ideas sound silly to some people, but when we realize how much technical skill and knowledge has been acquired during the past fifty years, it is apparent that few technical and scientific problems are without solutions. Today peacetime uses for atomic power are actually being developed. A few years ago most Americans were unfamiliar with the word "atom"; today, everyone uses it.

The United States has the greatest industrial development. Indust-

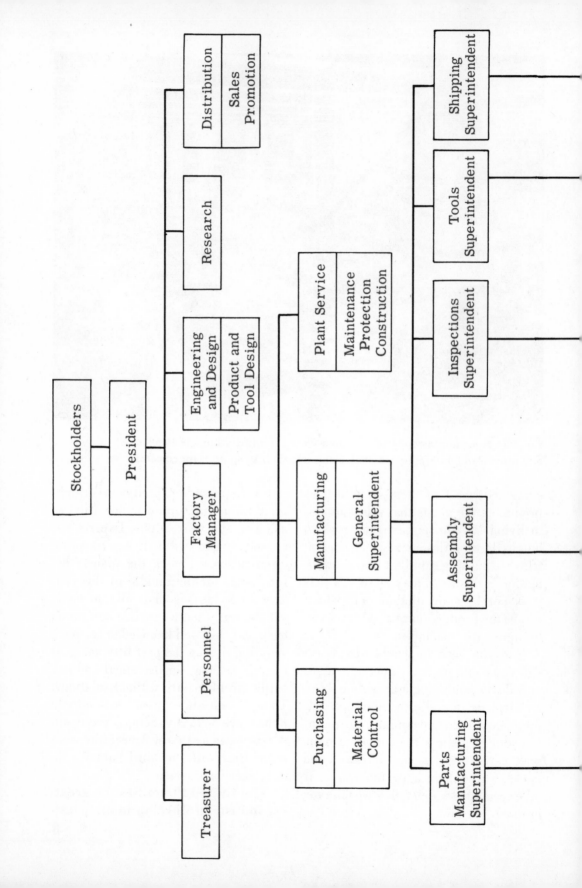

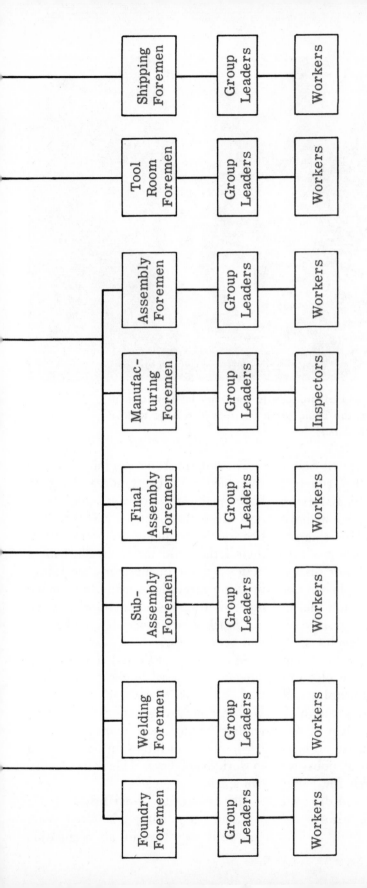

Fig. 1.3. Flow chart showing the personnel organization of a manufacturing industry. The stockholders are the owners of the company. They have invested their money to buy stock. They elect a board of directors, and the directors appoint the president, who is responsible for operating the plant. Small groups of workers are supervised by group leaders. The group leaders are responsible to foremen, who in turn are responsible to their superintendent, and so on up the line. In a large industry there may be fifty or more separate departments, each with a specific type of work. The activities of all these departments, which may include many thousands of employees, must be accurately coordinated so that the products can flow off the production line on schedule.

Fig. 1.4. Inspection and testing of products is important in American industry. Here outboard motors are being given test runs in a huge tank of water. (Courtesy: Evinrude Motors.)

trial development in the United States is greater than in any other country. We enjoy the highest standard of living in the world. The reason is that we have the greatest industrial development. Our industries produce more products of greater assortment at lower prices, which means that more people can use and enjoy them. Did you know that in the United States we have nearly 80 per cent of the world's automobiles, 50 per cent of the radios, and 60 per cent of the telephones? Nowhere else can one live as easily, comfortably, and healthfully. Why is all this possible? The answer lies in the nature of our people. We Americans thrive on freedom—freedom to work at jobs we choose; freedom to search for better ideas; freedom to invent and discover new things. The drive is always for something better.

The story of American industrial development is the constant searching for better materials, processes, and products. In some countries it is the practice for the people to do things just as their fathers did them. In the United States we put in museums the things that our forefathers made, and make our own to suit us now; and when these are finished, we proceed to make new and better ones.

American growth and development depend on our willingness and ambition to search always for the better. We use our imaginations; we enjoy getting better ideas than have been used. We want things and are willing to work to get them. This is the American spirit.

Occupational possibilities. If you had been living a hundred years ago your selection of an occupation would have been much easier. If your father were a carpenter or potter, for example, you would probably have become the same. There were fewer kinds of occupations in those days, too. The jobs involved in the manufacture of autos and airplanes, for example, didn't even exist. Today you have more than 50,000 different occupations from which to choose. Imagine how difficult it would be to pick the necktie you liked best from among 50,000 of them.

From day to day and year to year these occupations come and go. New processes and products mean new and different jobs. Can you imagine the nature of the occupations required for the construction and operation of space stations? When an occupation is no longer needed the worker must learn a new one. You will probably change your occupation several times during your lifetime.

Choosing an occupation. We don't believe nowadays that a person is born into a job, that his occupation is determined at or by his birth. We don't believe, either, that he must necessarily follow in his father's footsteps. We know that a person can succeed in several different occupations. In the days of the horse and buggy a jack-of-all-trades was a "ne'er-do-well." Respectable people looked down on him because he did not stick to one job. Today we realize that if you can do one thing well you can do others just as well, providing that you are willing to learn.

The best way to decide if the new suit or dress fits you and looks well on you is to try it on. The best way to choose an occupation is to try it out. There are some "bugs" in this method, however. You might want to try out a dozen, but that would take years. You might find that a particular occupation didn't exist in your community, and thus the tryout would be impossible.

Modern industrial arts programs are designed to provide experiences in a wide variety of occupations common to American industry. You should get as many of these experiences as possible. They are try-out experiences to enable you to discover special interests and talents which can guide you in making occupational choices. After you have had experiences with a variety of materials, tools, processes, machines, and occupations you can select one or more of them to specialize in for your senior high school industrial arts courses. By means of movies, field trips through industries, and watching people at various jobs you can get information to help you choose your occupation.

If your industrial arts program doesn't offer experience in an occupation that you think you might prefer, perhaps you could arrange to get some try-out experience in it after school, on Saturdays, and during vacations. For example, if you wanted to be a dentist, you might try to get a spare-time job helping a dentist in some way so that you might get as near to his work as possible. You might run errands or keep his office clean.

Another good way to sample an occupation is to try it out through a hobby. Many famous people got their starts in hobbies at home. If you do not have a hobby, try to find one in industrial arts activities.

Does the government owe you a living? Some people have the idea that the government should provide them with jobs. This is done in countries controlled by dictators. If you lived in one of those countries you wouldn't need to worry about choosing an occupation; the government would do it for you. The freedom of occupational choice is another of the freedoms we possess in America. In this country we believe that each of us owes it to himself and to his community to work at occupations in which he can most benefit himself and society. A person who is a "drifter" doesn't help much to make our country greater. Choose an occupation of which you can be proud and in which you can excel.

Success and failure. When you take your field trips through industries, ask some employers what qualities make for success and why some people fail and are discharged. They will probably tell you that the reason for failure is seldom that the people can't do the job. It is usually because they are unwilling to follow directions, or are unable to get along with other workers, or come to work when they please. The person who learns to do his job well, who is willing and enthusiastic about it, and who has the ability to get along well with others, is the happy, successful person.

A business of your own. Think of this possibility, too, for an occupation. If you are the type of individual who would rather work for yourself than for someone else, try to get ex-perience in such work while you are in school. With your own home workshop you might repair furniture and appliances for people. You might manufacture an article which you could sell to friends. You might start a lawn-mowing company for the summer months, or a neighborhood newspaper. All you need is an idea and plenty of "push." Of course, if you discourage easily you won't enjoy being a businessman or an industrialist. That kind of work takes plenty of courage and stick-to-it-iveness.

Your Home Workshop

Have you been wishing for a workshop of your own where you could make all sorts of things in your spare time? Wishing strongly for something is the first step toward getting it. Let's look at some of the problems that may be standing in your way and see what answer we can find.

What can you do in a home workshop? Each of the chapters in this book is a source of many activities which you might like to carry on at home. Make a list of all the things you can think of which you would like to be able to do in a home workshop. You may want a shop in which you can work with one material such as wood, metal, or clay, or perhaps you would like to be able to work with several materials.

How much room will a workshop require? If you can have all the space you want for a shop you are very fortunate; most of us can't. Whether you can have the whole basement, or just a tiny closet, or a corner in your bedroom, or no room at all, there is a workshop for you. If you have a basement shop or one in the garage, the things you make may be quite different from those you would make in a closet or in your room. You know how mother is about your making messes.

Suppose you have no space at all in which to set up a shop. You have two choices: (1) to do those things that require no extra room, such as drawing, designing, collecting, and making scrapbooks, or (2) to use portable equipment that can be stored out of the way when not in use. With such equipment you can build model airplanes, autos, and boats, make pottery, or do printing, photography, and the like. You can work in your bedroom, the kitchen, or perhaps the bathroom.

What will it cost? Some people have spent thousands of dollars equipping home workshops; others have made their own equipment as part of the fun. You can spend as little or as much as you wish.

There are many items of equipment that you can build in industrial arts, for example, a model airplane construction kit; a photographic printer, enlarger, and safelight; a work bench and table; screwdrivers, hammers, and other small tools; a screen printing frame; a wood lathe, jig saw, and grinder; a potter's wheel, modeling tools, and bats. Some of these are illustrated in this book. Look through back issues of such magazines as *Popular Mechanics, Popular Science, Mechanics Illustrated, School Shop,* and *Industrial Arts and Vocational Education* for articles on building your own equipment.

If your father or mother or even the whole family were interested in the same hobby, perhaps you could furnish the workshop together. The cost could be shared and you could have wonderful times together. You could probably teach the others some of the things you were learning in industrial arts.

You may be able to sell things that you make in a workshop. Many people do. The products should be well designed and constructed so that the customers will be happy with them. One large company, which makes model airplane kits, grew from a home workshop. Two boys designed and built some hand-launched gliders of balsa for themselves, and when their friends saw them they, too, wanted some. The two boys made gliders for the youngsters in the neighborhood, and as the demand increased they gradually expanded their production, until now it requires a large plant.

When you select a hobby around which to build a workshop, plan on working at it for all the good you can get out of it. Only then will you have the most fun and learn the most. Try to become expert in the activity. People then will come to you for your opinion and advice. Perhaps you can then share your experiences with them and help them to get started in a home workshop project. If there isn't a club in your neighborhood centered around the activity in which you are interested, you may be able to organize one. Ask your teacher for some suggestions on starting it. Once you get a workshop started, you won't have any problem of what to do in your spare time. It will be occupied by your hobby.

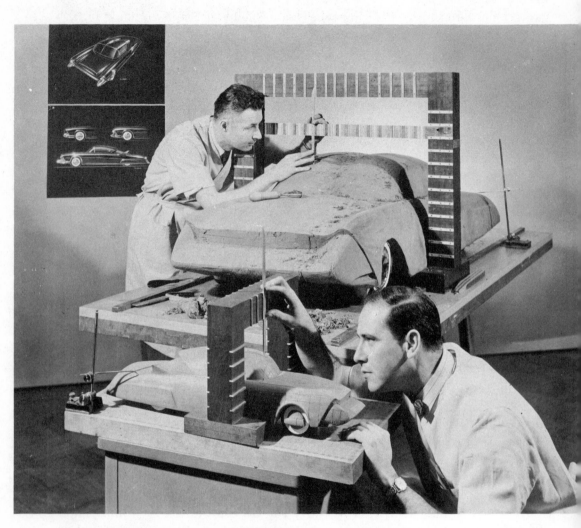

Fig. 2.1. Engineers and designers work together on tomorrow's automobiles. (*Courtesy: Ford Motor Co.*)

INDUSTRIAL
DRAWING
2 and DESIGN

Drawing is the best means we have for expressing many of our ideas. Words usually fail to describe technical things adequately because words so often have more than one meaning. (Look up the word *draw* in the dictionary, for example.) Not so with drawings. Each line, curve, and symbol usually has but one meaning. Consequently a Swedish engineer, for instance, although he may not be able to read the American language, can read the drawings done by American engineers. The reverse is also true.

A drawing can describe the shape and size of an object and the materials of which it is made, as well as how they are joined together. It may tell the kind of finish and the color. When it does all of this it is called a *working drawing*. An *assembly drawing* shows how several parts are fitted together.

You will find that it is very handy, both at home and at school, to be able to read and make drawings. When you can do this, then you can read and write the language of industry.

How Drawings are Used in an Industry

From the completed drawings prints are made for each department concerned in the plant. (See page 12.) The originals and their tracings are not used in the factory but are kept on file.

Idea sketches. The first drawings are idea sketches by the designers, who "dream up" products. They consider function, styling, and the like. (See pages 34-35.)

Design drawings. When the designers have agreed on the general idea

Fig. 2.2 Jonny checks a toy locomotive with the engineer's drawing of it. Details on this drawing are twice the actual size. (*Courtesy: The Lionel Corporation.*)

for the product, they make pictorial drawings, often in color, as well as scale models. (See page 35).

Engineering drawings. Design engineers take these drawings and solve the technical problems in the proposed product. They prepare specifications that call for particular kinds of materials, fastenings, and finishes and that tell, for example, whether parts are to be cast, pressed, or welded. They make working drawings which prepare the product for manufacture.

Tool engineering drawings. From these drawings the tool engineer designs any special tools, dies, jigs, and fixtures that will be needed in manufacturing the product.

Production engineering. From the working drawings the production department figures out how much of the various materials—welding rod, bolts, and the like—to order. It plans the production schedule, which shows how many items will be produced in a certain time.

Manufacturing. The pattern shop, foundry, machine shop, welding shop, and the like, use the working drawings to make the setups on their machines and to check the products for accuracy.

Assembly. The prints help the workers in assembly departments to put the parts together.

Inspection. Inspectors check the parts and the finished products for

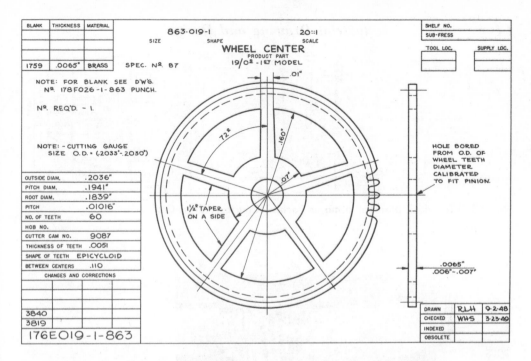

BLANK	THICKNESS	MATERIAL
1759	.0065"	BRASS

SPEC. Nº 87

WHEEL CENTER
PRODUCT PART
19/0² - 1ˢᵀ MODEL

SIZE   SHAPE   SCALE

SHELF NO.		
SUB-PRESS		
TOOL LOC.		SUPPLY LOC.

NOTE: FOR BLANK SEE D'W'G.
Nº 178F026-1-863 PUNCH.

Nº REQ'D. - 1.

NOTE: - CUTTING GAUGE
SIZE O.D. = (.2033"-.2050")

OUTSIDE DIAM.	.2036"
PITCH DIAM.	.1941"
ROOT DIAM.	.1839"
PITCH	.01016"
NO. OF TEETH	60
HOB NO.	
CUTTER CAM NO.	9087
THICKNESS OF TEETH	.0051
SHAPE OF TEETH	EPICYCLOID
BETWEEN CENTERS	.110

CHANGES AND CORRECTIONS

3840

3819

176E019-1-863

.01"

7²

.160"

.07"

1½° TAPER
ON A SIDE

HOLE BORED
FROM O.D. OF
WHEEL TEETH
DIAMETER
CALIBRATED
TO FIT PINION.

.0065"
.006"-.007"

DRAWN	RLH	9-2-48
CHECKED	WHS	3-23-49
INDEXED		
OBSOLETE		

Fig. 2.3 (above). A working drawing for the center wheel in a wrist watch. The drawing was made twenty times as large as the wheel. (*Courtesy: Elgin National Watch* Co.)

Fig. 2.4 (below, right). The accuracy of the center wheel described in Fig. 2.3 is checked by a precision machine. (*Courtesy: Elgin National Watch* Co.)

quality according to the working drawings and specifications.

Occupations and drawing. Many jobs require that a person be able either to read blueprints or to make drawings. A *blueprint* is a printed copy of a drawing (see page 225). From the general manager of a factory to the foreman, almost all persons in important positions need these skills. If you can become skillful at drawing, that skill may not only help you to choose your future occupation but it may help you to get it.

Some boys and girls insist that they just can't draw, even before they really try it. If they think they can't they probably won't; if they think they can,

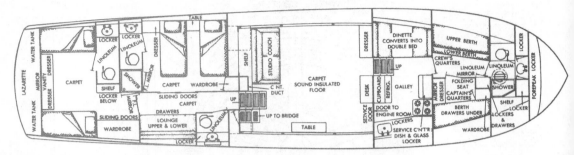

Fig. 2.5. The deck plan for a motor yacht. (Courtesy: Chris-Craft.)

Fig. 2.6 (left). The Yacht under construction. (Courtesy: Chris-Craft.)

Fig. 2.7 (below). The yacht on a trial cruise. (Courtesy: Chris-Craft.)

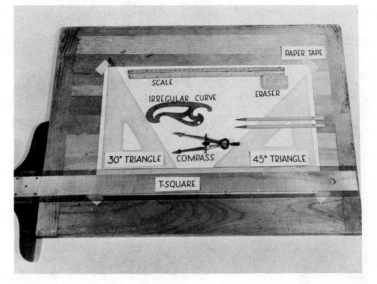

Fig. 2.8. A set of draw-
ing tools.

they probably will. In which group are you?

The Architect and Drawings

Houses, schools, city buildings, and factory buildings are planned by architects. Their drawings and specifications completely describe a building. The client for whom the building is to be constructed decides whether or not he wants it on the basis of these plans. The building contractor with his carpenters, bricklayers, and steel workers construct according to the plans. The plumbing, electrical, painting, heating, and ventilating contractors all use them. As the work progresses, the architect checks it against the plans. Can you imagine the troubles all these people might have if there were no drawings to guide them?

Drawing Tools

There are special tools for drawing just as there are for all crafts. The draftsman has a number of special tools, which enables him to do a better job more quickly. He uses drafting machines and electric erasers, for instance.

Drawing board. The drawing board is usually made of basswood or white pine and is available in many sizes.

T square. The T square, sliding up and down the left end of the drawing board, enables you to draw horizontal lines that are always parallel. The head of the square must be kept against the end of the board.

Triangles. With triangles you can draw angular lines and vertical lines. The 45-deg triangle is used for lines at that angle and the 30-deg to 60-deg triangles for those angles. Each is used on the T square, and they can be added together to make other angles; for example, 45 deg plus 30 deg equals 75 deg.

Architects' scale. The architects' scale is used for measuring on the

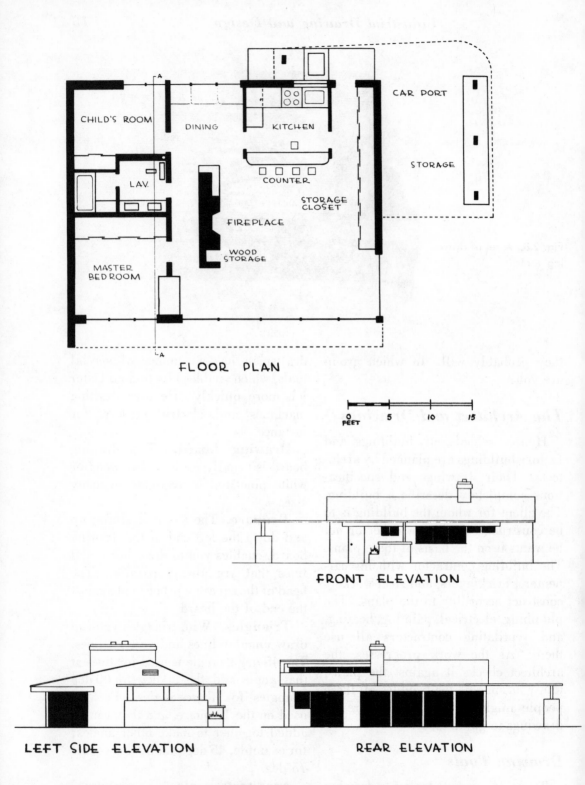

CHILD'S ROOM

DINING

KITCHEN

CAR PORT

STORAGE

LAV.

COUNTER

STORAGE CLOSET

FIREPLACE

WOOD STORAGE

MASTER BEDROOM

A

A

FLOOR PLAN

0 5 10 15
FEET

FRONT ELEVATION

LEFT SIDE ELEVATION

REAR ELEVATION

Fig. 2.9. An architect's drawing of a summer cottage. (*Designed by Joseph Mullane.*)

A SUMMER VACATION HOUSE

ACCOMMODATION

THIS VACATION HOUSE IS DESIGNED TO ACCOMMODATE A YOUNG COUPLE WITH ONE CHILD. A FLEXIBLE AREA FOR TWO OVERNIGHT GUESTS IS PROVIDED BY THE USE OF A FOLD-AWAY BED.

VENTILATION

THE EXTENDED ROOF OVER THE CHILD'S ROOM GIVES ACCESS TO MORE LIGHT AND VENTILATION. CROSS VENTILATION IS ACCOMPLISHED THROUGH THE SLEEPING AND TOILET AREAS BY THE SPACE ABOVE THE CLOSETS IN THE BEDROOMS.

CIRCULATION

ROOM TRAFFIC IS DIRECT FROM EACH OF THE LIVING AREAS — SLEEPING, EATING, AND RELAXING — TO THE OTHERS. THE GUESTS HAVE DIRECT ACCESS TO THE TOILET FACILITIES.

CONSTRUCTION

THE LARGE FIREPLACE HAS THE ADDITIONAL FUNCTION OF SUPPORTING PRE-STRESSED CONCRETE BEAMS — FROM WALL TO FIREPLACE TO WALL — AS MAIN MEMBERS OF ROOF SUPPORT.

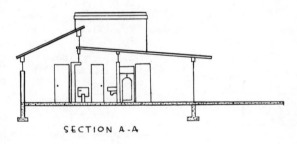

SECTION A-A

DRAWING SYMBOLS

THE ALPHABET OF LINES— A.S.A. STANDARDS

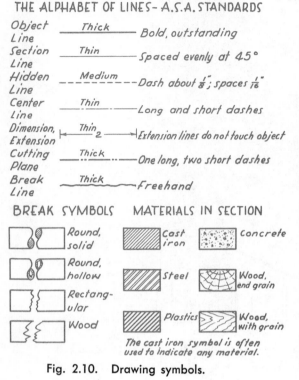

Object Line	Thick	Bold, outstanding
Section Line	Thin	Spaced evenly at 45°
Hidden Line	Medium	Dash about $\frac{1}{8}$"; spaces $\frac{1}{16}$"
Center Line	Thin	Long and short dashes
Dimension, Extension	Thin 2	Extension lines do not touch object
Cutting Plane	Thick	One long, two short dashes
Break Line	Thick	Freehand

BREAK SYMBOLS

- Round, solid
- Round, hollow
- Rectang-ular
- Wood

MATERIALS IN SECTION

- Cast iron
- Steel
- Plastics
- Concrete
- Wood, end grain
- Wood, with grain

The cast iron symbol is often used to indicate any material.

Fig. 2.10. Drawing symbols.

drawing. It has a foot marked off in inches and sixteenths as well as a foot squeezed down to 3 in., to $1\frac{1}{2}$, 1, $\frac{3}{4}$, $\frac{1}{2}$, $\frac{3}{8}$, $\frac{3}{16}$, and $\frac{1}{8}$ in. With these you can make true, accurate drawings smaller than the full size of the object to such proportions as $3'' = 1' - 0''$; $1'' = 1' - 0''$; and $\frac{1}{4}'' = 1' - 0''$.

Compass. This is the tool for drawing circles and parts of circles, as well as for stepping off distances. For the latter use, the pencil lead is replaced by a steel point.

Irregular curve. This is a plastic guide for drawing curves that do not have fixed centers as do compass curves.

Paper. There are special papers for technical drawing. You should have one that is tough and quite hard. The $8\frac{1}{2}$ by 11 in. size, or multiples of it, is the standard in industry.

Fig. 2.11. Electrical system for a toy electric locomotive. Notice the use of symbols. See p. 155 for electrical symbols.

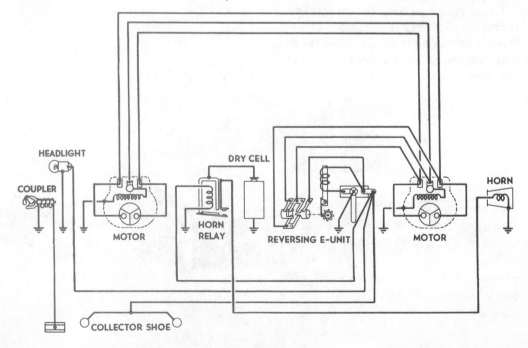

HEADLIGHT

COUPLER

MOTOR

HORN RELAY

DRY CELL

REVERSING E-UNIT

MOTOR

HORN

COLLECTOR SHOE

Pencils. Drawing pencils are graded by the lead. Those from 2H to 9H are hard; the H, F, HB, and B are medium; and those from 2B to 6B are soft. The more H's, the harder; the more B's, the softer. A 2H is recommended for drawing and an F for sketching and lettering.

Erasers. A ruby-typer eraser is good for removing lines, and an art gum or similar type for cleaning.

Paper tape. Paper tape is preferred to thumbtacks for holding the drawing paper in place on the board.

The Alphabet of Drawing

The language of drawing has an alphabet. You will learn it as you draw. There are certain types of lines that carry the same meaning in all technical drawing. Many symbols are used for convenience in drawing and ease in reading. These practices vary with different companies. Those suggested here are recommended by the American Standards Association. This is an organization that is attempting to make drawing practices more nearly the same for all industries.

Orthographic Drawing

An orthographic drawing shows the object in its true shape and size by means of several different views or separate drawings. Two or more drawings are needed to describe the object. The word *orthographic* comes from the Greek and means "true line."

The origin of orthographic views. 1. Picture in your mind a block suspended inside a clear plastic box.

2. As you look directly down on the top of the block you see its shape or outline. This outline is projected up to the top of the plastic box and then drawn on it.

3. The same is done for the front face and the right end of the block. It can also be done for the other faces, but it is usually not necessary.

4. Now open the box and lay it out flat. Here are three views of the block with the *front* at the lower left, the *right end* to the right, and the *top* above the front view. This is the correct position of these views in orthographic drawing.

Hidden lines. When details of the object cannot actually be seen in any view, they are shown by hidden lines. See the Alphabet of Lines (Fig. 2.10). If we make a cut in this same block, as is shown, note how hidden lines account for it. (See Fig. 2.17.)

How to Make an Orthographic Drawing

You don't need the plastic box when you make these drawings, but you must keep in mind the origin of the views.

1. Draw lightly the base line *AB* and the line *BC* at right angles to it.

2. Mark off the length and height of the object. Add lines *DF* and *EG*.

3. Mark off the width of the object on the top view. Add the lines to complete it.

4. Draw a line with a 45-deg triangle from the upper right corner of the front view.

5. Project the width from the top

Orthographic Drawing

An orthographic drawing shows the true shape of the object in *views*. Two, three, or more views are needed to show the object completely. The following drawings show how these views are determined.

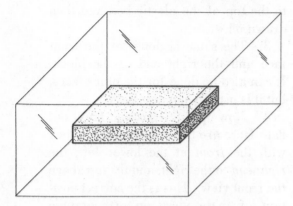

Fig. 2.12. Imagine an object, in this case a block, suspended inside a clear transparent plastic box, with its longest side to the front.

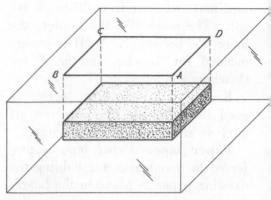

Fig. 2.13. As you look down at the top of the box you see the outline of the top of the block. This outline is projected up to the top of the box and drawn on it, ABCD.

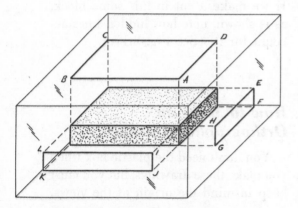

Fig. 2.14. When you look at the block from the right end, the end view, EFGH, is seen and similarly, the front view, IJKL, is obtained.

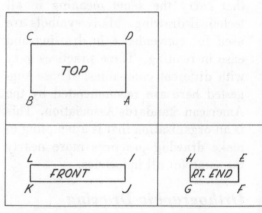

Fig. 2.15. When the top, front, and right end of the box are opened and laid flat, these three views appear in their proper positions. The top view is always directly above the front view. The right end view is always to the right of, and in line with, the front view. These positions are sometimes changed, but only for exceptional cases.

HOW TO MAKE AN
ORTHOGRAPHIC DRAWING

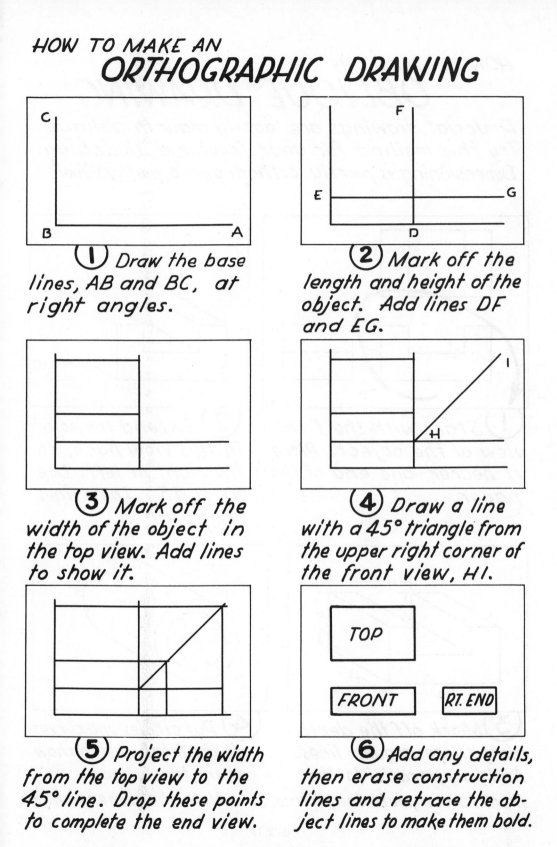

① Draw the base lines, AB and BC, at right angles.

② Mark off the length and height of the object. Add lines DF and EG.

③ Mark off the width of the object in the top view. Add lines to show it.

④ Draw a line with a 45° triangle from the upper right corner of the front view, HI.

⑤ Project the width from the top view to the 45° line. Drop these points to complete the end view.

⑥ Add any details, then erase construction lines and retrace the object lines to make them bold.

Fig. 2.16

HOW TO MAKE AN
OBLIQUE DRAWING

Pictorial drawings are easily made in oblique.
Try this method for your freehand sketching.
Dimensioning is partly orthographic, partly isometric.

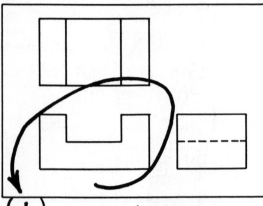

① *Start with the front view of the object. Place it nearer one end of the paper.*

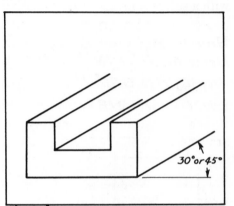

② *Extend the points in this view back, to the right or left. Use 30° or 45°. These lines are parallel.*

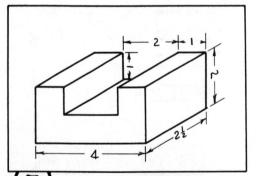

③ *Mark off the depth along these angular lines. Add lines parallel to the front to complete the picture.*

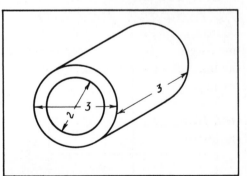

④ *Put circles and curves in the front view to show their true shape. Note the dimensioning.*

Fig. 2.17

view over to intersect the diagonal line. Drop those points down to complete the end view.

6. Now add any details, starting in the front view, and project them into the other views. Erase the construction lines lightly and trace over the views with a softer pencil to make them bold.

How to Make an Oblique Drawing

Oblique drawing is a fast, simple form of pictorial or picture drawing. It has an advantage over isometric drawing because one face of the object is always shown in its true shape.

1. Take the front orthographic view.
2. Add the third dimension lines, at 30 or 45 deg.
3. Mark off the third dimension and add parallel lines to complete the view.
4. Put circles and curves in the front view when possible; otherwise, draw them as in isometric.

Dimensioning. The front face is dimensioned just as in orthographic drawing; the others, as in isometric drawing.

How to Make an Isometric Drawing

In isometric drawings, unlike oblique drawings, the true shape of the object cannot be shown. A square is not a true square, nor is a circle a true circle. Actually it is an oval or an ellipse. Isometric drawings are pictures made mechanically, so you can do them easily. The word *isometric*

means in Greek "equal measure." It refers to the equal angles between the three axes, as shown in step 1.

1. Using a T square and a 30 to 60 deg triangle, lay out the nearest corner of the object, lines, *A, B,* and *C.*
2. Measure off the length, width, and height on these lines. Add lines *D* and *E.*
3. Add *F* and *G.*
4. Add *H* and *I.*
5. Add any details to the object. Remember to measure along the angular and vertical lines but never measure horizontally. Each dimension is placed in the same plane as the face that includes it.

Isometric circles. Circles are not shown in their true shape in isometric drawing. They are ovals or ellipses.

As a circle fits into a square, so an oval fits into a diamond. The curve touches the midpoint of each side; it is *tangent* at each midpoint. First construct the isometric square, then find the centers, *I* and *J,* and swing the four arcs from points *A, C, I,* and *J.*

Sections

Sections are used to show the inside of an object, how parts are put together, and the materials of which they are made. When you slice through a layer cake you can see the thickness of the frosting and the kind of cake. The cake is sliced with a knife, but in a drawing it is done with a cutting plane. This cut is only imaginary. You draw what you know is there but really can't see. When the cake or the object is cut clear across we call it a *full section;*

HOW TO MAKE AN
ISOMETRIC DRAWING
A TYPE OF PICTURE DRAWING - all dimensions are in one view

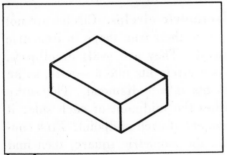

① Draw a vertical line, B, for the nearest corner. With 30°-60° triangles on T-square draw lines A and C.

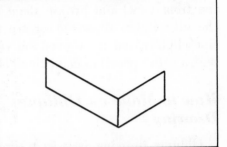

② Mark off length, width, and height on lines C, A, and B. Add parallel lines to complete the two sides.

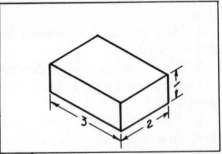

③ Draw the parallel lines to complete the view. Add any details and retrace the object lines.

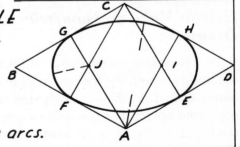

④ Dimensions are done isometrically. Hidden lines are not shown. Any isometric drawing starts with a box.

THE ISOMETRIC CIRCLE

① Draw an isometric square, ABCD.
② Draw lines EC, FC, AH, and AG bisecting opposite sides.
③ With points I and J as centers, swing the small arcs.
④ From points A and C swing large arcs.

Fig. 2.18

when half through, it is a *half section*. A partial cut is a *partial section*.

Sectioning is indicated by a symbol consisting of light, uniformly spaced lines at 45 deg to the right or left. For your drawings this spacing will usually be from 1/16" to 1/8". This effect is *cross-hatching*. (See Fig. 2.23.)

Dimensioning

Dimensions specify size and give locations of holes, cuts, parts, and such. All dimensions up to and including 72 inches should be given in inches, and when all dimensions in the drawing are in inches, no inch symbols (") are used.

Location of dimensions. Dimensions should be so located that there can be no question as to what or where they apply. Follow these tips:

1. Put the dimension on that view which most clearly shows the part being dimensioned.

2. Dimensions should be readable from the bottom or the right side of the drawing.

3. Do not dimension from or to hidden lines. A center line should not be used as a dimension line.

4. It is generally better to place the dimensions outside the object, between the views. Can you tell why?

5. Arrange consecutive dimensions in a straight line, with the over-all dimension outside of them.

6. Start extension lines about 1/16" from the object.

Drawing to Scale

For greatest accuracy, working

Fig. 2.19. Marene cuts her birthday cake. Until it was cut one couldn't tell what kind of cake was beneath the frosting. Drawings in section cut away an object to show interior detail.

DIMENSIONING PRACTICE
(ACCORDING TO AMERICAN STANDARDS ASSOCIATION PRACTICE)

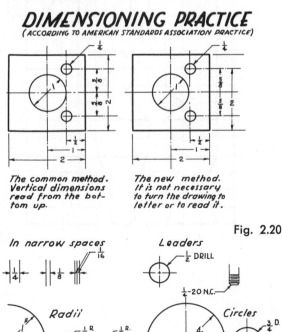

The common method. Vertical dimensions read from the bottom up.

The new method. It is not necessary to turn the drawing to letter or to read it.

Fig. 2.20

SOME DRAWINGS TO MAKE
① DRAW 3 VIEWS OF EACH LETTER
   IN YOUR FIRST NAME
② DRAW THEM IN OBLIQUE, TOO

Fig. 2.21

AN ALPHABET FOR DRAWINGS

ABCDEFGHIJK

LMNOPQRST

UVWXYZ UPPER CASE

abcdefghijklmno

pqrstuvwxyz ?!&

lower case · letters

1234567890

$\frac{1}{8}, \frac{1}{4}, \frac{3}{8}, \frac{1}{2}, \frac{5}{8}, \frac{3}{4}, \frac{7}{8}, \quad 14\frac{5}{8}$

VERTICAL LETTERING IS DONE IN
THE SAME MANNER. COUNT THE
STROKES IN RHYTHM AS YOU LETTER.

Fig. 2.22

CAMPER'S
GRIDDLE AND FRY PAN

SEE PHOTO, FIG. 4.59.

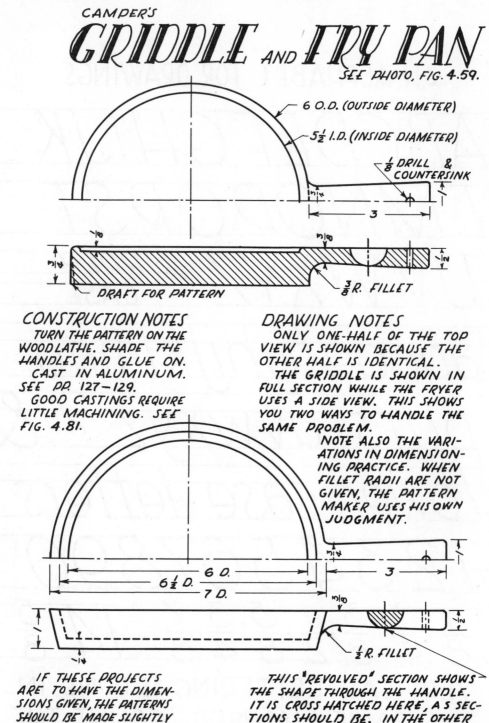

6 O.D. (OUTSIDE DIAMETER)

5½ I.D. (INSIDE DIAMETER)

⅛ DRILL & COUNTERSINK

3

DRAFT FOR PATTERN

⅜ R. FILLET

CONSTRUCTION NOTES

TURN THE PATTERN ON THE WOOD LATHE. SHAPE THE HANDLES AND GLUE ON. CAST IN ALUMINUM. SEE PP. 127–129.

GOOD CASTINGS REQUIRE LITTLE MACHINING. SEE FIG. 4.81.

DRAWING NOTES

ONLY ONE-HALF OF THE TOP VIEW IS SHOWN BECAUSE THE OTHER HALF IS IDENTICAL.

THE GRIDDLE IS SHOWN IN FULL SECTION WHILE THE FRYER USES A SIDE VIEW. THIS SHOWS YOU TWO WAYS TO HANDLE THE SAME PROBLEM.

NOTE ALSO THE VARI-ATIONS IN DIMENSION-ING PRACTICE. WHEN FILLET RADII ARE NOT GIVEN, THE PATTERN MAKER USES HIS OWN JUDGMENT.

6 D.

6½ D.

7 D.

3

½ R. FILLET

IF THESE PROJECTS ARE TO HAVE THE DIMEN-SIONS GIVEN, THE PATTERNS SHOULD BE MADE SLIGHTLY LARGER TO ALLOW FOR THE SHRINKAGE OF THE METAL AND THE MACHINING.

ADD ⅛" TO THE DIAMETER.

THIS "REVOLVED" SECTION SHOWS THE SHAPE THROUGH THE HANDLE. IT IS CROSS HATCHED HERE, AS SEC-TIONS SHOULD BE. IN THE OTHER DRAWING THIS CROSS HATCHING WAS OMITTED FOR THE SAKE OF CLARITY.

A DRAFTSMAN USES HIS OWN JUDGMENT IN SUCH CASES.

28   Fig. 2.23

DO-ALL TRACTOR

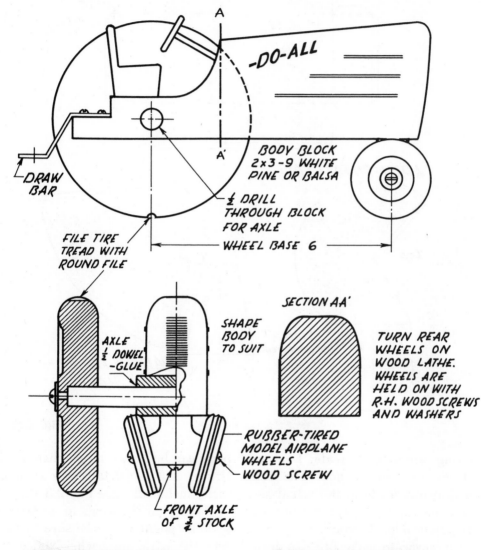

A

-DO-ALL

A'

BODY BLOCK
2 x 3 - 9 WHITE
PINE OR BALSA

¼ DRILL
THROUGH BLOCK
FOR AXLE

DRAW
BAR

WHEEL BASE 6

FILE TIRE
TREAD WITH
ROUND FILE

SHAPE
BODY
TO SUIT

SECTION AA'

AXLE
½ DOWEL
-GLUE

TURN REAR
WHEELS ON
WOOD LATHE.
WHEELS ARE
HELD ON WITH
R.H. WOOD SCREWS
AND WASHERS

RUBBER-TIRED
MODEL AIRPLANE
WHEELS
WOOD SCREW

FRONT AXLE
OF ¾ STOCK

CONSTRUCTION NOTES

MAKE EACH PART AND
SMOOTH AND PAINT IT
BEFORE ASSEMBLING.
DESIGN YOUR OWN
TRIM AND RADIATOR
GRILL FOR AN UP-TO-DATE
MODEL.
VISIT A TRACTOR DEALER.

DRAWING NOTES

ONLY ENOUGH DETAILS ARE
GIVEN TO SHOW YOU THE IDEA.
MAKE A WORKING DRAWING
OF THE TRACTOR, WITH DIMEN-
SIONS, BEFORE YOU BUILD IT.
DRAW IT FULL SIZE.
CAN YOU DESIGN A TRAILER
OR AN IMPLEMENT TO FIT?

Fig. 2.24

DEVELOPING PATTERNS

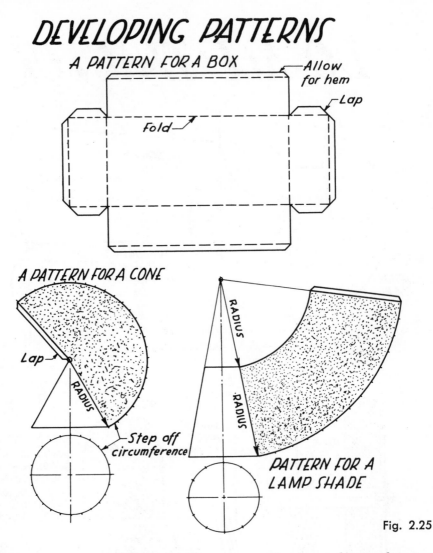

A PATTERN FOR A BOX

Allow for hem

Lap

Fold

A PATTERN FOR A CONE

Lap

RADIUS

Step off circumference

RADIUS

RADIUS

PATTERN FOR A LAMP SHADE

Fig. 2.25

drawings are made to scale; freehand sketches are usually not. The full-size drawing, made to the actual size of the object, is preferred whenever it is practicable. It would be quite a task, however, to make full-size drawings of the *USS United States* or of the parts of a wrist watch. One is too large and the other is too small. Accurate drawings of the ship can be made smaller than full size. For example, one inch on the drawing might equal fifty feet on the ship. Watch

parts can be drawn larger than actual size so that the details can be more easily included. (See Fig. 2.3.)

Make your drawings to as large a scale as possible and be sure to indicate the scale on each. Notice the scales given on various drawings in this book. Some common scales are; $\frac{1}{4}'' = 1' - 0''$, meaning, $\frac{1}{4}''$ on the drawing equals $1' - 0''$ on the object; $1'' = 1' - 0''$; Half Size; and Full Size.

Making tracings. In industry the

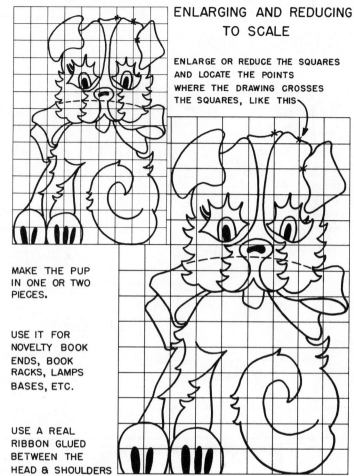

ENLARGE OR REDUCE THE SQUARES
AND LOCATE THE POINTS
WHERE THE DRAWING CROSSES
THE SQUARES, LIKE THIS

MAKE THE PUP
IN ONE OR TWO
PIECES.

Fig. 2.26

USE IT FOR
NOVELTY BOOK
ENDS, BOOK
RACKS, LAMPS
BASES, ETC.

USE A REAL
RIBBON GLUED
BETWEEN THE
HEAD & SHOULDERS

here's 'HONEY'
SEE WHAT YOU CAN MAKE WITH HER

Fig. 2.27

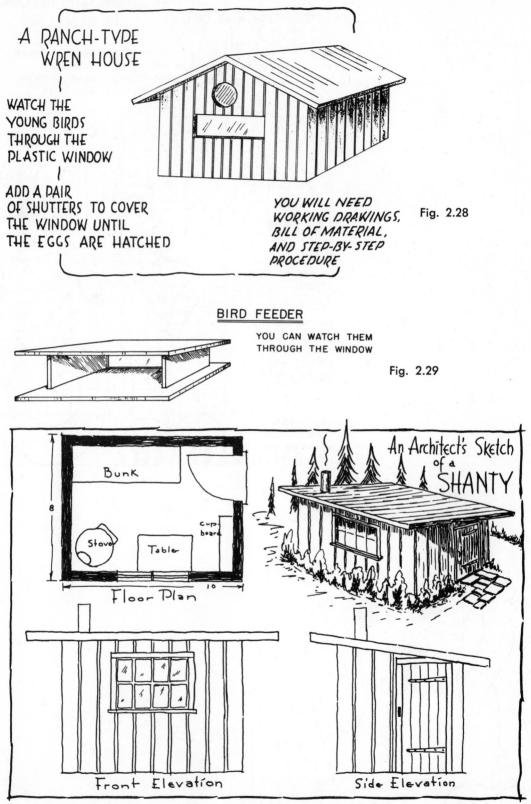

A RANCH-TYPE WREN HOUSE

WATCH THE YOUNG BIRDS THROUGH THE PLASTIC WINDOW

ADD A PAIR OF SHUTTERS TO COVER THE WINDOW UNTIL THE EGGS ARE HATCHED

YOU WILL NEED WORKING DRAWINGS, BILL OF MATERIAL, AND STEP-BY-STEP PROCEDURE

Fig. 2.28

BIRD FEEDER

YOU CAN WATCH THEM THROUGH THE WINDOW

Fig. 2.29

Bunk

Stove

Table

cup-board

8

10

Floor Plan

An Architect's Sketch of a SHANTY

Front Elevation

Side Elevation

Fig. 2.30

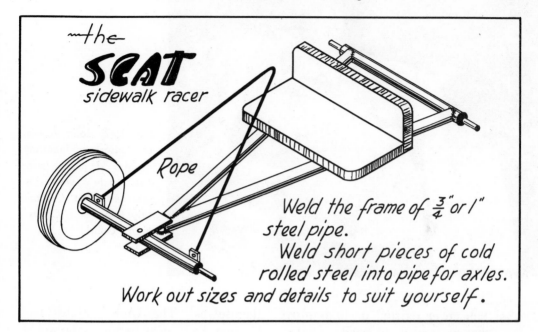

—the
SCAT
sidewalk racer

Rope

Weld the frame of $\frac{3}{4}$" or 1" steel pipe.
Weld short pieces of cold rolled steel into pipe for axles.
Work out sizes and details to suit yourself.

Fig. 2.31

original drawings do not go out into the shop. Tracings are made and, from these, the prints. Each department needing prints can then have them. To make a tracing, fasten a piece of transparent tracing paper over the drawing. Trace the drawing with an H or an F pencil. Make the lines dark and bold. If the light in the printing machine cannot go through your lines, they will be sharp and clear on the print.

SOME USEFUL INFORMATION

Circles

Diameter $= 2R$
Circumference $= 3\frac{1}{7}$ (or 3.1416) $\times D$
Area $= 3\frac{1}{7} \times R^2$ (or $R \times R$)

Areas

Square $= L \times L$
Rectangle $= L \times W$
Triangle $= \dfrac{A \times B}{2}$

Volumes

Cube and rectangular box $= L \times W \times H$
Cylindrical tank $=$ Area of bottom $\times$ Height

Units of measurement

LENGTH

1 ft (1') $=$ 12 in. (")
1 yd $=$ 3 ft
1 rod $=$ 16½ ft
1 mile $=$ 5280 ft
1 in. $=$ 2.54 cm (centimeter)

WEIGHT

1 lb $=$ 16 oz
1 ton $=$ 2000 lb
1 oz $=$ 28.35 gram (g)

LIQUID

1 pint $=$ 16 oz
1 quart $=$ 2 pt
1 gallon $=$ 4 qt

AREA

1 sq ft $=$ 144 sq in
1 sq yd $=$ 9 sq ft
1 acre $=$ 43,560 sq ft

VOLUME

1 cu ft $=$ 1,728 cu in (12 $\times$ 12 $\times$ 12)
1 cu yd $=$ 27 cu ft

Designing Your Own Projects

Designing begins with a problem. It may be to invent or create a product

Fig. 2.32. John Vajner of Anderson, Indiana, designs a model car. The side view is sketched first. (*Courtesy: Fisher Body Craftsman's Guild.*)

that has never existed or to improve one that is commonly used. The inventor of the airplane worked without the aid of books or schooling in aeronautics, and without having seen other airplanes; still he designed a machine for traveling through the air. He did it by trial and experiment until he succeeded. Airplane designers today can take advantage of a half century of aviation know-how, and with it they can improve the airplane to the limit of this knowledge.

When you design your own project you can have it the way you want it. You don't have to be satisfied with a project just like those made by others. You will have much more fun making things when you "cook them up." When you have designed something it means that you have thought seriously about it and have come up with an idea. This process is good experience for you.

Our country needs people who can and are willing to think seriously for

themselves. The United States has become the leading nation in the world because each of us is encouraged to have new, different, and better ideas. There is a constant demand for better answers to problems. Our industrial development has been so great because new and better ideas for products, processes, and machines are constantly being developed.

How an industrial designer works. An industrial designer is a most unusual person. It is he who "cooks up" the original products which industry produces in quantity. He is a combination of engineer, for his understanding of materials, tools, and machines; inventor, for his imagination; and artist, for his ability to make things beautiful. When he is assigned a design problem, he works in this manner:

1. He first finds out just what the problem is so that he can determine the exact purpose or function of the proposed product.

2. He then determines all of the limitations under which he must work; for example, he must know who the product is intended for, who will use it. The probable selling price always limits him. It is important to know where the product will be used, as indoors or outdoors. Such limitations affect the design.

3. He studies similar products designed by others and makes many sketches of possible ideas. He makes scale models of the ideas in order to show them better. He changes, adds to, and lays aside ideas until he finally settles on those he thinks best.

4. These proposals are then laid, for criticism, before a jury made up of such company experts as other designers and engineers, the plant manager, sales manager, president, and vice-presidents. The jury decides whether or not to accept the proposed product for manufacture. Frequently changes are suggested, or the idea may be rejected. The jury studies it very carefully because the product must sell.

5. *Pilot* (or *trial*) *models* are sometimes made and tried out in various parts of the country to find out what consumers think of them before the plant is tooled up to produce them.

6. When the design is accepted, working drawings are made so that materials can be ordered and special tools, machines, and jigs can be made. The plant is then made ready to turn out the product in quantity.

7. Consumer acceptance of the product is carefully watched to find out how well it pleases those who use it. From time to time it is improved as weaknesses show up and as competition gets keen.

How to go about designing your projects. It makes good sense for you to follow a procedure similar to that of the industrial designer when you design a project:

1. Think through the problem so that you know exactly what the purpose of the project is and what it has to be able to do.

2. Find out what the limitations are. For example, if you have no equipment for welding metal, then you may not be able to use a welded con-

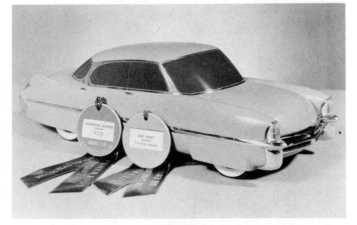

Fig. 2.33. This model car was designed and built by Gerald Grabcheski, Elizabeth, New Jersey. It won a scholarship for him in the junior division of the Fisher Body Craftsman's Guild competition. (Courtesy: Fisher Body Craftsman's Guild.)

Fig. 2.34. This chair was given to an industrial designer to improve the appearance, increase the comfort, and lower the production cost. This is a "redesign job," as the designer calls it. (*Courtesy: Lawrence Blazey.*)

Fig. 2.35. After the redesigning, the chair is much improved. It even looks more comfortable, and the cost was cut 3¢. The shape of the seat was obtained by having people sit on a block of soft clay. (*Courtesy: Lawrence Blazey.*)

struction. If you are not yet able to operate certain machines, you may have to design the project to be made by hand.

3. Find out how the problem has been solved by others.

4. Using rough sketches, put down your ideas so that you can study them.

5. Make small-scale models from these sketches to see how the project will actually look or work.

6. Get the criticisms of your classmates and teacher. These suggestions may help you to improve the idea.

7. When the idea is workable and acceptable, make a full-size model, if practicable. If not, make an accurate scale model, refining the design to make it attractive and interesting, and then try it out on your jury again.

8. When it meets with your complete approval, make a working drawing of it and from this construct the project. Have your jury judge it again. The more experiences you and your classmates get in designing, the better you can judge design. Sometimes the criticisms may not make sense to you. Study them anyway. You will often find that they contain good suggestions.

What good design is. When a project or a product is well designed, it scores highly on the following measures:

1. *Function.* The project has a usefulness; it was intended to serve a purpose. It should be so designed that it serves this purpose well.

2. *Durability.* The project should be so designed that it will serve this function for as long as was intended. A piece that is to be used, say, for

only an hour, must be designed differently from one that must last for a year. The tendency in industrial arts is to build things too strong. Often too much of too heavy material, too securely fastened together, makes the article too heavy, too massive, and too amateurish in appearance.

3. *Economy.* The project should be so designed that it can be produced economically. This means not only the conserving of materials but the selection of economical materials as well. Too much durability is wasteful, too. Economy requires that the materials be simply formed and put together.

4. *Material.* The project should be made of materials that are suitable and appropriate when function, durability, and economy are considered. The material should be so used that it retains its identity. For example, if the product is made of clay, then it should look as though it were made of clay instead of being an imitation of wood, metal, or other materials. Any finish that you put on a beautiful piece of wood should be one that enhances rather than conceals its beauty or that makes it appear to be a wood that it is not. No amount of walnut stain can change poplar into walnut. Be honest with materials.

5. *Construction.* Construction methods should be appropriate to function, durability, economy, and material. They should make it possible for the project to serve its purpose well and for as long as desired. Simple methods are preferred to complicated ones and they should be suited to the material. Nails, for example, are excellent devices for fastening boards together to

Fig. 2.36. A contemporary chair, emphasizing comfort, usefulness, and simplicity of form and construction. (*Courtesy: J. G. Furniture Co., Inc.*)

Fig. 2.37. Scale models show ideas better than drawings. These are coffee tables. Note the paper clip; it gives an idea of the size of the models.

Fig. 2.38. A model of a desk designed to meet the needs of the person who designed it.

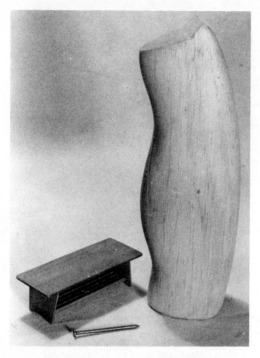

Fig. 2.39. A small scale model of a coffee table and a full-size balsa model of a lamp base.

make a dog house, but they should not be used to fasten fine woods together when you make a coffee table.

6. *Beauty*. The product is most beautiful when its form and shape reflect its function and when they originate from that function. A good example of this is a claw hammer. *Its form is determined by its function.* Nothing else is necessary, although a beautiful finish on the head and handle makes it more desirable. Beauty is not added to the project after it is built; beauty is built in. Lines, curves, color, texture, and finish must be appropriate to the function, material, and construction. The well-designed project has a beauty that lasts and lasts. You don't tire of it. It is simple rather than ornate.

7. *Personality*. A project may score highly on the preceding qualities and yet it may not be really interesting. It should give the feeling that the designer has built some of himself into it. It should have individuality, and

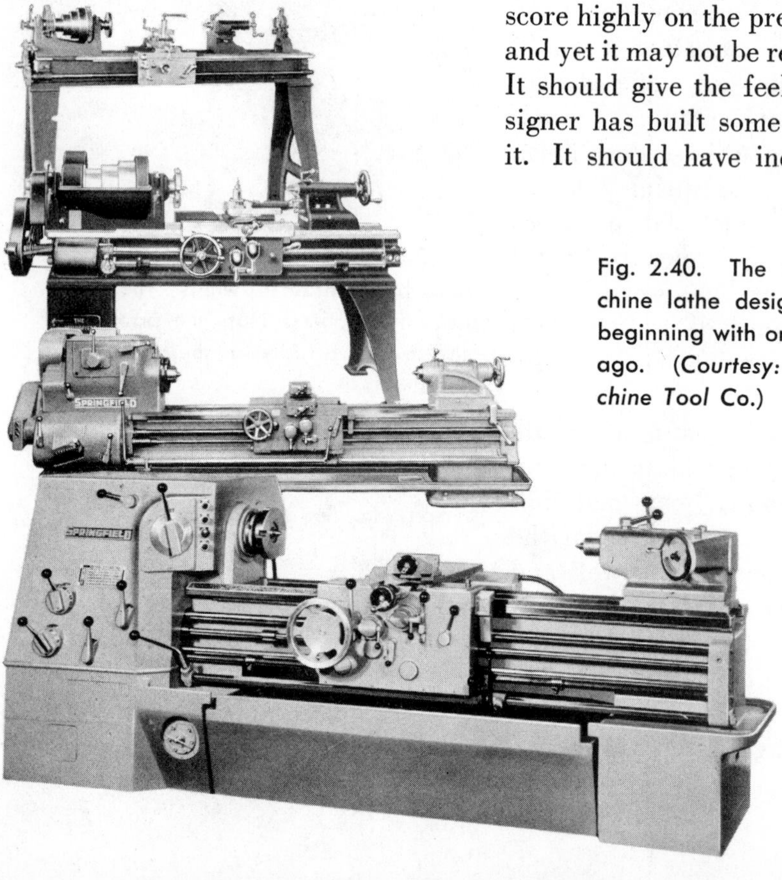

Fig. 2.40. The evolution of machine lathe design is shown here, beginning with one built sixty years ago. (*Courtesy: Springfield Machine Tool Co.*)

Fig. 2.41. The evolution of the common flat iron. The appearance has changed through the years, but note that the basic shape, the boat hull, is used in all the irons. This means that it is still the best shape for ironing and pressing. (*Courtesy: Walker Art Center.*)

thus show that the designer has taken the problem seriously and intended that the article be a credit to his reputation. Without this quality the product seems cold and impersonal, as though it were designed by a machine and not a person. Many mass-produced articles lack this quality, and consequently we as consumers treat them indifferently.

Design for beauty. Some people insist that if they like the appearance of an article it is beautiful; but just because one likes it doesn't make it a good design. There are some guides to beauty in design which you can study and apply. With them you can more easily know when a design is beautiful and good.

1. The basic form of a product is determined first of all by the *function*. (See Fig. 2.44.) The form is defined

SOME *free forms*
FOR BOWLS AND TRAYS OF CLAY, ART METAL, AND CARVED WOOD

Fig. 2.43. A free form copper tray, and the pattern from which it was made.

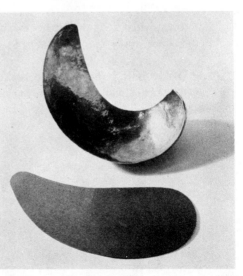

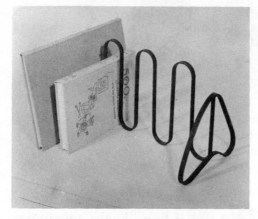

Fig. 2.44. A contemporary book rack employing the principle that "form follows function."

usually preferable. Rectangles, ovals, and free forms are more interesting than are squares and circles.

3. *Balance,* which refers to a state of *equilibrium* within the design, means that the object is neither top-heavy, nor bottom heavy, nor lopsided. When a design is arranged about a center line so that the parts on each side are alike, it has *symmetrical balance*. When the design is so arranged that the balance cannot actually be measured or laid out with a ruler, and yet one gets the feeling that balance does exist, it has *informal balance*. This is the more interesting of the two. Fig. 2.44 is symmetrical and Fig. 2.45 is *asymmetrical* (meaning "not symmetrical").

4. *Emphasis* means that the design has a center of interest; that is, one part of it is most important and is the point of the whole design. All other parts are subordinate to this main part just as, in a flower, the blossom is the center of interest; the stem and leaves support it and help to make it all the

by lines and curves that give shape to areas (two-dimensional figures, those with length and width only) and masses (shapes with three dimensions, length, width, and thickness or height).

2. *Proportion* is the relationship of dimensions and can be expressed as a ratio; for example, when the width is 20 in. and the length 30 in., the proportion is 20:30, or 2:3. Odd ratios such as 2:3, 3:5, 5:7, 7:9 are

Fig. 2.45 (below right). In this front view of the book rack, rhythm repetition and balance are easily seen.

Fig. 2.46 (below left). The triangular ends of the book rack are simple in form, yet fully functional. Note that the rack is off center, yet balance is adequate.

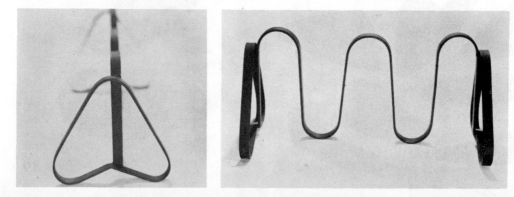

more beautiful. In Fig. 2.44 the center of interest is the part that holds the books.

5. *Unity* is present in a design when one's eye follows through and among the various parts with ease rather than having to jump from one part to another. It means that there is a one-ness about the design rather than an assortment or conglomeration of miscellaneous items which have no particular relationship to one another.

6. *Rhythm* is obtained by repeating lines, curves, forms, colors, and textures within the design. In Fig 2.45 rhythm and unity are easy to see.

7. *Harmony* results when all of the elements or parts in a design get along well together. However, there are times when too much harmony makes a design uninteresting and monotonous. Variety is then needed just as salt and pepper is needed to make good food more tasty.

8. *Texture* is the condition of the surface of a material. Burlap has a very coarse texture; copper sheet has scarcely any visible texture. Different woods have different textures. Compare a piece of cherry or poplar with a piece of oak or walnut. Texture can be applied to materials to make them more interesting (see Fig. 7.31). Any texture that is natural to a material should be so used that this naturalness is preserved. When a texture is applied, it should be appropriate to the piece and to its function. Excessive textures are excellent dust catchers.

9. *Color selection* is important in any design. It is closely related to finishes that are applied to materials to improve their appearance and to protect them. A project may be most interesting before color or finish is added. After that it may be junk. Colors have qualities which help you to choose them wisely. Yellows, oranges, and reds are warm colors. They suggest warmth, fire, cheerfulness, action, boldness. They shout loudly and must be used with restraint to keep them from becoming too "noisy." Blues and greens are cool colors which produce feelings of coldness, quiet, formality. Colors have seasonal qualities, too. Reds, browns, and deep, dull greens are common in the fall, and light yellow, yellow-greens, and lavenders are appropriate for spring.

Selecting colors for your projects. These suggestions can help you to make color choices:

1. Make one color *dominant* in the design. This is the main color and it may be the only one.

2. Select the main color to be most appropriate to the project. Consider the qualities of colors as just described. Here are some examples: If the project is to be used by a baby, use soft, light colors. If it is a child's toy to be played with out-of-doors, use bright, cheerful colors. If it is to become part of the furnishings in a room, either make the color harmonious with the other furnishings or make it contrast with them. For a football poster the colors should be lively and loud; for one announcing a P.T.A. meeting, they should be less loud and more dignified. The fact that you have a favorite color doesn't mean you should use it on everything or in large quantities.

COLOR WHEEL

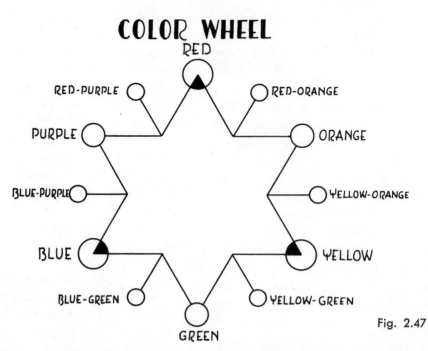

RED

RED-PURPLE

RED-ORANGE

PURPLE

ORANGE

BLUE-PURPLE

YELLOW-ORANGE

BLUE

YELLOW

BLUE-GREEN

YELLOW-GREEN

GREEN

Fig. 2.47

3. When more than one color is to be used, select colors that will make the main color appear more beautiful. You may get some ideas from a color wheel. To construct such a wheel (see Fig. 2.47), use the same paints as you will use on your project.

Two-color combinations. Two neighboring colors on the wheel can be used together. Since they are related, they get along well. Such colors are called *analogous.* Some examples are yellow and yellow-green, blue and blue-violet.

Two colors opposite on the wheel can be used together. With one of them the main color, use only a little of the opposite color. This combination is known as *complementary.*

Three-color combinations. The three colors may be adjacent on the wheel, as blue-green, blue, and blue-violet. You can also select three which are spaced equal distances apart on the wheel, or you can use any one color

with the color on each side of its complement. This is the *split-complementary* scheme.

4. Black, white, grays, and such colors as cream, ivory, tans, and browns are neutral, that is, they get along easily with the colors on the wheel.

5. Always try out your selections on some scrap material before using them on a project.

Signs and Posters

Signs and posters are silent salesmen. They have something to sell or to tell. The first duty of a poster is to draw attention to itself and then to get people to read its message.

Attention is attracted by the location of the poster or sign and by its color, layout, and letter style. A poster may be perfectly made, but if it is not placed where it can be easily seen, it cannot do its telling.

42

AN ALPHABET FOR
SIGNS AND POSTERS

ABCDEF
GHIJKLM
NOPQR
STUVW
XYZ1234
567890

Fig. 2.48

Choose colors that are most appropriate for the particular sign or poster. (See page 44.) Two or three colors including that of the background are sufficient. The more additional colors you use, the more difficult it becomes to handle them well. The layout, or arrangement, of the words and illustrations is important. The words must be so arranged that they can be easily read. Use as few as possible, too. Use illustrations to draw attention and to help explain the message and be sure that they are related to it. Simple letter styles are most effective. Use one style only in your first signs and posters. You will need to study and practice to be good at lettering just as you must to play a musical instrument or drop-kick a football well. Start out on the alphabet shown on page 27. Rule guide lines for various sizes of letters, then take each letter of the alphabet and form it many times with a soft pencil. Make the strokes rapidly instead of trying to draw them. Check your work frequently with the originals and with your teacher.

Some Group Projects

1. Visit a building under construction and look over the prints from which it is being built.
2. Visit the engineering department of a local industry, an architect, and the highway engineering department to watch engineers and designers at work.
3. Collect pictures of old and new autos and discuss the changes in engineering and body styling.

Roadside Sign

USE A MATERIAL WHICH WILL STAND THE WEATHER.

Fig. 2.49.   Ideas for signs.

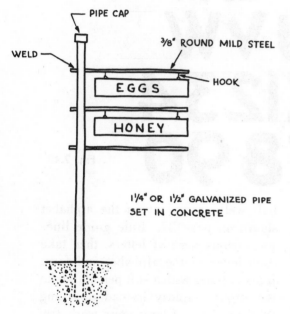

PIPE CAP

WELD

3/8" ROUND MILD STEEL

HOOK

EGGS

HONEY

1¼" OR 1½" GALVANIZED PIPE
SET IN CONCRETE

Fig. 2.50.   More ideas for signs.

Fig. 2.51.   More ideas for signs.

1045

R.L. JONES

YOUR NAME ON THE LAWN

4. Design and build a scale model of the city of the future.

5. Design and build scale models of a space station and a space ship for interplanetary travel.

Some Things to Draw

1. Make a full-size drawing and template for a milk pitcher to make of clay.

2. Make a stretch-out pattern full size for a sheet metal small-parts box.

3. Make working drawings for any of the projects illustrated in any of the chapters in this book.

4. Design a Christmas card or linoleum block or stencil printing.

5. Design a poster announcing an industrial arts exhibit, ball game, or other activity.

6. Design an identification bracelet.

7. Design a free-form copper dish. Make the pattern, too.

8. Design and draw a shack you would like to have and make a model of it.

9. Draw a floor plan for a dream workshop you would like to have at home.

See If You Can Find Out

1. How pencils are made.

2. How an architect goes about designing a building.

3. Why the American Standards Association is setting up standard drawing practices.

4. Why decimals are used rather than fractions in some dimensioning.

5. What perspective drawing is.

6. Why you should learn to design things rather than copy them.

7. The names of some important industrial designers and the products they design.

8. What aircraft "lofting" means.

9. How the full-size patterns for some airplane parts are made photographically.

10. How to read a set of house plans.

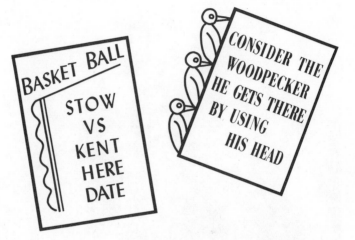

Fig. 2.52. Poster ideas.

Some Sources of Ideas and Information

Books

1. Barton R. L. and Donnel, J. *Modern Industrial Drawing*. Austin, Texas: The Steck Company, 1954.

2. Bradley, G. B. *Design in the Industrial Arts*. Peoria, Ill.: Charles A. Bennett Company, 1946.

3. Coover, Shriver L. *Drawing, Sketch- and Blueprint Reading*. New York: McGraw-Hill Book Company, 1954.

4. Dal Fabbro, Mario. *Modern Furniture Design and Construction*. New York: Reinhold Publishing Company, 1949.

5. Fleming, J. W., Barich, D. F., and Smith, L. C. *Applied Drawing and Sketching*. Chicago, Ill.: *American Technical Society*, 1950.

6. Fryklund, V. C. and Kepler, F. R. *General Drafting*. Bloomington, Ill.: McKnight and McKnight, 1949.

7. Hale, E. M., McGinnis, H., and Hill, C. L. *Introduction to Applied Drawing*. Bloomington, Ill.: McKnight and McKnight, 1952.

8. Van Doren, Harold. *Industrial Design*. New York: McGraw-Hill Book Company, 1940.

Booklets

Drawings and Drafting Room Practice. American Standards Association, 70 East Forty-fifth Street, New York 17, N.Y.

Films

Behind the Shop Drawing. Rental. Audio-Visual Center, Indiana University, Bloomington, Ind., and Audio-Visual Aids Library, Pennsylvania State College, State College, Pa.

Fig. 3.1. A modern use for wood. Small pieces of wood are held together with glue, making a laminated construction that is much stronger than the ordinary type of wood framing. (Courtesy: American Forest Products Industries.)

3 The WOOD INDUSTRIES

In the days of 1776 trees were used chiefly for lumber and fuel. Today they are the raw material used in many huge industries. Trees provide material for lumber, veneer, wallboard, insulation, paper, chemicals, plastics, and foods which are used in more products than we could list on this entire page. Today the lumberjack and the carpenter are but a few of the men who earn their living with trees and lumber. Scientists, chemists, engineers, and designers have developed new materials and products from trees, thus creating new jobs that did not exist a few years ago.

About trees. Lumber-producing trees are classed as *hardwoods* and *softwoods*. Hardwood trees, such as maple, birch, oak, and walnut, have broad leaves which are shed in the fall. Most softwoods, pines, firs, hemlock, and spruce, come from trees that have needles rather than leaves. A tree grows by adding new growth just underneath the bark and on the tips of roots and branches during the growing season. The age of a tree can be told quite accurately by counting the *annual rings* in the stump. The area from one ring to the next is a year's growth.

About lumber. Most of the wood in trees cut commercially is made into lumber and pulp. Boards that are sawed directly from the log are called *rough lumber*. After seasoning, or air drying, the rough lumber is usually *kiln-dried* (a kiln is a large oven) to make it hold its shape and size better. After being surfaced to thickness, width, and length, it is ready for use.

Lumber is usually sold by the board foot, a unit measuring 1 in. by 12 in.

47

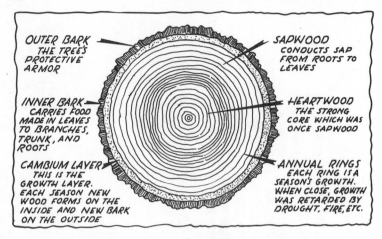

OUTER BARK
THE TREE'S
PROTECTIVE
ARMOR

SAPWOOD
CONDUCTS SAP
FROM ROOTS TO
LEAVES

INNER BARK
CARRIES FOOD
MADE IN LEAVES
TO BRANCHES,
TRUNK, AND
ROOTS

HEARTWOOD
THE STRONG
CORE WHICH WAS
ONCE SAPWOOD

CAMBIUM LAYER
THIS IS THE
GROWTH LAYER.
EACH SEASON NEW
WOOD FORMS ON THE
INSIDE AND NEW BARK
ON THE OUTSIDE

ANNUAL RINGS
EACH RING IS A
SEASON'S GROWTH.
WHEN CLOSE, GROWTH
WAS RETARDED BY
DROUGHT, FIRE, ETC.

Fig. 3.2. How a tree grows larger. (From U.S.D.A. Chart M-5159 Rev. 1948.)

by 12 in. Some building lumber is sold by the lineal foot. Lumber is graded by different systems. Soft-

Fig. 3.3. An early American log cabin, typical of pioneer architecture. These buildings are in Schoenbrunn Village, near New Philadelphia, Ohio.

woods for building purposes are classed as *select* for finish and trim, or *common*. Hardwoods are graded as first, seconds, and common. Lumber is available as rough or surfaced. S2S means "surfaced 2 sides."

Plywood is built up of layers of veneer, or thin wood sheets with the grain of one sheet at right angles to the next. They are glued and pressed into panels. The veneer is generally cut from the log by peeling, just as paper is unwound from a roll. A long blade peels it off as the log rotates. Plywood is sold in sheets of standard sizes such as 4 by 12, 4 by 10, or 4 by 8 ft and smaller. Plywood panels faced with cabinet wood veneers as walnut, oak, and mahogany are available.

Pressed woods are new forms of sheet wood made from wood chips that have been processed and pressed into sheets. They are more resistant to warping than is plywood of the same thickness and are less costly.

Defects in lumber. Common defects in lumber which you can easily recognize are warping or twisting; cup-

Fig. 3.4 (above left). This man is a "high climber." He climbs the giant trees, trimming off branches, and then cuts off the top. (*Courtesy: American Forest Products Industries.*)

Fig. 3.5 (above right). The high climber "tops" a giant Douglas fir. This is done before the tree is felled. (*Courtesy: American Forest Products Industries.*)

Fig. 3.6 (below). Felling a Douglas fir with a power saw. The saw blade is an endless chain to which teeth are fastened. (*Courtesy: American Forest Products Industries.*)

Fig. 3.7. Sawing logs into lumber. The man on the carriage moves the log into a huge band saw, which slices off boards. (Courtesy: American Forest Products Industries.)

Fig. 3.8. Sawing a smaller log into several boards at one time with a Swedish gang saw.

ping, in which one side of the board is hollow and the other high; and checking, or the small cracks on edges, ends, or faces.

Conserving forests and woods. Twenty-five years ago boys and girls were told that the forests would soon be used up. This would have been true had not a tremendous program of tree planting been started. Each year now our new wood growth equals about 98 per cent of the amount that is cut or destroyed. Tree farming has become a going business in twenty-five years.

Forest fires are more effectively controlled today, too. Yet in 1949 more than 15,000,000 acres of forests were burned. Each year such fires cause needless and inexcusable waste of trees as well as loss of life and property. Nine out of ten forest fires are caused by the carelessness of people.

Industry uses more parts of the trees today than it did formerly. Limbs, twigs, and even bark, leaves, and sawdust are converted into other materials and products.

Design and Woods

Pre-twentieth-century styles have been used so long in wood products that we sometimes assume that projects we make must be modeled after those styles to be good. This is not a true assumption. Using modern materials, processes, and ideas without being limited by the designs of historical cabinetmakers, you should so design your projects that they serve today's purposes. Such a procedure does not show a lack of appreciation for the work of those cabinetmakers. They

Fig. 3.9. Giant lathes peel thin sheets of wood, called "veneer," from logs just as paper is unrolled from a roll. (*Courtesy: Douglas Fir Plywood Association. A.F.P.I. photo.*)

Fig. 3.10. Stacks of pulpwood logs that will be ground up, cooked, treated, and made into paper.

designed for their times. Let us design for ours. See if you can "dream up" some unusual ideas for wood projects—some that are different and better than any you have seen. Remember, no design is so good that someone can't improve on it.

When You Work With Wood

Wood is a friendly material. The trees from which the wood came were friendly to all. They sheltered the birds, fed the squirrels, shaded the cattle from the hot sun, slowed and calmed destructive winds and water, and made homes for millions of people. But wood can be very obstinate and "ornery" when you don't treat it right. It refuses to be smoothed with dull tools. It goes to pieces when nailed too close to the edge. It shrinks when cold and dry and swells when warm and damp. When the wrong wood is used, your project is less useful and beautiful than it might have been.

The best way to get acquainted with wood is to work with it, to give it a chance to show how well it can serve you. Some wood is soft and some is hard; some is dark and some is light; some is splintery and some is smooth; some is strong and some is weak; some stand the weather and some cannot "take it." Your teacher will show you various kinds of woods and will help you to select the best one for each project you make. You will need to get well acquainted with the tools described on the following pages, too, because the more skillful you become with them, the more you will enjoy woodworking. Remember, the best piece of wood is not always in the middle of the board.

Woodworking Tools

Many different tools have been designed for working with wood. Each of them is intended to perform a certain process. The oldest was probably a sharp stone or shell for cutting and scraping. Hand tools are rarely invented today; the greatest develop-

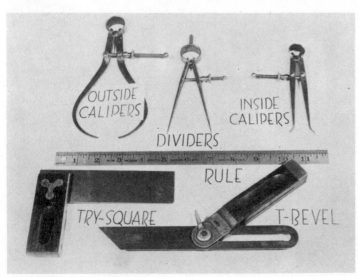

Fig. 3.11. Some layout and measuring tools used in woodworking.

Fig. 3.12. Marking a board square for sawing, with the *try-square*.

Fig. 3.13. Checking the end of a board for squareness.

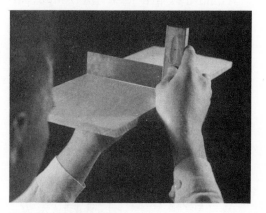

Fig. 3.14. Checking a face of a board for flatness.

Fig. 3.15. Marking an angle on a board with the sliding *T-bevel*.

ments are in machine processes, an example of which is electronic gluing in which synthetic glues are cured electrically to form perfect bonds. The tools and machines described here perform the common, most used processes.

Measuring Tools

Measuring tools are designed to help you work accurately to dimension.

The rule. A steel rule is used for measuring and as a straight edge. If you use a wood rule, set it on edge when measuring.

The try-square. This tool is used for measuring, for checking right angles (checking for square), and as a straight edge. A six-in. blade is best for your purposes. The steel square is a larger model.

The T bevel. This is an adjustable device for transferring angles. The blade and handle are set at the desired angle and locked. The T bevel is especially handy for checking chamfers and bevels.

The calipers. These are tools for measuring inside and outside diameters. When setting, the caliper is laid on a rule to get the dimension.

The dividers. This tool is similar to a compass used for laying out circles and arcs, except it does not hold a pencil. It is useful for finding centers, for stepping off distances, and for dividing lines.

MEASURE TWICE, SAW ONCE!

Handsaws

Handsaws are used for rough cutting: the crosscut saw for cutting across the grain, and the ripsaw for cutting with it.

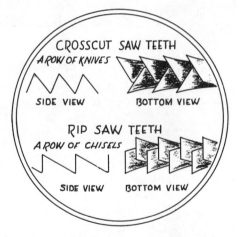

Sizes. Blade lengths vary from 16 to 26 in. The coarseness of the teeth is given in points per inch. A general purpose crosscut saw is a 22 in., 10 point saw, and a ripsaw, a 24 or 26 in., 5 point saw.

Care of handsaws. To cut straight, a saw must be straight and sharp. Use a handsaw only on wood. Hang it up when you are not using it. The saw handle breaks easily when the saw is dropped.

How to crosscut:

1. Square a line across the board.
2. Clamp the board flatwise in the vise.
3. The idea is to cut just outside the line, so place the saw teeth accordingly. With your thumb as a guide, about two inches above the teeth, start the cut with slow, short strokes.
4. Gradually lengthen the strokes until most of the teeth are used. Move your thumb away. A sharp saw requires little pressure. If the saw sticks, you are pressing too hard.
5. Ease up with short strokes as you finish the cut. Hold the piece being cut off to avoid splitting.

Fig. 3.17. Start a saw cut with a pull stroke. This is a cross-cut saw for cutting across the grain.

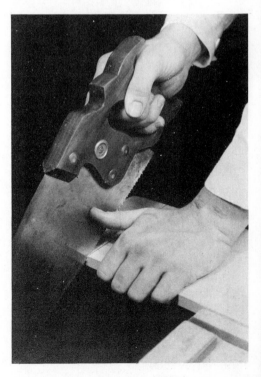

How to rip:

1. Mark the line.

2. Clamp the board vertically in the vise and saw as for crosscutting.

Safety sense. A dull saw chews more fingers because it skids in starting. Ease up as you finish the cut to avoid skinning your knuckles. Hang the saw on the tool panel so that the teeth don't stick out ready to "bite" someone.

The backsaw. The backsaw is used for making accurate cuts, as in joints, and for cutting to length. Blade lengths are usually from 10 to 16 in. The coarseness of teeth for these lengths is usually 13 points per in.

Care of the saw. Never use the backsaw for rough cutting. Keep it

Fig. 3.18.   Using a *rip* saw to saw a board with the grain.

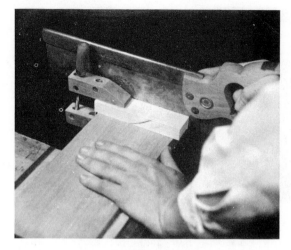

Fig. 3.19.   Sawing a board off to accurate dimension with a *back* saw and a guide block.

hung up when not in use to prevent dulling of the teeth and bending of the blade or the back.

How to cut a board to length:

1. Square a line across the board.

2. Clamp the board flatwise in a vise.

3. Clamp a straight piece of wood over the mark for a guide.

4. Keep the blade snug against the guide as you draw it slowly back and forth over the face of the board.

5. Little pressure is needed on a sharp saw. Lift up slightly on the last few strokes so that the saw doesn't break through.

How to cut a dado:

1. Mark out the dado with a square.

2. With a guide, as above, cut to the depth on each side.

3. Clean out the center, using a wood chisel as near the width of the dado as possible.

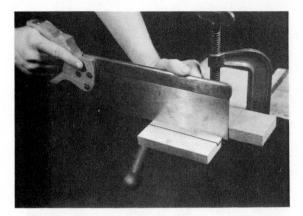

Fig. 3.20. Cutting a dado with a back saw and guide block. The dado is marked out with a try-square.

How to cut a rabbet:

1. Mark out the rabbet with a square and make the end cut.

2. Make the face cut using a guide.

The miter box. The miter box is a device in which wood can be sawed accurately to desired angles. The saw is swung to the angle, and with the wood held firmly against the fence, the cut is made. Be sure to figure the angle correctly before you saw.

The coping saw. The coping saw

Fig. 3.21. Cutting the end grain for a rabbet (see Fig. 3.49).

is used for cutting curves in wood not thicker than an inch. It is not intended for cutting straight lines. It cuts best with a vertical, pull stroke as in a jig saw rather than as a handsaw.

Blades. Two types of blades are used: pin end and loop end. Round blades with spiral cutting edges are available. These cut in any direction without turning the blade. Some blades cut plastics and soft metals.

Inserting a blade. Unscrew the handle three or four turns and press

Fig. 3.22. Making an angular cut with a *miter box*. This cuts angles from 45° to 90°.

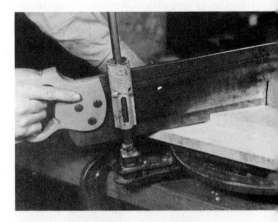

the saw frame against the bench until the blade can be slipped into the grooves. The teeth should point toward the handle. Then tighten the handle.

Cutting curves. Clamp the board flat on the edge of the bench. Holding the saw vertically, start with short, quick strokes. Press forward only enough to keep the teeth cutting. If the blade sticks, you are pressing too hard. Keep the blade cutting as you turn the frame to go around the curves. For fine detail sawing, use a saddle or

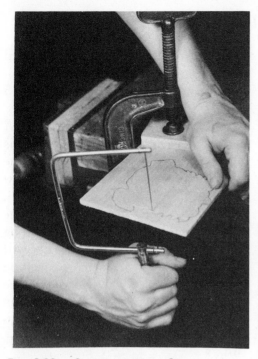

Fig. 3.23. Cutting out a figure with the *coping* saw. You may prefer to clamp the wood to a bench, as shown here.

Fig. 3.24. You can use a V-block to support the work for the coping saw. Hold it firmly so that it can't jump up and down.

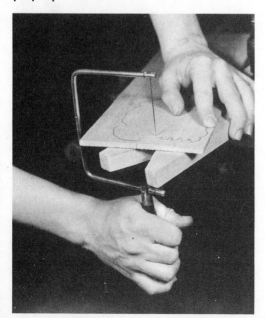

V block, to support the material. The blade should cut close to the V.

Cutting a hole. Bore a $\frac{1}{4}$-in. hole near the line in the waste stock. Stick the blade through the hole and insert it in the frame.

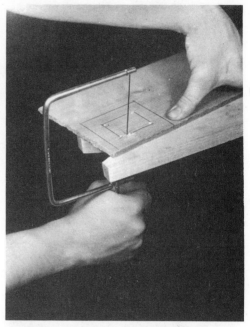

Fig. 3.25. Cutting out a hole in a piece of wood with the coping saw.

Hand Planes

Hand planes are designed to make wood surfaces smooth and flat. There are many types of planes, some for general use and others for special purposes. The following are those you are likely to use:

Block plane. This is a small plane, about 6 inches long, which can be used in one hand. It is handy for model building, planing chamfers, and other light work.

Smooth plane. This is the next larger plane, usually 8 to 9 inches long. It is your best all-round plane. Use both hands on it.

Fig. 3.26. A book rack in contemporary design. It is very simple, yet very functional. Make a full-size drawing, then cut out the ends with coping saw, jig saw, or band saw.

Fig. 3.27. When your plane is really sharp it will cut a beautiful shaving.

Jack plane. This is the general purpose plane for a carpenter or cabinetmaker. Lengths vary from 11 to 15 inches.

Some tips on using planes. A plane is useless unless the blade is sharp and properly adjusted for the job. Your teacher will show you how a sharp, well-adjusted plane cuts. Note the shavings and that the plane shaves smoothly rather than chewing or tearing the wood. Your teacher will show you how to keep the plane iron sharp and adjusted. When your plane is not in use, lay it on its side. Can you figure out why? Planes with cast-iron beds can be dropped only once. Why?

How to plane the face of a board:

1. Clamp the board on top of the

Fig. 3.28. Four common hand planes. Use the one which best fits the job and you.

JACK

SMOOTH

BLOCK

MODELER'S

bench or in a vise. Make a few trial cuts as you adjust the blade for thin shaving.

2. Now plane over the entire surface, in the direction of the grain, frequently checking for flatness with a try square. Should the grain roughen, plane from the opposite direction.

3. Hold the plane at a slight angle to, but push in the direction of, the grain. Lift the plane on the return stroke.

How to plane an edge:

1. Mark the line to which you will plane and clamp the board in a vise, close to the line.

2. Hold the plane firmly and squarely on the edge and at a slight angle to it, push it slowly from one end to the other.

3. Check for trueness with a straight edge, then with a try square check the edge for squareness with the face.

How to plane an end:

1. The blade must be very sharp and set for a thinner cut than when planing an edge. Square a line across the board as near the end as possible and clamp it in a vise, close to the mark.

2. Holding the plane firmly and squarely on the end and at a slight angle to it, push it slowly and steadily. If you plane clear across, the wood will split at the far corner, so plane from each edge toward the middle.

How to plane a board square.

Using the suggested procedures for planing and checking for true with the try square, follow these steps:

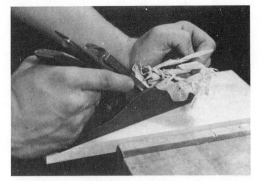

Fig. 3.29. Planing a face. Hold the plane at a slight angle to the grain of the wood, but push it with the grain, not across it.

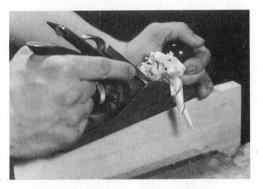

Fig. 3.30. Planing an edge. Hold the plane at a slight angle. Push it along the entire edge.

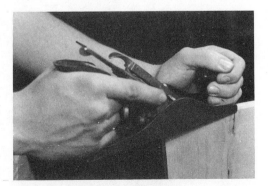

Fig. 3.31. Planing the end grain. The plane must be held at an angle so that the blade slices the wood.

1. Select the best side of the board for the No. 1 face. Test it for true. Plane off any high spots.

2. Plane an edge straight and square with this face.

3. Plane one end straight and square with the face as well as the edge.

4. Mark and saw off the board about $\frac{1}{16}$ in. longer than desired. Plane this end to the mark, making it square with the face and the edge.

5. Mark off the width from the true edge. Plane to this mark. Keep the edge square with the face and with each end. If there is too much wood to plane, rip off the excess with a saw.

6. Plane the No. 2 face true and the board to the desired thickness.

Chisels and Gouges

The wood chisel. The wood chisel is used for fitting wood joints and for shaping. It causes more injuries than any other shop tool because it is so often misused. *Butt* chisels are short and husky; *socket* chisels are long and slender. Size is given as the width of the blade. Sizes range from $\frac{1}{4}$ to 2 in.

How to use a wood chisel:

1. Use only a sharp chisel. Ask your teacher how to sharpen it.

2. Use as wide a chisel as the job will permit and make sure that the handle is on securely.

3. Be sure to clamp the work tightly in a vise or on the bench so that you can use both hands on the chisel. Use a mallet on the chisel only when you must have the extra force.

4. When making *paring* or shaping cuts use one hand on the handle and the other on the blade so that you can control the cutting.

5. Never let one hand or finger get out in front of the chisel while cutting. Always cut away from yourself. When you lay the chisel down, place it so that the edge is protected.

Gouges. A gouge is a chisel with a curved cutting edge. It is used as a chisel for hollowing and shaping.

Carving chisels. These are small chisels and gouges with cutting edges

Fig. 3.32. A set of wood chisels and a set of carving chisels.

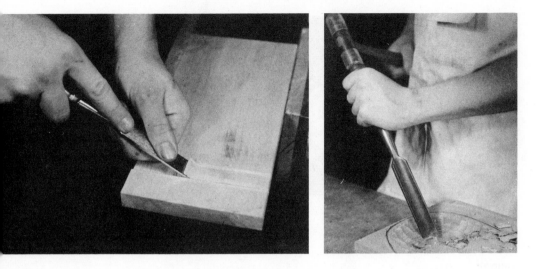

Fig. 3.33 (above left). Cleaning out the waste for a dado with a wood chisel. Use both hands on the tool. The bevel should be down.

Fig. 3.34. (above right). Hollowing out a tray with a gouge and a mallet.

in assorted shapes to suit various cuts. The chisels illustrated are used by hand only, not with a mallet. They will cut wood, linoleum, and other soft materials.

How not to use chisels:

1. A chisel is not for prying open cans of paint.

2. It is not for prying open boxes.

3. It is not a screwdriver.

4. It should not be carried in your pocket.

Knives

Knives are used mostly for whittling and carving. Those with replaceable blades are easiest to use and to keep sharp.

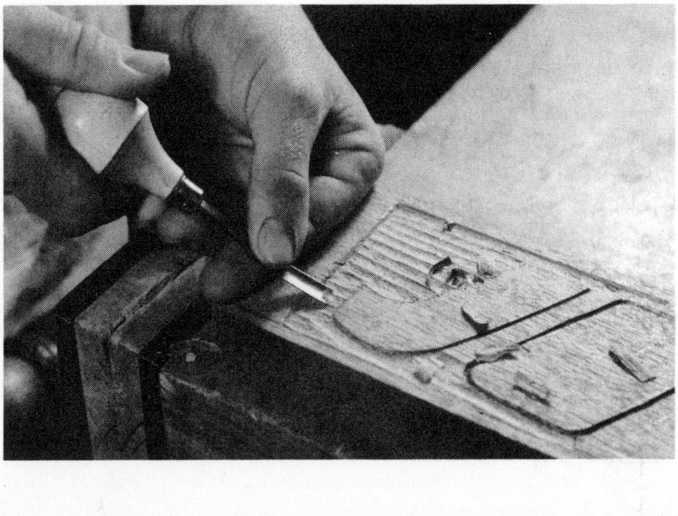

Fig. 3.35. Using a carving chisel to cut away the background of a carving. This tool is a gouge. The outlining was done with a V-shaped tool, a veining tool.

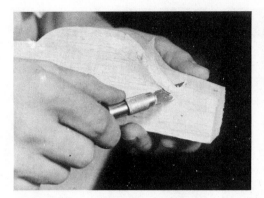

Fig. 3.36. Roughing out a model auto from a block of balsa with a knife. Remember, cut away from yourself.

Fig. 3.37. Smoothing a sawed curve with a cabinet file.

Cutting safely. Keep these pointers in mind and you won't cut yourself again with a knife:

1. Use only a sharp knife. The dull one may not cut wood, but it causes most injuries.

2. Always cut away from yourself.

3. Never carry an open knife in your pocket, even for a moment or two in the shop.

4. Use a knife for cutting, not for prying or in place of a screwdriver.

Wood Files

Wood files are used for smoothing curves, usually on the edges of boards after they have been sawed out. The two common types are the *wood rasp* with coarse teeth for rough cutting, and the *wood file* (sometimes called the *cabinet rasp*) with finer teeth for smoother cutting. The most used shape is the half round. It has one side round and the other flat. Wood files are also round or square. Common lengths are 8, 10, and 12 inches. Do not use any file without a handle.

How to shape an edge with a file:

1. Clamp the board in a vise with the edge to be filed as horizontal as possible. Clamp the edge close to the vise.

2. With one hand holding the point and the other the handle, push the file diagonally across the edge; lift on the return stroke and repeat. A file cuts better this way than when rubbed back and forth.

3. Use the curved side for hollow curves and the flat side for flat edges and convex surfaces. Clean the teeth frequently with a file card. Work down to the mark so that there will be a minimum of sanding to do.

4. Watch the edge as you file. The wood should be quite smooth and clean cut. If the file roughens the edge, change the direction of the filing. File from the opposite side or at a different angle to the edge.

The Brace and Bit

The brace and bit together are used

Fig. 3.38. Boring a hole with an auger bit and brace.

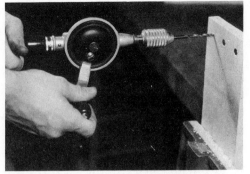

Fig. 3.39. Using the hand drill.

for boring holes in wood. The brace is used with other tools, as countersinks and screwdriver bits.

The brace. Braces are made with or without ratchets (for working in close quarters). The jaws can grip both round and square shanks. Brace size is given as the swing—the diameter of the circle swung by the handle as the brace is turned. A 12-inch swing is a common size.

Auger bits. Auger bits are wood-boring tools. The most common sizes bore holes from ¼ to 1¼ in. in diameter. The number on the shank is the diameter of the hole in sixteenths; for example, a No. 5 bores a ⁵⁄₁₆-in. hole.

Care of the brace and bits. A drop of oil is occasionally needed in the head of the brace. The bits need sharpening periodically. Ask your teacher to demonstrate this. If a bit gets bent, lay it on a scrap board and roll it over slowly until the high side comes up. Rap this with a soft mallet.

How to bore holes:

1. Unscrew the chuck on the brace a few turns, insert the tang, and tighten.

2. Press the point of the lead screw in at the center of the desired hole. Press against the head of the brace with one hand and, with the other, turn the handle clockwise. To cut fastest, press firmly but turn slowly.

3. When the screw point comes through the back side, stop and reverse the direction to remove the bit. Finish the boring from the opposite side. This procedure prevents splintering.

The Hand Drill

The hand drill is used for drilling small holes, usually not larger than ¼ in., in wood, metal, plastics, or other material. It turns a straight shank twist drill bit. (See page 64.) The drill illustrated is typical; some have enclosed gears.

How to use a hand drill:

1. To insert a drill bit in the drill, grasp the chuck with one hand, and with the other turn the crank backward (counter clockwise) to open the jaws. Insert the bit, hold the chuck, and turn the crank in the opposite direction until it draws up snug.

2. Prick a center mark at the desired point, insert the point of the bit and, holding the drill handle with one hand, turn the crank clockwise. Use only enough pressure to keep the bit cutting. Ease up on the pressure as the bit breaks through the back of the material.

A safety tip. Since you can get a finger pinched in the gears when tightening or loosening the chuck, watch where you hold the drill.

The automatic drill. This tool is used for drilling small holes in soft materials. Pumping the handle up and down makes the bit revolve. Its special bits are kept in the handle.

Drill Bits

Drill bits are used in hand drills, drill presses, and portable power drills for drilling holes in woods, metals, plastic, and the like. There are several types, the most common being the straight shank *twist drills*. Sizes are designated by fraction, number, or letter. Common sizes range from $\frac{1}{32}$ in. to $\frac{1}{2}$ in. by 64ths, from No. 1 to No. 80 in the wire gauge, and from *A* to *Z* by letter. The size is stamped on the shank, but when the drill has been used, the marks are difficult to read. In this case find the hole that fits in a drill holder to get the size. *Carbon steel drill bits* are used for soft materials such as wood and plastic, and *high-speed steel bits* are used for metals.

Comparative sizes of drill bits. These are but a few of the more than a hundred sizes up to $\frac{1}{2}$ in. (* indicates nearest to fractional size):

Fractional Size	Wire Gauge	Letter
$\frac{1}{16}$	52*	
$\frac{3}{32}$	42*	
$\frac{1}{8}$	30*	
$\frac{5}{32}$	22*	
$\frac{3}{16}$	12*	
$\frac{1}{4}$		E
$\frac{5}{16}$		O*
$\frac{3}{8}$		V*
$\frac{7}{16}$		-
$\frac{1}{2}$		

How to use twist drills:

1. Use only sharp drill bits. A dull bit rubs and gets hot and, if forced, will break or burn. Ask your instructor to show you how to tell when a drill bit is cutting as it should.

2. Press only hard enough to keep the drill bit cutting. It should not bend under the pressure.

3. Oil is used as a coolant on the bit when drilling steel, and water is used on cast iron. No coolant is needed for wood, plastics, brass, copper, or aluminum.

Fig. 3.40.   A comic-book rack. All you need is a board and a few pieces of dowel rod.

Hammers

A hammer is probably the first woodworking tool you ever used. It is the handiest to have around. Several types are used:

The claw hammer. This is the hammer for driving and pulling nails. These hammers are sized according to the weight of the head. A 7-oz hammer is for small nails and brads; a 16-oz hammer is for general use. A claw hammer should not be used on cold chisels or any hard material that can mar the face because it makes nail driving difficult.

How to drive a nail:

1. Grasp the hammer as shown and tap the nail lightly to start it, so that it stands by itself.

2. Drive the nail down flush with the surface with accurate blows. At first it takes a lot of courage to strike the nail hard, but with practice you should be able to drive a 6d nail with three or four blows.

Fig. 3.41. Driving a nail. Use all of the hammer handle. Note how the nails are slanted; they hold better this way.

How to pull a nail. The claws of the hammer are intended for pulling nails. To protect the surface of

Fig. 3.42. Pulling a nail with a claw hammer.

the board, lay a block under the head. This procedure gives added leverage, too, and makes pulling easier.

The nail set. This is a slender punch for setting the heads of brads and finish nails below the surface so that they may be hidden with filler. Place the set squarely on the head and, with the hammer, drive it down 1/32 to 1/16 in.

Upholsterer's hammer. This is a tack hammer with one end magnetized for holding and starting tacks. Once started, the tack is driven with the other end.

Soft-face hammers and mallets. Soft-face hammers have replaceable plastic faces. In woodwork they are used for the same purposes as are mallets; for example, driving wood chisels and tapping joints together. Mallets have soft heads, usually of wood, rubber, or rawhide.

Nails

Although the carpenter depends on nails for fastening lumber, the cabinetmaker uses glue and, now and then, small nails. The ordinary types of carpenters' nails are *common, casing,* and

NAILS

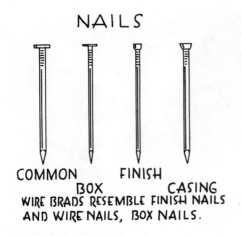

COMMON   FINISH
    BOX   CASING
WIRE BRADS RESEMBLE FINISH NAILS
AND WIRE NAILS, BOX NAILS.

Fig. 3.43.   Kinds of nails.

finishing. Sizes are given as 6d, 8d, and so on. The "d" is called "penny." Originally in England the price of nails was so many pennies per 100; for example, 8d per 100. The larger the nail the more they cost.

COMMON SIZES OF CARPENTERS' NAILS

Size	Length (in.)		
	Common and Box	Casing	Finishing
2d	1	1	1
4	1½	1½	1½
6	2	2	2
8	2½	2½	2½
10	3	3	3
12	3½	3½	3½
16	4	4	4
20	4½		
40	5		
60	6		

Wire nails and brads. Wire nails are similar in appearance to common nails and wire brads are similar to finishing nails. Wire nails and brads are made in a greater assortment of lengths and diameters, however. Sizes range usually from ¼-in. No. 20 to 3-in. No. 10. The larger the "No.", the smaller the diameter. A No. 15 brad is approximately ⅛-in. in diameter and is about twice as thick as a No. 20 brad.

How to make nails hold better. Slanting the nails gives them more holding power. (See Fig. 3.41.) Stagger them so that they don't fall into the same grain line and split the wood. Wire brads, casing nails, and finishing nails are usually set. (See page 65.)

Screwdrivers

The original use for a screwdriver was to drive wood screws, but it is so handy for prying open cans, boxes, and such that manufacturers usually make some of them rugged enough to do this. There are two distinct types: those for *slotted* screws and those for *recessed* head screws (Phillips head). Sizes of the former are given by the length of the blade; a 4-inch and a 6-inch screwdriver will do most of

Fig. 3.44.   Installing a wood screw with a screwdriver.

your work. For recessed screws, pick the screwdriver to fit.

How to drive screws:

1. Pick the screwdriver that fits the screw snugly.

2. Insert the bit in the slot and hold it there with one hand while you turn the screwdriver with the other hand. Keep the screwdriver in line with the screw.

Screwdriver bits. These bits are used in an auger brace for driving screws easier and faster. Blades are available for both types of screws.

The countersink (brace type). This tool, used in an auger brace, cuts a tapered hole to fit the head of a flat-head wood screw.

How to countersink a hole:

Fig. 3.45. Countersinking a hole for a flat-head wood screw.

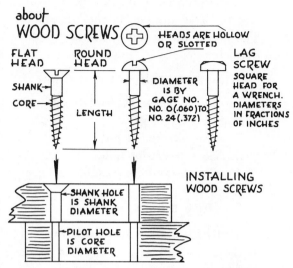

1. Insert the point in the screw hole and turn the brace clockwise.

2. After two or three turns try the screw. The head should lie flush with or just below the surface.

Wood Screws

Wood screws hold better in wood than do nails and they can be easily removed to permit taking a project apart. There are a great many kinds of wood screws. They vary by head, material, finish, slot, and thread as shown in this table.

Head	flat, round, oval
Material	steel, aluminum, brass
Finish	bright, blue, cadmium, chromium
Slot	straight, recessed (Phillips)
Thread	regular, drive type.

Those that you will use most often are the flat-head bright (F.H.B.) and the round-head blue (R.H.Bl.) with either slotted or recessed heads.

Sizes. Both lengths and diameters vary. The most common lengths are from ½ to 3 in. with diameters from 4 to 12 in. A screw size is indicated as, for example, 1 in. No. 6, 1½ in. No. 8. The number is the diameter. The larger the number, the larger the diameter.

How to install wood screws:

1. Select the screw and the screwdriver (see page 66).
2. Bore the shank hole.
3. Bore the pilot hole.
4. Countersink the shank hole, if needed.
5. Drive the screw.

Drill bit sizes for wood screws:

Screw diameter	4	5	6	7	8	9	10	11	12
Shank drill	⅛	⅛	⁵⁄₃₂	⁵⁄₃₂	³⁄₁₆	³⁄₁₆	³⁄₁₆	⁷⁄₃₂	⁷⁄₃₂
Pilot drill	¹⁄₁₆	³⁄₃₂	³⁄₃₂	⅛	⅛	⅛	⅛	⁵⁄₃₂	⁵⁄₃₂

Smaller pilot holes can be used in soft wood than in hard wood.

Glues and Cements

Glues and cements can make stronger joints in wood than can nails or screws. They can be used when nails or screws would be inappropriate. A good glue joint is actually stronger than the wood itself.

Several kinds of glues are available: animal, fish, casein, synthetic, and plastic. Animal and fish glues can be had in liquid or in flakes for melting. They are not waterproof. Casein glue is made from milk and is purchased in powder form to be mixed with water.

The synthetic glues are usually in powder form to be mixed with water. Be sure to follow the manufacturer's instructions. Liquid plastic in tubes, like model airplane cement, is useful in the assembly of small pieces of wood. But because it dries so quickly it would be difficult to use for gluing boards together for a table top, for example.

Rubber cement, although not for gluing wood together, is a very handy adhesive. Use it for cementing paper, cloth, leather, paper patterns to wood and metal, and the like. When dry it can be rubbed off the surface.

Some tips on gluing:

1. When gluing boards edge to edge, alternate the grain to counteract warping.
2. Pressure is needed when gluing boards together. Adjust the clamps to fit before applying the glue. Do not remove the clamps until the glue is dry, usually 4 to 24 hours.
3. Glue surfaces must be in full contact to get strong joints.
4. Apply glue quickly to both surfaces, using no more than necessary to cover. Excess glue oozes out. Wipe off the excess of water-mixed glues immediately with a damp cloth. Scrape off the excess of quick-drying cements.

Fig. 3.47. The end grain is alternated when boards are glued edge to edge.

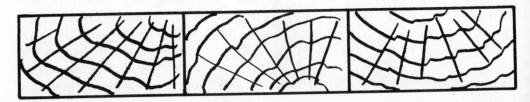

Fig. 3.48. A table top being glued. Pressure by clamping is necessary for strong joints.

Clamps and Clamping

Clamps are used for holding and pressing when a vise is not suitable. Use the type and size best suited for the job. Protect the work from jaw marks by inserting pieces of wood.

"C" clamps. These are general purpose clamps, shaped like a "C," for holding pieces of wood face to face. Sizes are given in inches, referring to the maximum opening.

Hand screws. These are for general clamping, too, but are especially useful when the sides of the work being held are not parallel. Common sizes have openings ranging from 6 to 14 inches.

Bar clamps. Bar clamps are for holding large work, especially for gluing boards edge to edge, as for table tops. Sizes are given in feet and refer to the maximum opening.

Finishes

Finishes are applied to wood to protect and preserve it, to make it more useful, and for color and texture. A thorough sanding of the surface is usually necessary before a finish is applied. Consult with your teacher about the selection of a finish for your projects. Always read the instructions on the label of a can of finish before using it.

Shellac and wax. This is an easy finish to apply. It is dust proof and leaves the wood in its natural color. Brush on a coat of white shellac thinned two parts of shellac to one of alcohol. When dry, usually 20 to 25 minutes, rub lightly with 6-0 sandpaper until the surface feels smooth.

Apply several coats of paste polishing wax, letting each dry and then rubbing it to a luster before applying the next. Four or five coats are sufficient. Put the wax inside a soft cloth when applying it. Clean shellac brushes in alcohol.

Oil and wax. Oil finishes bring out the natural beauty of woods most effectively. They are easiest to apply, dry dust free, but require much rubbing.

With a rag, swab on a coating of a mixture of two parts warm linseed oil and one part of turpentine. After it has soaked in for about an hour, wipe off the excess. Let it dry overnight, then rub it hard with a soft cloth until it shines.

Apply as many coats as you wish, one per day, but at least three or four. When thoroughly dry and rubbed, apply two coats of wax as for the shellac finish.

Tempera. Tempera paints are water-mixed opaque colors used for decorative purposes. They are easier to use than is enamel for painting designs. First seal the surface of the wood with a thin coat of shellac. Sand it smooth when dry. Stir the tempera and add water until it brushes smoothly, covering in one coat. Tempera that is too thick will peel.

When the design is dry, spray on a coat of clear lacquer to protect the tempera. Cut the lacquer with lacquer thinner until it sprays easily. A fly spray gun will do. Tempera brushes are cleaned with water.

Enamels and varnishes. Enamels are opaque, waterproof colors used when a slow-drying, weather-resistant finish is desired. Some are made of natural oils and gums and some are synthetic, so be sure to read the instructions on the label.

Enamels are commonly applied to the bare wood and brushed in. After 24 hours of drying they are hard enough to sand lightly with fine sandpaper. Lay on a heavy second coat, brushing from the center of the surface out to each end. This coat should be just heavy enough that brush marks will level out, thus leaving a mirror-like surface. When possible, let the enamel set for an hour in a horizontal position to avoid runs. On vertical surfaces paint with vertical strokes. Two coats are usually adequate.

Varnish is a clear enamel and is applied in the same manner. Spar varnish is waterproof. Brushes are cleaned in paint thinner followed by hot water and soap.

Lacquer. Lacquer is a synthetic liquid plastic. It is water proof and weather resistant and dries in 15 to 20 minutes. Airplane dope is lacquer. For brushing, use a slow-drying lacquer thinner to cut the lacquer; for spraying, use a fast-drying thinner. Lacquers spray better than they brush.

On porous woods, like balsa, mix some whiting with the first coat to act as a filler. Brush this on. When dry, sand it smooth and add six to eight coats by brush or spray of the desired color, allowing about 15 to 20 minutes between them. No sanding is done between these coats because each coat dissolves the one beneath, thus resulting in one thick coat. When the last coat is dry, apply a coat of thinner to help smooth the surface. Let this dry and then rub well with fine rubbing and polishing compound until you have a soft, lustrous, automobile-type finish. Clean brushes and spray gun with lacquer thinner.

Abrasives

In the process of making a smooth

surface on wood, sandpapering follows filing, planing, and such tool processes. Coarse sandpaper removes tool marks and finer sandpaper removes the scratches made by the coarse. Three kinds of sandpaper are common; flint, garnet, and aluminum oxide. Flint is least costly and is recommended for woods that tend to gum up and clog the grit. Garnet cuts faster and lasts longer than flint; and aluminum oxide cuts faster and outlasts garnet. Sandpaper is not sand glued to paper, rather it is paper coated with tiny, sharp pieces of hard, crushed rock or other abrasive. Aluminum oxide abrasive is made from bauxite in an electric furnace and is much harder than flint or garnet rock.

A COMPARISON OF GRITS
(adapted from Behr-Manning classification)

	Flint	Garnet	Aluminum Oxide
Coarse	No. 2	No. 1½	No. 40
Medium	No. 1½	No. 1	No. 50
	No. 1	No. 0	No. 80
	No. ½	No. 2/0	No. 100
Fine	No. 0	No. 3/0	No. 120
	No. 2/0	No. 4/0	No. 150
Very fine	No. 4/0	No. 6/0	No. 220
	No. 6/0	No. 8/0	No. 280

Note that for flint and garnet the larger the number, the coarser the grit, and the more "O's", the finer. The aluminum oxide numbers are screen-mesh size through which the grit was sieved.

Using sandpaper. Cut the sheet into four approximate squares on a paper cutter (this keeps the cutter sharp). Use one piece at a time on a wood or rubber sanding block for

SOME CUTS AND JOINTS IN WOOD

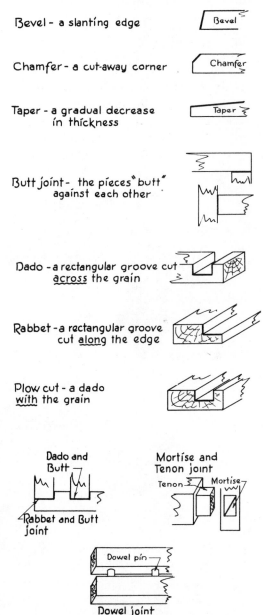

Bevel - a slanting edge

Chamfer - a cut-away corner

Taper - a gradual decrease in thickness

Butt joint - the pieces "butt" against each other

Dado - a rectangular groove cut across the grain

Rabbet - a rectangular groove cut along the edge

Plow cut - a dado with the grain

Dado and Butt

Rabbet and Butt joint

Mortise and Tenon joint

Dowel joint

Note the use of oblique drawings and symbols

smoothing flat surfaces. For inside curves wrap the paper around a piece of dowel or other suitable shape. Always sand with the grain of the wood, using only enough pressure to keep the sandpaper cutting.

The Jig Saw

The jig saw is a power-coping saw. A short blade moves up and down, cutting on the down stroke. It saws

wood, cardboard, plastics, and such soft metals as aluminum, copper, and brass. Jig saws are available in bench and floor models in sizes ranging from 12 in. for model making to 36 in. or more for industrial use. A saw with a swing of 18 in. or 24 in. (it will cut stock this wide) is best for all-round use.

Limitations. It is as important to know what not to cut on a jig saw as it is to know what to saw.

Fig. 3.50. The jig saw, or scroll saw, cuts fine detail in thin materials. (Courtesy: Rockwell Manufacturing Co.)

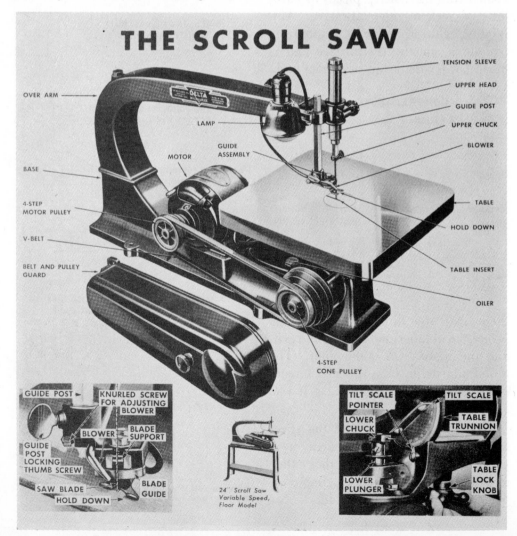

THE SCROLL SAW

1. The jig saw is not designed for cutting straight lines. Use a handsaw or circular saw.

2. It was not made to cut heavy stock, like 2 by 4's. One-inch stock is the maximum.

3. It cannot do every job that a coping saw can. You will still need to use a coping saw now and then.

4. It does not cut as fast as a band saw, so take your time. The longer you can saw without breaking a blade, the more expert you are.

Cutting speeds. The saw cuts best when run at the proper speed for the material. If the speed is too slow, you will tend to force the cutting; if it is too fast, you will not keep up with it. The fastest speeds are used on woods and the slowest on metals. Your teacher will show you how to set the speed.

Blades. Jig-saw blades are usually 5 in. in length and are available in various combinations of thickness, widths, and t.p.i. (teeth per inch). The blade should be selected for the kind of sawing to be done. The thinner the material being sawed, the greater the number of t.p.i.; the sharper the curves, the narrower the blade. Sheet metal requires a blade with finer teeth than does wood. For your usual sawing in wood, a blade about 0.110-in. wide, 0.020-in. thick and with 10 t.p.i. is recommended. This blade can be used on plastics. For sheet metals use blades with 20 to 30 t.p.i.

Installing a blade:

1. Remove the table insert and turn the motor by hand to get the vise at the bottom of the stroke.

2. Insert the blade, teeth pointing down, in the lower vise. Align the blade in the guide and tighten the vise. Then clamp the top end securely. Do not use a wrench or pliers unless the vises are designed for them. There should be not less than ½ in. of blade in a vise.

3. Turn the motor slowly by hand to see that the blade is in correctly. If it bends, the upper vise must be moved down the blade or the upper housing raised slightly to add tension. Replace the table insert. Have your teacher check the blade before you turn the motor on.

Order of sawing. Sometimes you cannot saw completely around a pattern without stopping because of extra sharp curves and abrupt changes in direction. These make several separate cuts necessary. Plan the order of cutting before you start sawing so that

Fig. 3.51. When the curves are too sharp, the cut is made from each side toward the center.

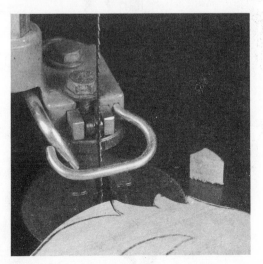

Fig. 3.52. To cut out a hole, the blade is installed through a small drilled hole.

you won't have to do much backing out.

How to saw:

1. Check for the proper blade and speed.

2. Adjust the hold-down fingers to press the work lightly against the table.

3. Guiding the work with both hands, push it just fast enough to keep it cutting. When making a turn, keep the blade cutting or it will twist and break.

4. To cut out holes, drill a ¼-in. hole near the line in the waste stock and install the blade through it.

Safety sense. The jig saw is a very safe machine, but carelessness can make it cruel. Read and heed:

THE BAND SAW

UPPER WHEEL GUARD
GUIDE POST LOCK SCREW
LAMP ATTACHMENT
ARM
SLIDING BLADE GUARD
BALL BEARING BLADE SUPPORT
BLADE GUIDES
TABLE
GUIDE POST
BLADE SUPPORT LOCK SCREW
BLADE GUIDE LOCK SCREW
BLADE
TABLE INSERT
BLADE SLOT
ALIGNMENT PIN
MITER GAGE GROOVE
BALL BEARING BLADE SUPPORT ADJUSTING SCREW
ADJUSTING SCREW FOR BLADE GUIDES
TABLE CLAMP
REAR BLADE GUARD
LOWER WHEEL GUARD

TILT POINTER
TABLE TILT SCALE
TABLE TRUNNION
LOWER BALL BEARING BLADE SUPPORT ADJUSTMENT NUT
LOWER BALL BEARING BLADE SUPPORT
LOWER BLADE GUIDE
SAW BLADE
LOWER BLADE GUIDE ADJUSTMENT NUT
TABLE LOCK KNOB
GUIDE POST
GUIDE BRACKET
BLADE GUARD
BALL BEARING BLADE SUPPORT ADJUSTING NUT
BLADE
BLADE GUIDE ADJUSTING NUT
BLADE GUIDE PIN
BALL BEARING BLADE SUPPORT
BLADE GUIDE PIN
GUIDE PIN ADJUSTING SCREWS

14" Wood- and Metal-cutting Band Saw
20" Wood-cutting Band Saw
36" Wood-, Metal-, and Sprue-cutting Band Saw

Fig. 3.53. The band saw has an endless saw blade. (Courtesy: Rockwell Manufacturing Co.)

Fig. 3.54. The band saw cuts curves in heavy material.

Fig. 3.55. Slicing a block of wood on the band saw, using the fence clamped to the table.

1. Keep your fingers to the side of the blade, never in front of it.

2. Use as slow a speed as is consistent with good cutting.

3. The light should shine on the work, not in your eyes.

4. Shut off the motor as soon as you are finished.

5. Never talk to a person while he is operating the saw.

The Band Saw

The band saw is a versatile machine. It has an endless blade around two wheels like a flat belt around two pulleys. It cuts curves and straight lines in thin and thick materials such as woods, plastics, and metals. It cuts faster but not as finely as does a jig saw. There are two common types, the wood cutting and the metal cutting.

The size is measured in inches from the blade to the frame across the table.

A 14-in. band saw is recommended for home and school use. Contrast this with band saws used in lumber mills for ripping logs, which have blades a foot wide.

Limitations. The limitations are in the nature of overloading:

1. Wide blades cannot make as sharp turns as can narrow blades. A ¼-in. blade will cut curves of 1-in. radius and larger. Curves that are too sharp bind the blade.

2. Heavy work can overload the blade. The saw may be able to accommodate a piece of balsa wood 6 in. thick but not be able to cut more than 3 in. of hard maple.

Blades. Blades are purchased to fit the saw and the total length is specified. For a 14-in. saw, blades from

75

THE DRILL PRESS

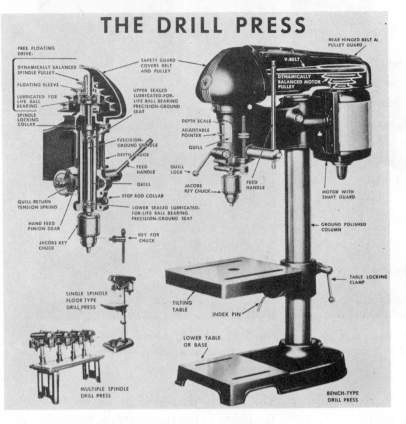

Fig. 3.56. The drill press. (Courtesy: Rockwell Manufacturing Co.)

⅛ to ½ in. wide are available for cutting wood, or metal, or plastic with the appropriate tooth style.

How to use a band saw. Before using the band saw for the first time have your teacher "check you out." Each time you use it make sure that all adjustments have been made beforehand.

1. Set the top blade guide so that it just clears the work.

2. Turn on the switch and, holding the work with both hands, feed it slowly into the teeth.

3. Cut on the outside of the line, using only enough pressure to keep the blade cutting. The blade must be cutting as you follow a curve or it will bind and break.

4. Follow a plan for cutting as described for the jig saw. You can pull the blade off the wheels backing out of tight places.

Safety sense. A band saw can be hard on fingers. Watch where you hold them.

1. If the blade is dull, don't use it. It will burn and break.

2. Keep the light focussed on the spot where the blade is cutting.

3. Keep your fingers to the side of the blade, never in front of it.

4. Make no adjustments on the machine while it is running.

5. When you are finished, shut off the motor and, after the saw stops, drop the blade guide down close to the table.

6. To watch someone operate the saw stand behind him and to the right. Do not speak to him while he is sawing.

7. If the blade breaks or comes off, stop the motor.

The Drill Press

Originally the drill press was for drilling holes; but with the many attachments now available, it is also used for boring, mortising, routing, shaping, sanding, grinding, buffing, and like processes. Drill presses are made in a wide range of sizes to suit a wide variety of jobs. The *single spindle type* (it drills one hole at a time) may be small enough to drill holes so tiny you can hardly see them or large enough to take locomotive parts. The *multiple spindle type* drills two or more holes at once and is an industrial production machine.

Limitations. Limitations on the use of a drill press are determined by the drill chuck, the size and shape of the work that can be accommodated, and the drill bit itself. A different chuck is required to hold a No. 80 drill bit from that required for a ½-in. size. High-speed bits should be used for drilling metals.

Drill speeds. Different size drill bits require different speeds, and different materials being drilled may require different speeds. See your teacher's chart on drill speeds. He will show you how to change speeds on your drill press.

Lubricants. It is necessary to use lubricants to protect the drill bit when drilling certain materials. Cutting produces heat and if this heat is not carried away the bit may get hot enough to turn blue, which means that it has lost its hardness and will no longer hold an edge. On hard steel use kerosene; on mild steel, cutting oil. Drill cast iron, aluminum, copper, plastics, and wood dry.

How to drill. These are general suggestions for drilling all materials:

1. Insert the drill bit and tighten the chuck with the key. Adjust the belt for the proper speed.

2. When possible, clamp the work to the drill press table. Use a V block to hold round stock. Always clamp metals. Put a piece of scrap wood under the work whenever possible to prevent drilling into the table.

3. Metals must be center punched for drilling.

4. Raise the table as near to the drill bit as possible and lock it in position with its center hole directly under the bit.

Fig. 3.57. Chucking a drill bit. Always use a chuck key to lock the bit securely.

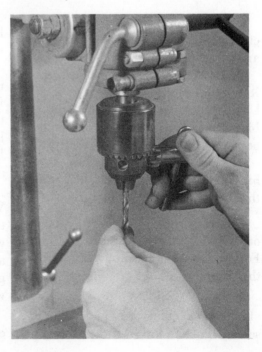

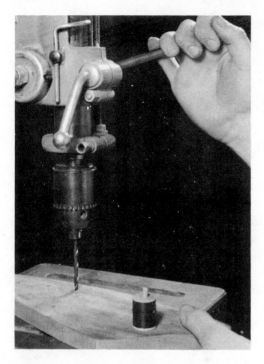

Fig. 3.58. Drilling a hole in a piece of wood. This is a rack to hold spools of thread. Small pieces should be clamped to the table.

5. Turn on the motor and start the cut with only slight pressure until you are sure the location is correct.

6. If a lubricant is needed, keep it dripping slowly on the bit as it cuts. Use only enough pressure to keep the bit cutting. Raise the bit from the hole occasionally to clear out the chips.

7. Ease up on the pressure as the bit cuts through the other side. Raise the bit and shut off the motor.

Drilling safely. The drill press is one of the safest of shop machines. Follow these suggestions to keep it that way.

1. The work must always be clamped or otherwise held securely, so it will not be jerked away from you.

2. The belts must be guarded to protect fingers and hair.

3. Use an eye shield to guard against flying chips of metal.

4. Be sure you get the necessary instruction before you use any attachment on the drill press.

Drilling troubles. The following will help you troubleshoot drilling problems:

Trouble	*Remedy*
1. Drill gets too hot.	Use a sharp drill. Use a lubricant. Clean chips from the drill bit. Use a faster feed.
2. Drill doesn't cut.	Sharpen the drill. Use a slower speed.
3. Drill squeals.	Use a sharp drill. Keep the drill cutting. Use a lubricant.
4. Drill breaks.	Use less pressure on the bit. Hold the work steady.

The Circular Saw

The circular saw, also known as a bench or table saw, is a most useful machine for woodworking. It deserves considerable respect, and anyone who takes lightly the common sense rules for its use is likely to get hurt. Your teacher may not permit you as a junior high school student to operate the saw. If so, it means that he feels you are not ready for it. The chances for injury are greater than on the jig saw. When he decides that you are ready to learn to operate this machine, he will probably demonstrate crosscutting and ripping first. The following is general information to acquaint you with the saw.

About the circular saw. The circular saw has a round, flat blade with

THE CIRCULAR SAW

TABLE
STOP ROD
MITER GAGE
RIGID TYPE SPLITTER MOUNTED GUARD
FENCE

FENCE ADJUSTMENT SCREWS
POINTER
REAR FENCE LOCK KNOB
FENCE CLAMP HANDLE
MICRO-SET KNOB

SAW TILT HANDWHEEL
SAW TILT SCALE
LOCK KNOB
SAW RAISING HANDWHEEL
SWITCH
SAWDUST CLEAN-OUT
CABINET BASE

REAR GUIDE BAR
REAR FENCE LOCK KNOB
FRONT GRADUATED GUIDE BAR
MOTOR
FENCE MICRO-SET KNOB
FRONT FENCE CLAMP HANDLE
CABINET
RUBBER CORD

SAW BLADE
CUPPED SAW BLADE FLANGE
ARBOR NUT
INNER SAW BLADE FLANGE
BEARING LOADING SPRING
PULLEY
SPACING COLLARS
SPANNER NUT
HEX JAM NUT
ARBOR with Modified Left Hand Acme Thread
ARBOR BRACKET
V-BELT
Sealed, Pre-loaded, Lubricated-for-Life Ball Bearing

10-INCH TILTING ARBOR CIRCULAR SAW

Fig. 3.59. *(Courtesy: Rockwell Manufacturing Co.)*

teeth cut into the rim. The common types of blades are the *rip*, the *crosscut*, and the *combination*. The blade turns at high speed and the work is fed into it only as fast as the blade will cut. A guard is kept over the blade. In some states this is required by law. A movable *fence* on the table is the

Fig. 3.60. Adjust the height of the saw blade so that it will just cut through the material.

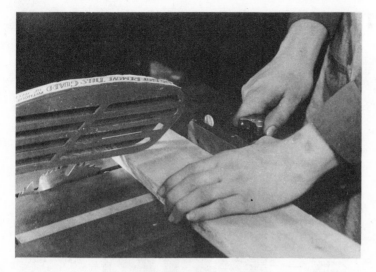

Fig. 3.61. When cutting across the grain, always use the cut-off attachment. It cuts many angles.

guide for ripping and a *miter gauge*, which slides back and forth in a groove, is for crosscutting. The size of a circular saw is the diameter of the blade. An 8-in. saw is a favorite for home and school shops.

How to crosscut:

1. Adjust the height of the blade so that it will just cut through the board. The farther the blade pro-

trudes, the greater the invitation to injury. The guard should be in the proper position covering the blade. Move the fence away, or remove it.

2. Lay the board on the table with its straight edge against the miter gauge and align the mark at which it will be cut with the blade. A blade usually removes about ⅛ in. of wood.

3. Turn on the motor and, holding the board against the gauge, push

Fig. 3.62. Ripping is done along the fence. See how the fingers are kept clear.

the miter gauge along the groove, slowly feeding the board into the saw. Stand behind the miter gauge, not in line with the blade. Push the board past the saw until it comes out from under the guard and the guard drops down on the table. Shut off the motor but do not pick up the end sawed off until the blade has stopped.

How to rip:

1. Remove the miter gauge and hang it up. Each time this falls to the floor some of its accuracy is lost. Set

4. Push the board through until it is free of the guard. Turn off the motor, and if the pieces are on the table do not pick them up until the blade has stopped.

Safety sense:

1. Always have your teacher check your saw setup before you turn on the motor, until he tells you that you can do it on your own. Machine adjustments are always made before the motor is started.

2. If the blade is dull, don't use it.

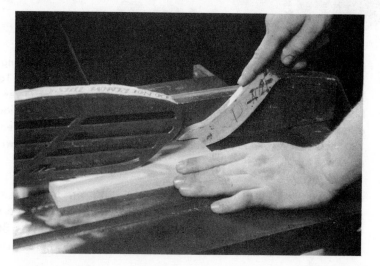

Fig. 3.63. Use a push stick when ripping thin pieces. It saves wear and tear on the fingers.

the blade as before and check the position of the guard.

2. Move the fence into position, using the scale on the front guide bar. Then with a rule check the distance between the fence and the closest saw teeth. Lock the fence.

3. Start the motor and, holding the board against the fence, push it slowly and steadily into the blade. Hold only the piece between the fence and the blade. When this piece is 3 or 4 in. wide, use one hand to hold it. When narrower, use a push stick.

Stand to one side of the blade when sawing.

3. Do not try to crosscut pieces that are too short to be held securely against the miter gauge. Do not rip pieces less than 6 in. long. Short, thick stock is easily jerked out of your hands.

4. Make sure that you have mastered ripping and crosscutting before trying other cuts, even though you have a saw at home.

5. No one other than the instructor should be standing near you as you

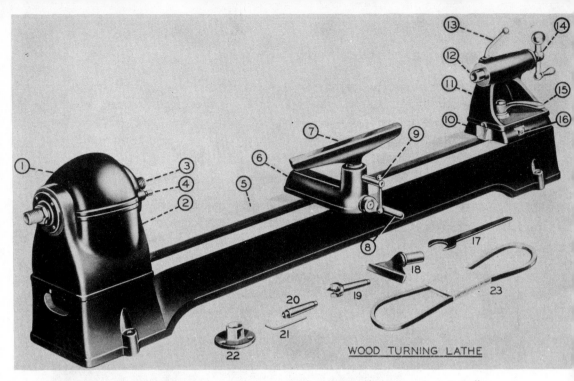

Fig. 3.64. Wood-turning lathe. *(Courtesy: Rockwell Manufacturing* Co.) 1. Pulley. 2. Headstock. 3. Headstock spindle. 4. Indexing stop. 5. Bed. 6. Tool rest support. 7. Tool rest. 8. Tool rest lock lever. 9. Tool rest adjusting screw. 10. Tailstock base. 11. Tailstock. 12. Tailstock spindle. 13. Tailstock spindle lock. 14. Spindle adjusting screw. 15. Tailstock lock. 16. Set-over screw. 17. Headstock wrench. 18. Short tool rest. 19. Spur center. 20. Cup center. 21. Allen wrench. 22. Face plate.

saw. No one should talk to you, nor should you talk to anyone.

6. Know where the blade is and where your fingers are at all times.

The Wood Lathe

The wood lathe is a machine on which wood is shaped into round and cylindrical forms—as bowls and legs —by means of a tool held and manipulated by the operator. Production lathes used in furniture industries are automatic. The operator pulls a lever which moves a cutter into the wood, thus making the entire cut at once. Sizes of wood lathes are given as *swing* and as the distance *between centers*. On a lathe with a swing of 11 in. and

36 in. between centers you can turn a piece as large as 11 in. in diameter and as long as 36 in. Shaping on the wood lathe is called *turning*.

Limitations. The wood lathe turns round shapes only, since the wood revolves against a tool. For large-diameter, heavy turning a heavy duty lathe is necessary to control the vibration.

Turning tools. Wood-turning tools are shaped to make particular types of cuts. A dull tool is useless; it makes dust instead of shavings. Tools must be sharpened frequently if they are much used, so you should learn how. When a tool is burned, nicked, or blunted by honing, it must be ground.

82

Between grindings the tools are honed to keep the edges sharp. A *slip stone* and an *oil stone* are used. The sharper you keep your tools the better turning you can do. Your teacher can show you how to keep your tools sharp.

Lathe speeds. As a rule, the faster the wood turns, the smoother the cut. Certain speed limits must be observed, however. If the wood is not perfectly centered and balanced, too much speed may cause it to fly out of the lathe. The larger the diameter of the piece, the slower it should revolve. A long piece such as a baseball bat billet should revolve more slowly than a short piece of the same thickness.

APPROXIMATE TURNING SPEEDS FOR
FACE PLATE WORK (R.P.M.)

Diameter of work	Rough-ing	Shaping	Sand-ing	Finish-ing
3"–4"	500–1000	1000–1500	1500–2000	2000
5"–6"	400–800	800–1200	1200–1500	1500
8"–10"	200–400	300–500	500–700	700

FOR SPINDLE TURNING

Diameter of work	Rough-ing	Shaping	Sand-ing	Finish-ing
1"–2"	500–1000	1000–2000	2000–2500	2500
3"–4"	400–800	800–1200	1200–1500	1500
5"–6"	300–500	500–800	800–1200	1200

If your lathe has but four speeds, do the roughing at the slowest, then increase one step at a time through the stages for shaping, sanding, and finishing.

Turning safely. Wood turning is fun; don't spoil it by being careless.

1. Roll up your sleeves and remove your tie if there is any chance of its getting caught on the work. (This saves wear and tear on the chin.)

2. Always make the setup and any adjustments in it before starting the motor.

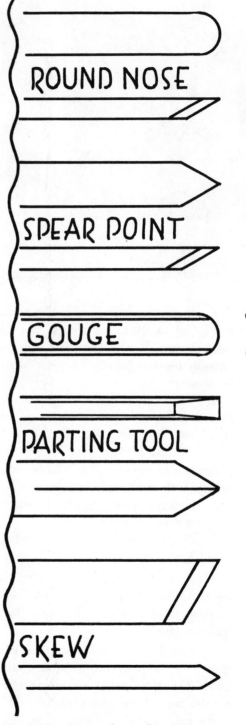

Fig. 3.65. A set of wood-turning tools.

ROUND NOSE

SPEAR POINT

GOUGE

PARTING TOOL

SKEW

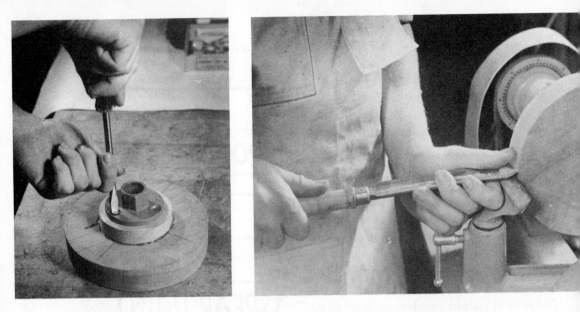

Fig. 3.66 (above left). Fastening the face plate to the block from which a bowl will be turned.

Fig. 3.67 (above right). Rough turning the bowl to true it, with the gouge.

3. Stop the motor and check the work frequently to see that it has not come loose. If you hear any strange noises, stop the lathe. The work may be loose.

4. Try to hold the turning tools so that the chips strike your fingers instead of your face.

5. If dust bothers you, use a respirator. Remember, a sharp tool makes little dust.

6. Always remove the tool rest before sanding.

7. When you leave the machine, turn off the motor.

There are two types of turning on the lathe: *face plate* and *spindle*. Face-plate work is best to start on, so let's make a bowl.

1. Get a piece of hardwood, like cherry or maple, from which a disc about 2 in. thick and 6 in. in diameter can be cut. Plane one side flat. This is the side next to the face plate. Cut out the disc on the band saw.

2. Make a full-size drawing of the shape you plan to turn. From this, make a template for the outside and for the inside.

3. Saw out a disc of scrap wood about 1 in. thick and ⅛ in. smaller in diameter than the foot of the bowl. Cut a disc of wrapping paper the same size. Now glue this block to the center of the bowl stock with the paper in between. Clamp them and let them dry.

4. Screw the small disc to the face plate. Do not screw into the bowl stock. Screw the face plate on the spindle.

5. Set the proper lathe speed. Adjust the tool rest parallel to the edge of the block at the center line and so that the block will just clear when turned by hand. Screw the tail center against the block.

6. Turn on the motor and hold a gouge firmly in both hands, on the tool rest square with the stock. Slide

it back and forth, using a forefinger as a guide, making thin cuts until the block is round. Move the tool rest when necessary to keep it close to the work.

7. Increase the lathe speed one step now for the shaping. Use a round nose tool, moving it from side to side as you peel off the shavings. Check the shape with the template now and then, with the lathe stopped.

8. Slide the tool rest out of the way and rough-sand the outside. Use a piece of 1-0 garnet paper on a felt pad. Keep the sandpaper moving from side to side below the center line. Follow with successively finer paper until the surface is free from all scratches.

9. To hollow the bowl, stop the lathe and set the tool rest across the front of the block on the center line and about ¼ in. away. Use the round nose tool again, sliding it back and forth from the left edge to the center. If you go beyond the center the wood tries to pick up the tool and hand it out to you. Use the inside template frequently.

10. Sand the inside as you did the outside.

Finishes. Use a finish that adds to the natural beauty of the wood. Try one of the following:

1. For a wax finish, which is the simplest of all, use a piece of soft cloth folded into a small pad. Coat this with paste polishing-wax and apply it to the revolving bowl. Polish each coat before applying the next. The more coats, the better, until there are about a dozen.

A piece of beeswax may be held against the bowl. The heat of friction melts the wax. When thoroughly covered, press a pad against it to force it into the wood. Repeat if desired.

Fig. 3.68 (below left). Hollowing out the bowl with the round nose tool. Keep the tool rest as close to the work as possible.
Fig. 3.69 (below right). Sanding the bowl smooth. Note that the tool rest has been removed.

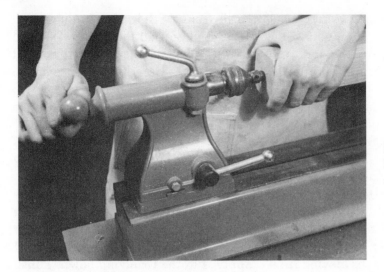

Fig. 3.70. Putting the ball bat billet between centers.

2. The French polish is an old-time cabinetmaker's finish. On a pad of cloth lay about a teaspoonful of white shellac. On this place four or five drops of boiled linseed oil. Hold the pad against the spinning bowl covering the surface and using moderate pressure. When the pad gets dry add more shellac and oil. Repeat until you have a mirrorlike finish. Protect the finish with two coats of paste polishing wax.

3. For a water-proof finish use clear lacquer. Remove the face plate and apply 10 to 12 coats of lacquer. When it is dry, place it on the lathe again and get a thick cloth pad and some lacquer polishing compound. Put a little of the compound on the pad and hold it lightly against the spinning bowl.

Spindle turning. Spindle turning is done between centers and enables you to make lamp bases, table legs,

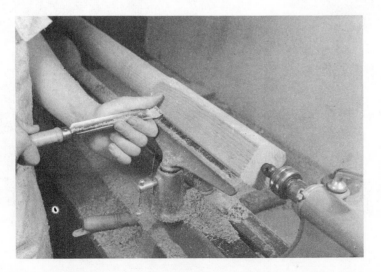

Fig. 3.71. Rough-turning the billet to the approximate diameter with the large gouge.

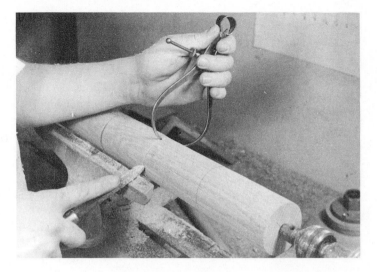

Fig. 3.72. Cutting down to the desired diameters at the stations. The parting tool does the cutting; an outside calipers does the checking for diameter.

ball bats, and the like. Here's how to turn a ball bat:

1. Make a full-size drawing of the bat, as shown.

2. For the stock, use straight-grained ash. This can be purchased in billet form for bats.

3. With a backsaw make shallow cuts across corners on each end of the billet. This marks the location of the lathe centers. Tap the headstock center into one end with a mallet. In-sert this in the headstock. Run the tail center into the other end and draw it up snug. Turn the stock a few times by hand to see that it is secure.

4. Set the tool rest to within ½ in. of the stock, on the center line and parallel to it. Use the slowest roughing speed. Have your teacher check the setup.

5. Rough-turn a section at a time with the gouge, using it as you did for the bowl. When the stock is round,

Fig. 3.73. Shaping the bat, using the cut-in stations as guides.

mark out the stations on it according to your drawing. Set a pair of calipers to the diameter of the first station, plus ⅟₁₆ inch. Cut into the diameter with a parting tool. Do this at each station. Now cut away the waste stock with a gouge. Use the round nose tool to shape the handle.

6. Sand the bat smooth and burn in your monogram for the trade mark on a flat-grain side. Saw off the stubs and apply a hot oil finish.

7. When it is dry, try it for a home run.

Some Group Activities

1. Visit a tree farm to see the cultivation of trees, then plant some seedlings on the school grounds, in the park, or at home. A tree becomes a monument to your thoughtfulness.
2. Visit an upholsterer's shop to watch him cover a piece of furniture.
3. Visit a house under construction to see how lumber is used.
4. Visit a museum to see tools and wood products made and used long ago.
5. Invite a forest ranger, furniture designer, architect, or chemist to talk to your class or to the school assembly.
6. Make some paper from wood pulp. (Your teacher can write to a paper company listed in source No. 3 *School Packet*, page 91, for instructions.)
7. Arrange an exhibit of wood products available today. Your furniture dealer may be glad to have you put it in his store window.
8. Repair or build some furniture or toys for a deserving family in your community.
9. Set up a wood products manufacturing plant in your school shop to mass produce a quantity of items needed by the Red Cross. Contact your local Chapter.
10. Build several bird feeders to be placed outside the windows of the elementary grades classrooms, on the school grounds or in the park.
11. Make up a set of safety rules for each machine you use.

Some Things to Find Out

1. What does a carpenter mean by "toe nailing"?
2. What is a mortise and tenon joint?
3. Which wood is the heaviest of all? The lightest?
4. Make a list of words that are part of the language of the woodworker.
5. See if you can find out how a tree grows.
6. What is the difference between plywood and veneer?
7. About how many different kinds of trees are there in the United States?
8. How fast do forest fires travel?
9. About how many people are employed in industries that are directly dependent on forest materials?
10. Why does wood insulate well against heat and cold?
11. What are some of the plastics that are made from trees?
12. Why does wood split more easily with the grain than against it?
13. What tools and machines for woodworking would you want in your workshop? Which should you get first?
14. What products are made from sawdust?
15. Learn to identify several common woods.

Sources of Ideas and Information

Booklets

1. *ABC's of Hand Tools.* General Motors Corporation, 1775 Broadway, New York, N.Y. Booklet and film.
2. *Safety in the Woodshop* (accompanies

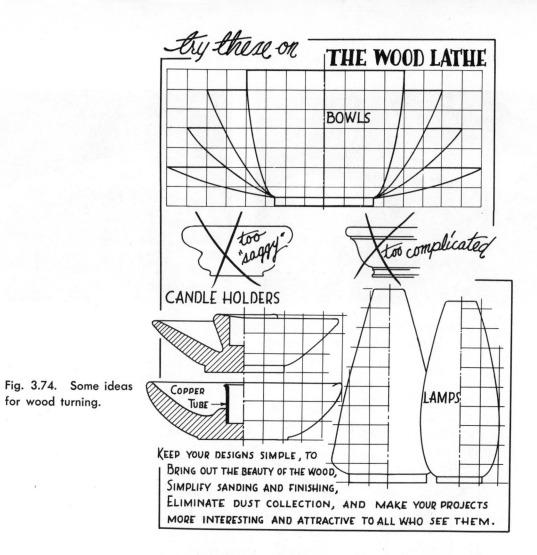

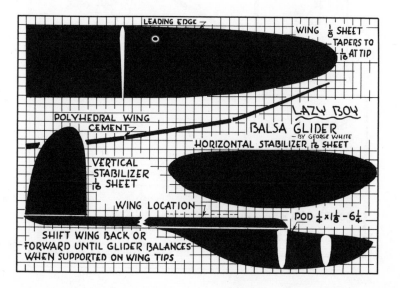

Fig. 3.74. Some ideas for wood turning.

Fig. 3.75. A glider.

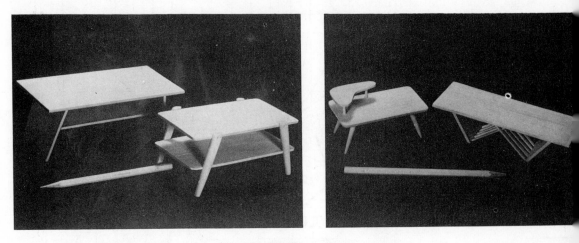

Fig. 3.76 (above left).   Scale models of coffee tables.
Fig. 3.77 (above right).   More scale models of coffee tables.

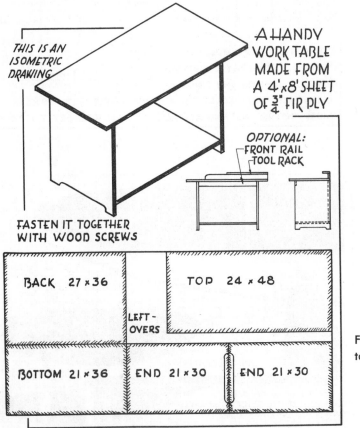

THIS IS AN
ISOMETRIC
DRAWING

A HANDY
WORK TABLE
MADE FROM
A 4'x8' SHEET
OF $\frac{3}{4}$" FIR PLY

OPTIONAL:
FRONT RAIL
TOOL RACK

FASTEN IT TOGETHER
WITH WOOD SCREWS

BACK   27 x 36

TOP   24 x 48

LEFT-
OVERS

BOTTOM 21 x 36

END 21 x 30

END 21 x 30

Fig. 3.78.   A handy work table.

a film strip by the same name). Carnegie-Illinois Steel Corporation, Pittsburgh, Pa.

3. *School Packet.* American Forest Products Industries, Inc., 1319 Eighteenth St. N.W., Washington 6, D.C. This is a collection of interesting, helpful booklets and charts, including a bibliography of other free materials and films.

4. The Forest Products Laboratory, U. S. Department of Agriculture Forest Service, Madison, Wisconsin. This is a public source of information on wood and its uses, technical and nontechnical.

5. *Use, Properties and Identification of American Woods* and *American Lumber Industry* (Basic Information Sources). Inquiry References Service, U. S. Department of Commerce, Washington 25, D.C. These are very comprehensive bibliographies.

6. *P.L. No. 27.* Western Pine Association, Yeon Building, Portland 4, Oregon. This is a list of good booklets and films.

Books

1. Feirer, John L. *Industrial Arts Woodworking.* Peoria, Ill.: Charles A. Bennett Co., Inc. 1950.

2. Fryklund, Verne C. and La Berge, Armand J. *General Shop Woodworking.* Bloomington, Ill.: McKnight and McKnight, 1946.

3. Groneman, Chris H. *General Woodworking.* New York: McGraw-Hill Book Company, Inc., 1952.

4. *The Use of Hand Tools and Portable Machinery.* New York: Delmar Publishers, Inc., 1946.

5. Sylvius, G. H. and Baysinger, G. B. *Safe Work Practice in Woodworking.* Chicago, Ill.: American Technical Society.
   Beautiful Woods. Frank Paxton Lumber Company, 5701 W. 66th Street, Chicago, Ill.

Films

1. See *School Packet,* above.
2. See *ABC's of Hand Tools,* p. 88.
3. See *P. L. No. 27,* above.

Fig. 4.1. Tapping an open-hearth furnace. Heavier than slag, the molten steel flows from the furnace first, and nearly overflows into the slag thimble at the right. *(Courtesy: United States Steel Corp.)*

The 4 METAL INDUSTRIES

It is not known how primitive man discovered metals and how to use them, but it might have been that he found some nuggets in the ashes of a campfire. He might have built the fire over a deposit of an ore and the heat melted some of it into metal. At any rate, it is known that copper was the first metal used by man, at least 8000 years ago. Accidentally or otherwise, he melted some copper with tin and produced bronze. This was the start of the Bronze Age, so called because tools and weapons were made of bronze. Copper was being used on our continent before the arrival of Columbus.

When early man discovered that he could hammer copper into useful forms and that he could melt it and pour it into holes shaped in sand, he started the metals industries. Even-

tually he learned to increase the heat of his fire by forced air. He used goat-skin bellows and was then able to melt iron from its ore. Hand- and foot-operated bellows were used for centuries until James Watt made his steam engine. With engine-powered bellows, greater heats were reached, making possible a better refining of ores.

The first iron making in America was near Jamestown, Virginia, at about 1640. Pittsburgh became the center of steel making about 1800 because both its iron ore and coking coal were convenient. Today the United States produces one half of the world's steel, which amounts to about 1400 pounds for each person in the country. About four fifths of the metal used here is iron and steel.

Metals are refined from minerals

93

dug from the earth, although some free metals are frequently found in the form of nuggets. Metals have luster and the ability to conduct heat and electricity, and can be fused together. Some are magnetic (iron and steel); some are very heavy (lead and mercury); and some are very light (aluminum and magnesium).

A COMPARISON OF COMMON METALS
(from *Machinery's Handbook*, courtesy The Industrial Press)

Metal	Melting Point Degrees F.	Pounds per Cubic Foot
Aluminum	1220	168.5
Brass		
(80% cop., 20% zinc)	1823	536.6
Bronze		
(90% cop., 10% tin)	1841	547.9
Copper	1981	554.7
Gold	1945	1204.3
Iron, cast	1990–2300	438.7–482.4
Lead	621	707.7
Magnesium	1204	108.6
Silver	1761	650.2–657.1
Steel	2500	486.7

If someone offered you a gold brick measuring 6 in. by 6 in. by 12 in. if you could carry it away, could you lift it? How much would it weigh?

Alloys. An alloy is the metal that results when two or more other metals are melted together. It has different characteristics from the metals of which it is made. Such qualities as hardness, toughness, and resistance to heat and corrosion are controlled by alloying. Steel is an alloy of iron and carbon. It is further alloyed with chromium, nickel, manganese, tungsten, and other metals to produce desired qualities. Most of the metals used in products today are alloys.

Here are some common ones:

Babbit—tin alloyed with copper and antimony
Brass—copper, with zinc
Bronze—copper, with tin
Pewter—tin with lead, bismuth, antimony, copper
Soft solder—tin and lead, usually 50/50
Stainless steel—Steel with chromium, nickel, molybdenum
Sterling silver—silver with copper

If your ring is 14 K. gold, it is 14 parts gold and 10 of other metal, usually copper. 24 K. gold is pure. The "K" stands for "carat."

Common metal shapes and sizes. The following list shows the usual ways in which measurements are given for the various metal shapes.

Sheet—Thickness is given by gauge number, in thousandths of an inch or in ounces per square foot.
Plate—This is in sheet form but usually 3/16 in. or more thick.

Fig. 4.2.   Common metal forms.

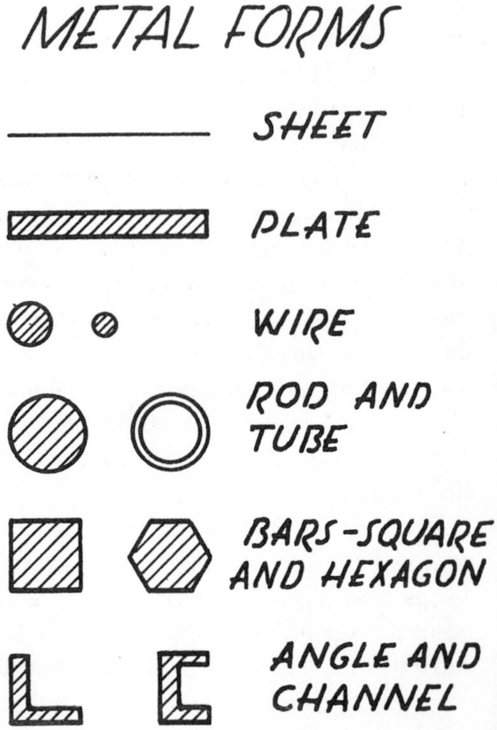

METAL FORMS

SHEET

PLATE

WIRE

ROD AND TUBE

BARS—SQUARE AND HEXAGON

ANGLE AND CHANNEL

Wire—Diameters of steel and copper wire are given by gauge number; of aluminum, in thousandths of an inch.

Rod—Diameters are in fractions of inches.

Band—Width and thickness is given in inches.

Pipe and Tube—Either inside diameter (I.D.) or outside diameter (O.D.) is given.

Angle—Thickness of stock and width of sides is given.

SHEET THICKNESSES

(from *Machinery's Handbook*, courtesy The Industrial Press)

	Steel	Aluminum and Copper		
Inches	Gauge * Manufacturer's Standard	Inches	Gauge**	Oz/Sq ft (copper)
0.0120	30	0.005	36	4
.0220	30	.010	30	
.0149	28	.0126	28	
.0179	26	.0159	26	
.0239	24	.0201	24	16
.0299	22	.0253	22	
.0359	20	.0320	20	24
.0478	18	.0403	18	
.0598	16	.0508	16	
.0747	14	.0641	14	48

* Manufacturers' Standard Gauge.

** Browne & Sharpe Gauge.

Thickness of aircraft aluminum is given in thousandths of an inch.

How Iron is Made

Iron is made in a *blast furnace*. Alternate layers of coke (partially burned coal), iron ore, and limestone are dumped into the furnace. The coke burns in a blast of hot air, reaching a temperature of about 3000°F. This melts the iron from the ore. The limestone melts and collects impurities which float on the surface of the molten iron. Then the iron is drawn off and either cast into pigs, as pig iron, or else used immediately for making steel.

Pig iron is further heated and refined to make cast iron, which is cast into many useful products such as machine parts, fire hydrants, boilers, and automobile engine blocks. Parts of

Fig. 4.3. Looking into the Hull-Rust open-pit iron mine at Hibbing, Minnesota. The ore is hauled to the docks on Lake Superior, loaded into boats, and shipped through the Great Lakes to steel plants. *(Courtesy: United States Steel Corp.)*

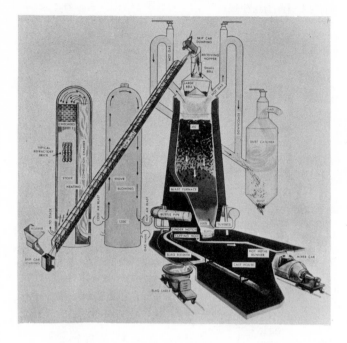

Fig. 4.4. A diagram of blast furnace operation in producing iron form ore. A skip car dumps the raw materials into the top of the furnace. The molten iron runs out at the bottom into the mixer car, which hauls it to the steel-making furnaces, or it is poured into molds as pig iron. (Courtesy: American Iron and Steel Institute.)

cast iron must be large and heavy because it is brittle and breaks easily.

How Steel is Made

Steel is iron at its strongest. The difference between steel and cast iron is in the amount of carbon they contain. Low-carbon steels are soft and easily formed. They contain only about 0.25 per cent of carbon. High-carbon steels are hard and stiff and contain as much as 1.7 per cent carbon. Cast iron has more than 1.7 per cent carbon and is brittle and porous.

Bessemer steel. Low-grade steels are made in the Bessemer converter. Molten iron from the blast furnace is poured into the converter and air is forced through it to burn out impurities and carbon.

Fig. 4.5. A flow chart of steel making. (Courtesy: American Iron and Steel Institute.)

FLOW CHART OF STEELMAKING

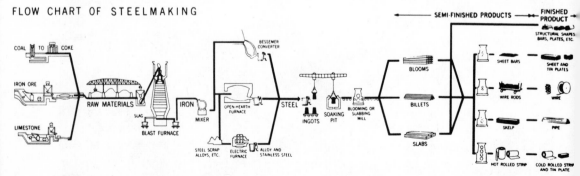

Open-hearth steel. Most steel is made in open-hearth furnaces. The hearth is a huge dish lined with fire furnaces where the melting and refining can be most accurately controlled. The necessary heat is produced by the

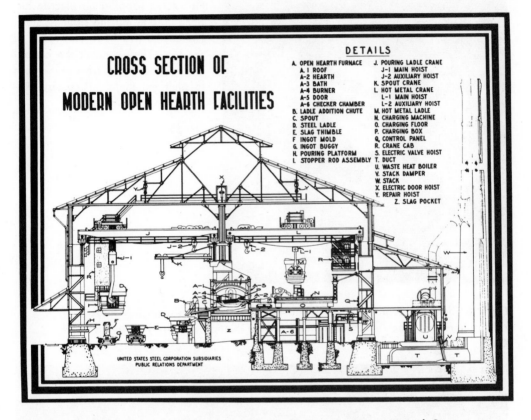

CROSS SECTION OF
MODERN OPEN HEARTH FACILITIES

DETAILS

A. OPEN HEARTH FURNACE
A. 1 ROOF
A-2 HEARTH
A-3 BATH
A-4 BURNER
A-5 DOOR
A-6 CHECKER CHAMBER
B. LADLE ADDITION CHUTE
C. SPOUT
D. STEEL LADLE
E. SLAG THIMBLE
F. INGOT MOLD
G. INGOT BUGGY
H. POURING PLATFORM
I. STOPPER ROD ASSEMBLY
J. POURING LADLE CRANE
J-1 MAIN HOIST
J-2 AUXILIARY HOIST
K. SPOUT CRANE
L. HOT METAL CRANE
L-1 MAIN HOIST
L-2 AUXILIARY HOIST
M. HOT METAL LADLE
N. CHARGING MACHINE
O. CHARGING FLOOR
P. CHARGING BOX
Q. CONTROL PANEL
R. CRANE CAB
S. ELECTRIC VALVE HOIST
T. DUCT
U. WASTE HEAT BOILER
V. STACK DAMPER
W. STACK
X. ELECTRIC DOOR HOIST
Y. REPAIR HOIST
Z. SLAG POCKET

UNITED STATES STEEL CORPORATION SUBSIDIARIES
PUBLIC RELATIONS DEPARTMENT

Fig. 4.6.   Modern open-hearth steel-making facilities. *(Courtesy: United States Steel Corporation.)*

brick in which scrap iron and limestone are loaded. Oil or gas flames are passed over it to melt the iron. Then molten pig iron from the blast furnace is added and the mixture is heated to about 3000°F. to burn out carbon and impurities. The furnace is then tapped and the steel is cast into huge chunks called *ingots*.

Electric furnace steel. The highest quality steel is made in electric current that arcs between the furnace's electrodes.

From ingots to usable steel. Steel sheet, plate, rod, bars, strips, angles, and other such forms are rolled from ingots. The hot ingot is run through a series of huge wringerlike rolls which squeeze it down into the desired thickness and shape. Some steel is dipped in molten zinc to give it a protective coating called *galvanize*.

Fig. 4.7. Tapping an electric furnace used in making stainless steel. Notice the two huge electrodes at the top. They conduct the current and serve as the sources of the heat to melt the metal. (Courtesy: Republic Steel Corporation.)

Fig. 4.8 (below). A thin ribbon of red hot steel speeds through this battery of rolling machines. Each machine makes the sheet thinner. (Courtesy: Republic Steel Corp.)

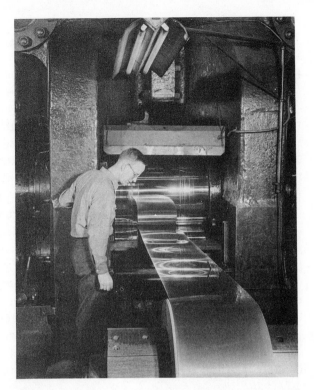

Fig. 4.9. Stainless steel is being rolled to produce a shiny, smooth surface. This steel does not rust or corrode as does ordinary steel. It is used for surgical instruments, automobile trim, architecture, chemical tanks, and the like. *(Courtesy: Republic Steel Corp.)*

You have seen this on pails, tubs, and garbage cans. When coated with tin, the steel sheet is called *tin plate,* the stock from which tin cans are made. There are enough tin cans made each year in the United States to supply each person with about 2000 of them.

Aluminum

Aluminum is an abundant material, being present in ordinary clay. Clay is actually an oxide of aluminum. It is not yet practical to refine the metal from clay; it is obtained instead from bauxite, most of which comes from Arkansas.

Because of its strength with lightness, aluminum is used extensively in aircraft. Because it conducts heat well it is used in cooking utensils; and because it is a good conductor of electricity and light in weight, it is used for cross-country electric power trans-

mission lines. It weathers well, so it is used as a building material. Aluminum is *ductile,* it is easily drawn out into a wire. It is *malleable,* which means that it is easily hammered or formed into shape.

In 1852 aluminum was valued at $545 per pound because it was difficult to refine. With the discovery of an electrical process in 1886 by Charles Martin Hall, a student at Oberlin College, the refining was simplified. Today, basic aluminum costs only about 15 cents per pound.

Pure aluminum is too soft for many uses. It is alloyed to give it stiffness, hardness, and great strength. The 2S grade (99 per cent pure) is recommended for the projects you make because it is easily formed. 17S and 24S are aircraft alloys containing copper, manganese and magnesium. They are very hard and stiff.

Copper

Copper is easily identified by its rich, reddish-brown color. It, too, is very ductile and malleable, but it is also very heavy. (See page 94.) It tarnishes (oxidizes) quickly. You can polish copper until it gleams only to have it dull in a day or so. The polish is preserved with clear lacquer. (See page 139.) Copper conducts heat well, a quality that makes it useful for such things as pots and pans, automobile radiators, and electric refrigerators. Almost one half of the copper produced in the United States goes into electrical uses. It is an excellent conductor of electricity. It is used for

in foundries. Metal molds are called *dies* and the casting process is *die casting*.

Rolling. This is the process described on page 118.

Extruding. Molten metal is forced through dies which give it shape, like tooth paste from a tube.

Drawing. Metal is pulled through dies to change its shape or size. Different diameters of wire are obtained by drawing.

Forging. This is the hammering process, as described on page 122.

Machining. These are the finishing processes by which a formed part is cut to the final shape and size. Sometimes it is a hand process and

Fig. 4.10 (left). Some of the parts for toy electric trains are cast in metal molds. This is called die casting. *(Courtesy: Lionel Corp.)*

alloying with steel, aluminum, gold, silver, and other metals. We get most of our ore from the western states Arizona, Montana, Utah, and Nevada. The largest known deposits are in Chile.

Industrial Processes for Forming Metals

Casting. Molten metal is poured or forced into cavities of the desired shapes in sand, plaster, or other metal. When cool it is hard and has the shape of the cavity. This is the process used

sometimes it is done automatically.

Pressing, stamping. Metal sheets, hot or cold, can be shaped by pressing into steel dies. The lower die is made to the shape of the desired part. The metal is laid over it and is pressed to that shape by the upper die. Sheet metal parts for toys, automobiles, airplanes, and many other products are formed by pressing.

Powdered metal is also pressed into solid shapes in dies. Then it is *sintered*, or heat treated, to give it strength.

Fig. 4.11 (above right). Extruded aluminum pipe emerges from a hydraulic press. Molten aluminum is pushed through dies to shape it. When the metal cools, the shape is retained. *(Courtesy: Aluminum Company of America.)*

Fig. 4.12. Steel jaws of the machine in the foreground grasp the end of an aluminum rod and pull it through holes in the die, in front of the men, reducing it in size. This is called "drawing." *(Courtesy: Aluminum Company of America.)*

Fig. 4.13. Today forging is done by huge drop hammers. The metal is placed in dies and hammered to shape. The piece shown is an airplane propeller blade. *(Courtesy: Aluminum Company of America.)*

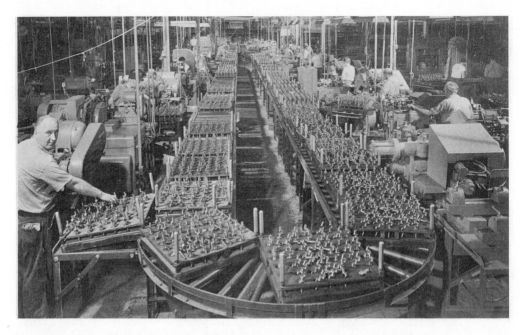

Fig. 4.14. Crankshafts for outboard motors are being machined to the correct size and finish. Each man and his machine perform one operation and then the piece moves on to the next machine. *(Courtesy: Evinrude Motors.)*

Fig. 4.15. Metal sheets are pressed into shape between dies. Auto body panels are being formed here. The upper half of the die moves slowly down, pressing the sheet into the lower half. *(Courtesy: Ford Motor Co.)*

Fig. 4.16. This machine presses powdered metal into solid metal parts. Those shown are wheels for toy electric trains. (Courtesy: Lionel Corp.)

Fig. 4.17. Sheet metal can be formed by spinning. A circular disc is placed in a special lathe and as it revolves it is pressed into shape over a mold. (Courtesy: Aluminum Company of America.)

Spinning. Spinning is the process for shaping circular sheets of metal into bowl-like forms. The disc is pressed into shape over a form as both revolve in a lathe. Some of your mother's pans have probably been spun. Light reflectors, airplane propeller spinners, and such concave forms of light metal are spun.

Hand Tools and Processes

Some common tools and processes are used with common metals. Get acquainted with these tools; they are the ABC's of metal working.

rule is a convenient, accurate measuring tool, providing you read it correctly. Remember, "Measure twice, cut once."

Scriber. The scriber is a thin, pencil-like tool of steel. Use it to mark fine lines, when scratching the metal is not objectionable. A pencil is used on soft metals.

Square. With a square, lines can be marked at right angles to an edge. It is also used to check flat surfaces, the accuracy of corners, and edges that are to be squared to other edges. If you drop a square or use it as a

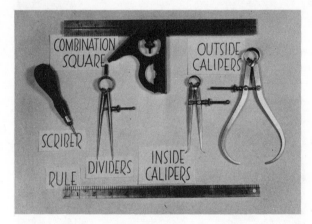

Fig. 4.18. Layout and measuring tools used by the metalworker.

Layout and measuring. The first step in metal working is usually the laying out of the work. Metal to be removed must be measured and marked off before cutting. Holes to be drilled must be located. Measuring and layout is done with *rules, scribes, squares, dividers,* and *calipers.* You can work to very close dimensions with metals, so do your measuring accurately.

Rules. The twelve-inch steel bench

hammer, it may no longer be square.

Dividers. The dividers is used to *scribe* arcs and circles and to measure and step off distances. Set the two points at the desired distance on a rule. To scribe a circular curve, the center should be pricked slightly with a sharp center punch.

Calipers. The outside caliper is used to measure thickness; the inside caliper, to measure openings. To use a caliper, adjust it to slide snugly over

Fig. 4.19.   Use both hands on the hack saw.

the stock or into the opening. Then hold one leg on the end of the rule and read the dimension at the other.

Combination square. This instrument is used to lay out lines and angles. It includes a *protractor* which can be set at any angle and a center head which is used to locate centers on the ends of round stock.

The hack saw. The hack saw saws metal as the handsaw saws wood. Blades are made in different lengths and with fine, medium, or coarse teeth. Fine teeth are for sawing thin material and coarse teeth for thick. The blade should be placed in the frame with the teeth pointing away from the handle and should be kept taut when sawing. The work should be held in a vise with the saw line close to the jaws to prevent chatter. With one hand holding the fore end and the other the handle,

use long, slow strokes with just enough pressure on the blade to keep it cutting instead of rubbing. Ease up on the pressure as the blade cuts through the opposite side.

Files. Files are hardened pieces of steel with sharp ridges or teeth that scrape and shear off the metal. They are made in a variety of shapes and sizes and for many different materials. Files are usually *single cut* or *double cut*. The first has all of its teeth slanting in the same direction, and the other has two sets of teeth crossing each other. The single-cut file is for fine, smooth cutting; the double-cut, for fast rough work. Chose a file to suit the job, but never use it without a handle. Files are very brittle and often break when dropped. They should not be placed so that they can rub together. When the teeth get shiny they are dull

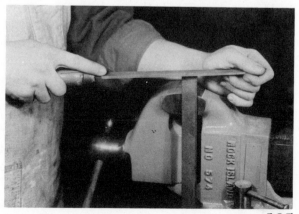

Fig. 4.20.   Use both hands when filing.

and the file should be replaced. If your file squeaks on the metal should you oil it? Why?

Use both hands on the file. Insert the work in a vise with the mark close to the jaws. The file cuts on the push stroke and should be lifted on the return. Clean the teeth frequently with a *file cleaner*. When small pieces get stuck between the teeth, pry them out with the pick supplied with the file cleaner. A clogged file will scratch the

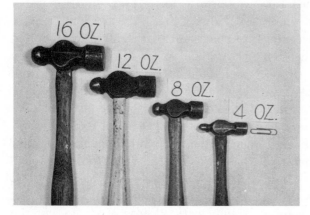

Cold chisels. A cold chisel is a hardened piece of tool steel with the cutting end sharpened as a wedge and the other end blunt to receive hammer blows. It is made to cut cold steel or other metals. Use as heavy a chisel as possible and hold it so that if the hammer misses the target it won't hit your hand. Light metal such as band iron can be cut in a vise by shearing it off with a chisel. To cut round rod, notch it on opposite sides, then bend

Fig. 4.21. An assortment of ball peen hammers.

surface of the work.

Draw-filing produces a smooth finish. Hold the file in both hands at right angles to the stroke then pull it toward you over the work.

Hammers. The *ball peen hammer* is the metal worker's hammer. There are many types of hammers for special purposes. (Some are described on pages 113 and 119.) Hammers are usually sized by the weight of the head as, 12 ounce, 24 ounce, and so on. Try to select the hammer which best fits the job to be done and which you can use most easily and safely.

it back and forth until it breaks. A chisel's cutting edge should usually be ground to a 60 degree included angle.

Drilling. Small holes can be drilled with a hand drill. (See page 63.) However, a portable electric drill, or a drill press, is much easier to control. (See page 77.) Straight-shank, high-speed twist drills are recommended. (See page 64.)

To drill a hole, first center-punch the location to keep the drill from wandering. Select the correct drill and tighten it in the chuck. The work should be clamped to a bench or in a vise. Pres-

Fig. 4.22. Hold a cold chisel so that if the hammer misses, it won't hit your hand. Metal can be easily sheared off in a vise with a cold chisel.

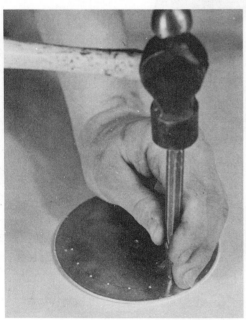

Fig. 4.23. Before a hole is drilled in metal, the mark should be center punched.

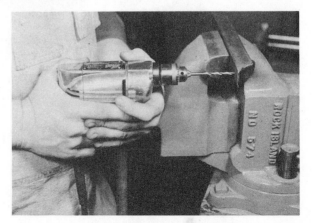

Fig. 4.24. A portable electric drill makes drilling easy.

Fig. 4.25. Bend band iron in a jig to get smooth, even curves.

Fig. 4.26. Make a bending jig like this to form the bookrack in Fig. 2.44.

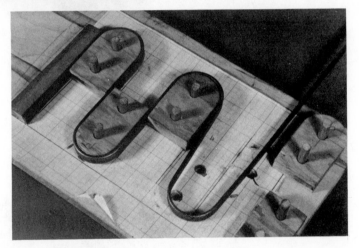

Fig. 4.27. This is the jig for the ends of the bookrack in Fig. 2.44.

sure must be applied to force the turning drill into the metal. Too much pressure bends and breaks small drills. Always ease up on the pressure as the drill comes through, to keep it from grabbing. (See page 139 for information about lubricants.)

Forming metal. Metal hoops, curves, and scrolls are formed most easily in a bending jig, of which there are several types. Adjust the jig to fit the metal band, then insert the band and bend it slightly. Move it into the jig a little and bend again. Repeat this process until the curve is complete. (See page 123 for information regarding the forming of hot metals.)

Punches. Punches are of the chisel family and there are many types to serve many purposes. A machinist's hand punch is for general use, as removing rivets, bolts, and the like from holes and for punching holes in sheet metal. Lay the sheet on the end grain of a block of wood or on a block of lead, and with a ball peen hammer drive the punch through the sheet just far enough to make a hole.

Riveting. Riveting is the process of fastening pieces of metal together with rivets. They are made in several different heads. The common ones are

Fig. 4.28. Riveting the fuselage of an F-84 Thunderjet. The man on the outside is using the riveting gun. The other is bucking the rivet to form a head. *(Courtesy: Aluminum Company of America.)*

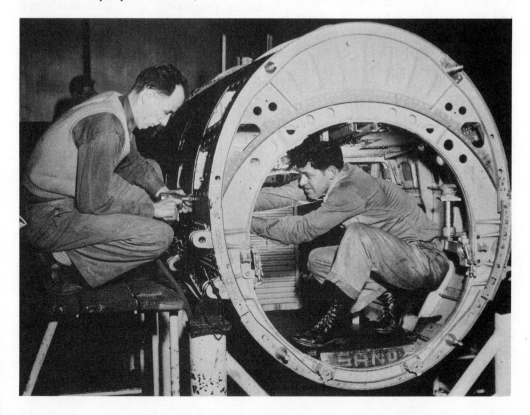

round, flat, and countersunk, or flush. Ordinarily the rivet is of the same metal as that being riveted.

A rivet should fit snugly into the hole. Drill the hole the same size as

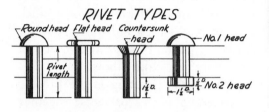

RIVET TYPES

Fig. 4.29.   Rivet types.

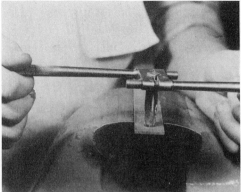

Fig. 4.30.   Tapping a hole in an aluminum lamp bracket. This tap cuts threads for the pipe nipple to which the socket screws.

the rivet shank. The shank should be just long enough to extend beyond the work, a distance equal to one and one-half to two times the rivet diameter. A rivet block is used to hold the head and to absorb the hammer blows in forming the No. 2 head. Do this with the face of a ball peen hammer. The No. 2 head should be about twice the diameter of the rivet and half as thick as the rivet shank. To remove a rivet, center-punch the No. 1 head and drill through it with a drill bit just in under the diameter of the hole. Snap the head off with a pin punch (a slender punch).

Threads. The spiral cut on a bolt and in a nut is a thread. When the two threads match, the nut screws onto the bolt. Threads can be cut with *taps* and *dies*. The die cuts the thread on a bolt, and the tap cuts the thread in the nut. The common thread types are National Coarse (N.C.) and National Fine (N.F.) A ¼-in. bolt with the N.C. thread has 20 t.p.i. (threads per inch), and one with the N.F. has 28 t.p.i.

To tap a hole it must first be drilled to the proper tap size. This is always smaller than the bolt diameter. Consult your teacher's drill chart to find the size. Tighten the tap in a tap wrench, then insert the end in the hole and turn the tap clockwise as you gently press down. If cutting oil is needed, use it frequently. (See page

Fig. 4.31.   Cutting   threads on a rod with a threading die.

139.) Turn the tap backward about a quarter turn for each revolution to clear out chips. Taps are very hard and brittle. The small ones break easily and plug the hole very effectively.

To thread a bolt or a rod select the correct die and lock it into the die size indicated on the tap is the diameter of the bolt.

Art Metal Products and Tools

Art metal products include bowls, trays, table service, jewelry, and the like, usually made from aluminum,

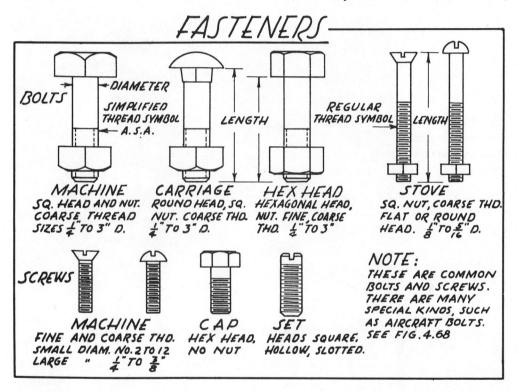

Fig. 4.32. Some common fasteners.

stock (the holder). Grind a slight chamfer on the end of the rod to make it easier to get the die started. Press the die into the stock and turn it slowly clockwise, using a lubricant if needed. Reverse the direction a half turn occasionally to break up chips. The size indicated on a die is the diameter of the rod which it will thread, and the

brass, copper, silver, or pewter. Most of the common, hand, metal working tools are used, plus a number of special ones described here.

Jeweler's saw. The jeweler's saw is similar to a coping saw except for its adjustable frame. It is used to cut fine details in the design. Blades come in many widths, from those as slender

Fig. 4.33. Paul Revere made this sugar bowl and cream pitcher of silver. He was one of the great American silversmiths. *(Courtesy: Metropolitan Museum of Art.)*

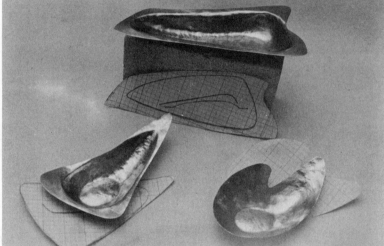

Fig. 4.34. Some free-form copper trays and their flat patterns.

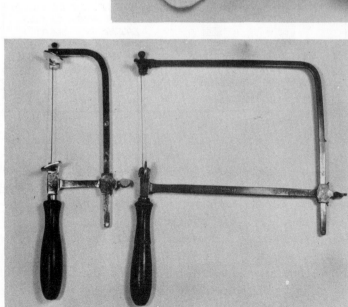

Fig. 4.35. Jeweler's saws. Note the slender blades.

as horse hair to those 1/16 in. wide, with various numbers of teeth per inch.

Needle files. Regular files are used for coarse cutting; needle files, for fine detail. Since they are slender and delicate, they must be used carefully.

Hammers. Hammers for art metal work are made in three types and in many shapes and sizes. *Raising hammers* usually have ball-shaped ends. They are used to tap and stretch the metal into rough, hollow forms from the inside. *Forming hammers* have rounded oval faces and are used to form round edges and for raising bowl shapes from the outside. *Planishing hammers* have flat faces and are round or square in shape. They are used to smooth and finish formed surfaces.

Art metal hammers must not be used for anything else; if the faces get nicked, they will mar the surface of soft metals.

Stakes. Stakes are heavy pieces of steel or cast iron in different shapes which are used as anvils. Metals are formed over them. Their surfaces must not be nicked.

Form blocks. These are pieces of hard wood on which metal is roughly formed. Blocks for raising hollow pieces have shallow cups into which the metal is hammered. Blocks can be cut to fit particular shapes.

Chasing tools. These are small chisel-like tools for cutting lines and designs in metal. A soft-face hammer or mallet is used to tap them.

Fig. 4.36. A set of art metal hammers.

Fig. 4.37. An assortment of stakes over which art metals are formed.

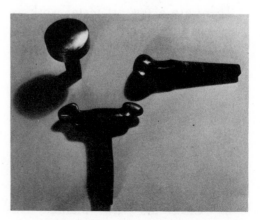

Fig. 4.38. Sawing with the jeweler's saw.

Daps and dapping dies. Daps are punchlike tools with a ball end for raising beads or dome shapes. The metal is placed on the dapping die and is tapped into the hole with a dap and a mallet.

Basic Tool Processes

There are a few art metal working processes which you will often use.

Sawing with the jeweler's saw. The measure of your skill with this tool is not only how close to your pattern you can cut but also how much sawing you can do with one blade. Here is how:

1. Draw the design on paper and cement it to the metal with rubber cement.

2. Select the saw blade. The thinner the metal, the finer the teeth.

For 18-gauge metal use a blade with 15 to 20 t.p.i.

3. Clamp the blade in the upper vise of the frame with the teeth pointing toward the handle. Fasten the lower end and then draw the blade up taut.

4. Hold the metal flat on a V-block and saw with a slow, easy up-and-down stroke. Put only enough forward pressure on the blade to keep it cutting.

Piercing. Piercing is the sawing out of openings within the metal. Drill a hole in the waste, insert the saw blade, clamp in the frame as before, and then saw.

Filing. File parallel to the edge of sheet metal instead of across it when you are using a regular file. Needle files can be used in any direction. Select the shape that best fits the section being filed. Be sure to remove any burrs and sharp edges.

Forming. Shallow bowls and trays can be most easily made by forming them into openings cut to the desired shape in wood blocks.

1. Trace the outline of a tray on the block and cut out the inside on the jig saw. Round the top inside edge a bit with a wood file. Nail this to another block for a base.

2. Cut out the metal about ½ in. larger than the opening on each side. Drive several wire brads into the form around the opening to hold the metal in place.

3. With a forming hammer tap lightly around the edge, stretching the metal down into the form. Tap around and around, gradually working down to the bottom. When the metal hardens and resists stretching, *anneal* it. (See page 116.)

4. When the tray is fully shaped remove it and trim the edges. You

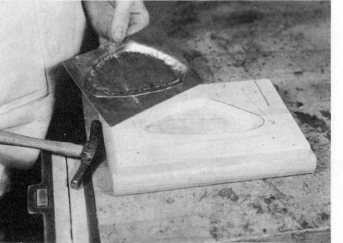

Fig. 4.39.   An opening cut in a block of scrap wood makes a good mold in which to form metal trays.

Fig. 4.40.   Tapping a copper dish into the mold. 18-gage sheet is just right for this work.

should then planish it on a flat stake.

Raising. Raising is a means for shaping sheet metal on a stake or form block. This is more difficult than the forming process just described, but it has greater possibilities.

1. With a pencil compass, mark several concentric circles ¾ in. apart around a 4-in. or 5-in. disc of 18-gauge copper or aluminum.

2. Hold the disc with the outer circle over the hollow in the raising block. With a raising hammer tap around the outer circle, turning the disc as you go to space the dents evenly. Strike each blow with equal force but not so hard that the metal is stretched out of shape.

3. Follow around the circles tapping toward the bottom. If the bowl needs more shaping after you have

gone over it once, repeat the process. Remember to anneal the metal when it begins to resist.

Annealing. Annealing is a softening process. If you keep your metal soft you can do much shaping with it; when it gets hard from hammering, it tears easily. To anneal copper and brass heat them to a dull red in a flame large enough to cover the metal, then quench in water.

To anneal aluminum first wipe some lubricating oil on it, then heat it until the oil burns off. Quench in water.

Planishing. Planishing smooths the surface and makes the metal stiff and hard. It leaves small, shallow, overlapping facets which are a mark of good craftsmanship. To planish, select a stake that fits the curve of your bowl as closely as possible. Place

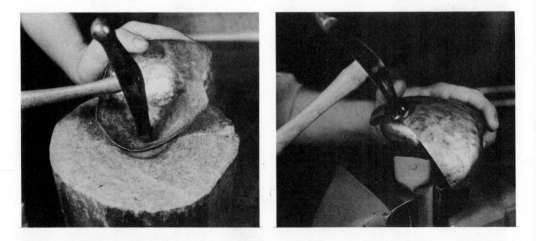

Fig. 4.41. Raising a dish on a form block—a hollow cut in the end grain of a heavy block of wood.

Fig. 4.42 (above right). Planishing the dish on a stake. This removes the large hammer marks and smooths the surface.

the bowl over the stake and with the planishing hammer tap over the surface, working around the bowl and gradually moving down to the bottom. Try to make the marks overlap evenly. Polish them occasionally with fine steel wool to check your progress.

Chasing. Line designs are easily applied by chasing.

1. Draw the design in pencil on the metal and select the chasing tool that fits best.

2. Lay the metal on a board and tap the tool lightly with a mallet as you follow the design, moving toward yourself. Go over the lines several times until they are deep enough.

Etching. Since some acids attack metals, they can be used to etch designs. Prepared etching solutions, called *mordants*, are safer to use than are raw acids and do a better job.

1. Clean the metal with fine steel wool and scouring powder. Try to keep your fingers off the clean surface.

2. Trace your design on the metal with a pencil and then paint out all areas that are not be eaten away, with *asphaltum* paint.

3. Place the object in a glass tray and cover it with the mordant, after you have read the directions on the bottle.

4. After 10 or 15 minutes remove the metal, rinse it in water, and dissolve the asphaltum with kerosene or turpentine.

Soldering. Soldering is the process of joining pieces of metal by means of an easily fusible alloy, called *solder*, which when melted has an affinity for the metal. Ordinary soft solder is half lead and half tin. A flame is preferred for soldering art metal projects because they conduct the heat away so rapidly. (See page 121 for soldering with an iron.) Follow these suggestions:

1. Fit the pieces of metal closely

Fig. 4.43. Sweating two pieces of copper together in a flame. Use an old pair of pliers.

together, then apply flux to the surfaces to be joined.

2. Heat each piece until it melts the solder when it is touched to the fluxed surface. Keep it just hot enough that the solder will flow over the surface. Use only enough solder to give a thin coating; this is known as *tinning*.

3. Place two tinned surfaces together and reheat until the solder flows. If you must solder a joint close to the one already soldered, paint a coat of clay slip on the first joint to keep it from melting.

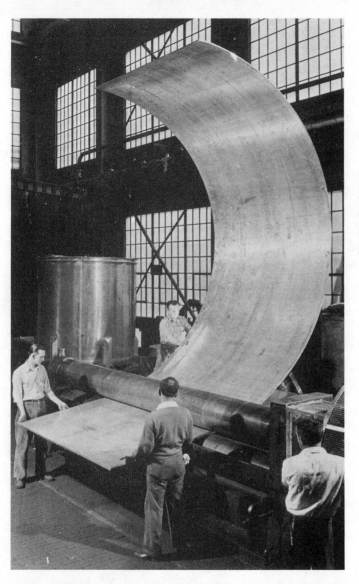

Fig. 4.44. Rolling the sidewall of a 45,000-gallon welded aluminum tank. (Courtesy: Aluminum Company of America.)

Finishing. See page 139 for finishing suggestions.

Sheet Metal Products and Processes

Sheet is one of the most commonly used forms of metal. You have seen the aluminum wrapper on breakfast cereal and candy bars. This is as thin as one usually finds sheet metal. It is called *foil*. Contrast this with armor plate and boiler plate. The first is a heavy steel which can shed bullets and shells. Boiler plate is usually one-half inch or more thick and when fabricated into a boiler can retain steam at hundreds of pounds pressure. Some boilers for powerful locomotives are made from plate as thick as six inches. The processess used in forming your sheet metal products are somewhat different from those for art metal products.

Sheet metal tools. In addition to many of the tools described in other parts of this chapter there are tools

Fig. 4.45. Hammers used in sheet metal work.

especially designed for sheet metal working.

Hammers. Riveting hammers are for *setting* rivets, that is, forming the second head (see page 109). Wooden *mallets* and soft-faced hammers are used in forming sheet metal because they do not stretch it as much as do metal hammers. An auto body repairman uses a *bumping hammer* to smooth out dents.

Stakes. Sheet metal can be formed by hammering over T-shaped anvils of steel called stakes. (See page 113.)

Punches. Holes in sheet metal are usually punched instead of drilled. This process is faster and more economical. You can do it by hand with a machinist's solid punch of the correct diameter, as described on page 109.

Groover. Seams are locked together with a groover. Use one that fits the seam and tap it with a mallet as you slide it along the seam. Lay the seam over an anvil while tapping.

Tin snips. These are heavy, scissor-type shears for cutting sheet metal. To cut, lay the sheet on the bench and slide the snip jaws over the sheet at the side of the cutting mark. Press down on the top handle and let the bench push against the bottom one.

Sheet metal machines. Sheet metals are processed by hand-driven and automatic machines. The *squaring shear* cuts off sheet to a straight line. Edges are turned and hems formed

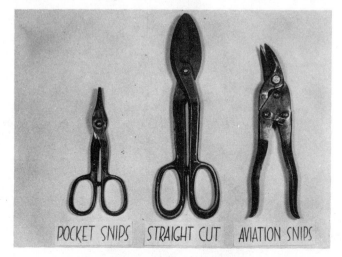

Fig. 4.46. Some snips for cutting sheet metal.

POCKET SNIPS   STRAIGHT CUT   AVIATION SNIPS

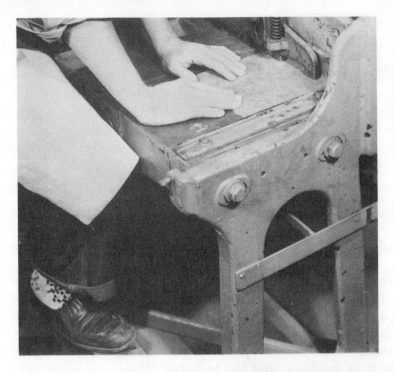

Fig. 4.47. Sheet metal is cut straight and square on the squaring shear. These are foot-operated.

Fig. 4.48. The bar folder is used for making bends in sheet metal.

Fig. 4.49. Slip rolls put curves in sheet metal. The grooves at the end of the rolls will curve wire.

on *bar folders* and *brakes*. Sheet is formed into round cylinders on a *slip roll*. Turned and wired edges are made on *rotary machines*. Sheet is pressed into form on *presses* (see page 102). It is cut to shape or punched on *punch presses*.

How sheet metals are joined. An auto body is made up of several pieces of formed sheet fastened together by welding. This is the commonest process for joining sheet metals. The joint may be welded continuously along its length or only in spots, called *spot welding*. Soft and hard soldering are used in place of welding in some products when little heat can be applied. Riveting is less common now than before the perfection of welding. (See page 141.) Hems and seams are the joints in such products as tin cans, pails, boxes, and heating ducts.

Hems and seams. This may sound more like dressmaking and tailoring than sheet metal work. There is a similarity, for a seam is a fold, whether in cloth or in metal. You may not have thought of the medieval armorer as a tailor, but he was, and a metal worker, too. A hem in cloth is sewed in place. In metal, the ends are folded, or hemmed, then hooked together and locked, making a seam. To stiffen the joint even more and to make it water tight solder is flowed into the folds.

Soldering. Galvanized and tin-plated steel can be soldered with a soldering iron (soldering copper). These metals do not conduct heat away

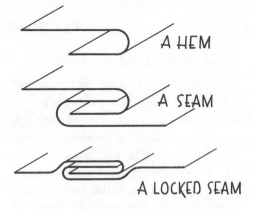

Fig. 4.50.   Some common folds for sheet metal.

as rapidly as do copper and brass. For the latter, a flame is preferred if the joint is large. Follow these steps for soldering:

1. Heat the copper until it will melt solder.

2. Wipe the tip clean with a damp cloth.

3. Dip the hot tip into flux and rub on a small amount of solder.

4. If the tip does not take the solder all over, rub it on a block of wood until it does. This is *tinning*. A well-tinned copper holds solder better and transfers more heat to the metal than does a dirty one.

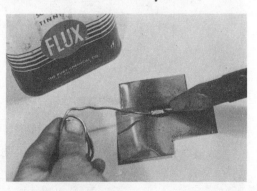

Fig. 4.51.   Soldering with a soldering iron.

And now to solder a joint:

1. The surfaces must be clean, but do not steel-wool the galvanizing or the tin plating. They are too thin. A good flux will usually do the cleaning.

2. Apply flux to the joint.

3. Hold the tip of the copper against the joint until the metal is hot enough to melt the solder, then add as much as is needed.

Forging

Forging is the process of shaping hot metal by hammering. It makes metal stronger and tougher. The village blacksmith shaped horseshoes, wagon-wheel rims, plow shares, and the like, on his anvil. As he struck the hot steel with heavy blows the sparks flew in all directions and glanced from his leather apron. In industry today hand forging has almost disappeared. It has been replaced by machines which, for ex- ample, can forge an automobile engine crankshaft with a few blows. You will enjoy forging. There is something fascinating about hammering red-hot steel; it is soft and plastic.

The forge. The forge is a furnace designed to heat metals quickly and at particular places. The old black-smith used wood or coal for fuel and a bellows for forced air draft. Modern forges are generally gas fired or electric. Do not operate your forge until your teacher shows you how.

The anvil. The anvil is a block of iron or steel with a flat face on top and a tapered horn on one end. On it most of the forming of hot metal is done in hand forging. The *face* is for hammering metal flat and straight; the *horn* is used for making curves. The square hole in the top is the *hardy hole.* Tools for cutting and shaping are held in it. The round hole, the *pritchel hole,* is for punching holes and shaping rod. Striking the face of

Fig. 4.52. Removing a forged part from a 2,000-ton press. The two halves of the dies forge the metal to their shapes. (Courtesy: Aluminum Company of America.)

the anvil with a hammer will make nicks in it which will show up as scars on the metal being forged.

Tongs. Use tongs to hold the metal while it is hot. These are long-handled pliers with jaws shaped to hold various sizes of metal. Do not keep the tongs in the fire while the metal is being heated.

Hammers. An engineer's hammer with a short handle and heavy head is ideal for general forging. The short handle makes it easier to control your aim. Use as heavy a hammer as you can safely swing.

Basic Forging Processes

When steel is forged it should be heated to a point between a bright cherry red and an orange. Too much heat burns the metal; too little, causes it to crack under the hammering.

Drawing out. The first shaping in the making of tools such as chisels and punches is drawing out. Hold the hot metal on the anvil horn and strike it several times with the face of the hammer, rotating it after each blow and working down toward the hot end. This procedure lengthens and tapers the stock. After the rough shaping, hammer the metal on the face of the anvil to smooth and straighten it.

Bending and forming. Angles can be bent over the edge of the anvil. For some bends a heavy vise is preferred. When making a bend a few inches from the end of the material, heat it, then quickly quench the end, leaving the section to be bent hot. To

twist bars, clamp one end in a vise and turn the other with a heavy wrench.

Cutting and shearing. Hot metal is cut on the anvil. Put a *hardy*, the blacksmith's cold chisel, in the square hole and lay the metal across the cutting edge. Strike it several blows with the hammer on both sides until it is nearly cut through. Then bend it back and forth until it breaks. Light bars can be sheared off in a heavy vise. Clamp the metal with the cut-off mark against the jaws and, with a cold chisel and hammer, shear it against the jaws.

Heat Treating

Without heat treating many tools and machines would be useless. It is the process by which soft steel can be made hard and hard steel, soft. In industry special heat-treating furnaces heat metal to temperatures controlled automatically. You can do yours in the forge. Heat treating includes

Fig. 4.53. Heating a piece of steel in a forge.

Fig. 4.54. With a hammer and an anvil the eye for the hook in the boat anchor is formed. (See Fig. 7.65.)

hardening, tempering, and annealing.

Hardening. Hardening is the first step in heat treatment. You have learned (page 96) that if steel is to harden it must contain carbon. Tool steel, a high-carbon steel, is hardened by heating and immediately quenching in oil or water. An expert can tell by the color of the steel when it is at the correct temperature for chilling. You may tell quite accurately by holding a small magnet to the steel. When the magnet no longer attracts the steel, the temperature is about right.

Tempering. Hardened steel is often so hard and so brittle that it is useless. Tempering is the process of removing excess hardness so that the steel, though still hard, is tougher. Polish the part of the metal to be tempered with aluminum oxide cloth. Slowly heat this part, removing it from the furnace frequently to watch for the colors. The first color notice-

able is a yellow, and as the temperature increases this changes to a straw, then to brown, purple, and blue. When you get the desired color for the tool you are making quench the piece in cold water. Hammers are quenched at the straw color, cold chisels and punches at purple, and screwdrivers at blue.

Annealing. Annealing is a softening process (see page 116). Since hardened steel cannot be readily machined, it is annealed, then machined, then hardened and tempered. To anneal a piece of steel heat it to a dull red and then cool it slowly in warm ashes, or let it cool down with the furnace. It should become as soft as it was originally.

Case hardening. Since mild steel, a low carbon steel, contains little carbon, it will not get very hard, but it can be given a hard outer shell by case hardening. The steel is heated red

124

and then placed in a compound rich in carbon. The hot surface absorbs carbon and becomes like tool steel. The steel is then reheated and hardened as is tool steel. Follow the specific instructions accompanying the compound you are using.

Safety sense. When you are forging or heat treating:

1. Wear a face shield while you are hammering the hot metal. The scale that flies is hot.

2. Wear gloves when necessary, and use tongs for handling hot metal.

Foundry Processes and Products

One of the first things that early man found out about metals was that they could be melted and cast into shapes in sand. Today this is a key process in the metals industries. Sand is still used for making molds into which large castings of molten metal are poured. Sand molds are broken up after each casting. Permanent molds of steel are used for producing great quantities of identical pieces, such as certain automobile parts of aluminum. Jewelry and dental structures are cast in plaster molds. The foundry industry has grown up around this process of shaping molten metal in molds. Today much casting is done automatically with metals compounded scientifically by *metallurgists* and melted in furnaces controlled automatically. As in all industries, certain tools and equipment are necessary.

Patterns. Patterns are the models from which the molds are made. They are identical to the finished casting in shape except that they are enough larger to make up for the shrinkage of the metal when it cools. Patterns

Fig. 4.55. Looking into the frame finishing shop at the Buckeye Steel Castings Company. The frames are one-piece steel castings for the trucks that hold the wheels of railroad cars.

Fig. 4.56. Lifting the drag, the lower half of a mold, from the pattern of a railroad car coupler. *(Courtesy: Buckeye Steel Castings Co.)*

Fig. 4.57. This is the cope, the upper half of the mold. *(Courtesy: Buckeye Steel Castings Co.)*

Fig. 4.58. Pouring the molds from a huge ladle. *(Courtesy: Buckeye Steel Castings Co.)*

126

are usually made of wood, metal, or plaster.

Flask. The flask is the metal box that holds the pattern and the sand. It has two parts: the upper is the *cope*, and the lower, the *drag*. It has two locating pins which permit it to be taken apart, the pattern removed, and then reassembled in exactly the same position.

Sand. The special sand used in foundry work is called *molding sand*. Before it is used it is tempered by water being added and the whole mixed thoroughly. The sand should be just damp enough to hold together. Squeeze a handful tightly and then break it in two. If it breaks clean and sharp, the sand is well tempered. Sand that is too wet is dangerous; the hot metal turns the water to steam, which may cause the mold to explode.

Melting furnace. The metal to be cast is heated in a melting furnace, which may burn gas, oil, electricity or coke. The metal is melted in a special container, a *crucible*, made of clay and graphite. Be sure to get the operating instructions from your teacher before you attempt to light the furnace.

Other tools. The *riddle* is a sieve for the sand. Sand is packed into the flash with a *bench rammer*. The *striking board* is a straight edge for leveling the sand acros the top of the flask. The *sprue pin* is a tapered, slender, wooden cone set in the sand to form the hole into which the metal is poured. The *riser pin* is similar and forms the hole for the air to escape as the metal

Fig. 4.59. A camper's outfit including grill, hamburger fryer, fry pan, and flapjack griddle. The last two were cast in aluminum. The hamburger fryer consists of two pans formed of black iron sheet, hinged together and brazed to wire handles. The legs of the grill fold to make it portable.

rushes in. The *gate cutter* is used to cut channels in the sand to carry the molten metal from the sprue to the mold and out the riser.

How to make a sand mold. The measure of a good sand mold is the accuracy with which the cavity is made from the pattern. Follow these

Fig. 4.60. The griddle patterns for the fry pan and griddle are made of wood to the exact shape desired for the castings.

127

suggestions as carefully as possible:

1. Place the drag on a molding board with the locating pins pointed down. Center the pattern with its flat side down on the board inside the drag. Dust the pattern with *parting compound.*

2. Riddle about a half inch of sand over the pattern.

Fig. 4.63. With the sand rammed firmly, the drag is turned over and the other side of the pattern is dusted.

Fig. 4.61. The griddle pattern is placed on the pattern board in the drag and dusted with parting compound.

Fig. 4.64. The sprue pins are pressed into position.

3. Fill the drag heaping full with unriddled sand and pack it firmly with the rammer. Strike the sand off evenly with the striking bar.

4. Place another mold board on top of the drag and carefully turn the drag over, with the boards held firmly in place. Remove the top board and place the cope on the drag. Set the sprue and riser pins in place, about

Fig. 4.62. Sand is riddled over the pattern.

Fig. 4.65. Cutting the gates, through which the metal will flow.

Fig. 4.66. The mold is filled with molten aluminum. Note the protective gear which is worn. This is protection against hot metal that might be spilled and that might splatter from the mold if the sand were too moist.

Fig. 4.67. The rough castings.

an inch from the pattern on opposite sides. Dust the pattern with parting compound.

5. Riddle, then fill with sand as before. Ram and strike it off.

6. Remove the pins and with your fingers shape each opening like a funnel.

7. Lift off the cope and set it down gently so that the sand is not disturbed. Tap the pattern lightly from side to side so that you can lift it out. Be careful not to damage the cavity. Cut the gates.

8. Blow off any loose sand with a bellows and replace the cope on the drag. The mold is now ready to pour.

Pouring the metal. When the metal is hot enough, lift the crucible out of the furnace with the tongs and pour it into the sprue hole in a continuous stream as fast as the hole will take it. When the metal comes to the surface in the riser, the cavity is full. After the metal has cooled, set the flask in the molding bench and dig out the casting.

Pattern making. Almost any simple shape can be used as a pattern. The important thing to remember when you make a pattern is that you must be able to remove it from the sand without damaging the cavity. The sides of the pattern must be tapered or rounded so that it can be withdrawn easily. This taper is called *draft*. Inside corners should be rounded too. They can be filled and

129

smoothed with wax. Wood and plaster of paris make good patterns. Shellac and wax them well before using them.

Safety sense. When you are working with molten metals,

1. Wear a face shield, gloves, and leggings.

2. Never add wet metal to molten metal, nor pour when the sand mold is wet. Can you figure out why?

3. Light a melting furnace with a torch, not a match.

4. Keep those pupils who are not actually helping with the pouring at a safe distance.

Metals Machining Processes

Products that originate as castings and forgings often require shaping or cutting to precise dimensions. Such

Fig. 4.68. These screws are an example of accurate machining. They are almost invisible to the naked eye, yet they are made so perfectly in dimension and weight that they are accurate to one-millionth of an ounce. They are used to true balance wheels in wrist watches. A needle and thread appear giant-sized by comparison. *(Courtesy: Elgin National Watch Co.)*

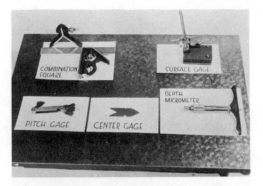

Fig. 4.69. Some layout and measuring tools for machine work.

processing is called *machining*. It involves a cutting away of metal, not a stretching, bending, hammering, or the like. The department in a factory which does this work is a *machine shop*. The skilled workers are *machinists*. The basic machines are machine lathes, drill presses, grinders, shapers, and mills. Automatic models are used for production.

Layout and measuring. All of the machining processes require layout, measuring, and setup. Layout refers to the actual marking of the locations for the cuts. Making the setup involves the adjustment of the machine so that the correct cuts are made. Measuring includes the measuring and checking of dimensions before and after cutting. (See pages 104-105 for the tools and techniques in layout.) Measurements are made with the aid of such devices as surface plates and gauges, depth gauges, screw pitch gauges, and micrometers.

Surface plate and gauge. A surface plate is a flat, true, iron surface that serves as the base line from which heights are measured on the piece being machined. A surface gauge is the tool used on the plate for marking the heights on the work.

Depth gauge. This is a narrow steel rule with a movable crosspiece. It is used to measure depths of holes and slots.

Screw pitch gauge. The number of threads per inch on a bolt or nut can be accurately checked with this tool. Find the blade that fits the thread and read the number on it.

Micrometer. A micrometer is the

are $^{100}/_{1000}$ in., or $^{1}/_{10}$ in., or 0.1 in. apart. There are four spaces between two adjacent numbers, as between 2 and 3 and 4. Each of these spaces is $^{1}/_{4}$ of $^{100}/_{1000}$, or $^{25}/_{1000}$, or 0.025 in.

How to read the micrometer:

1. Hold the mike in one hand and turn the thimble until it is closed. The reading should then be zero with the 0 mark on the thimble directly over the 0 mark on the hub.

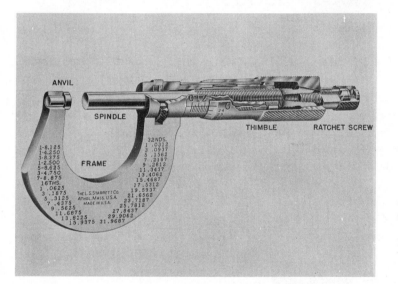

Fig. 4.70. The micrometer measures in thousandths of an inch. (Courtesy: L. S. Starrett Co.)

machinist's most used precision measuring tool. He calls it a "mike." There are styles for inside and outside measuring; all are read alike. The outside mike resembles a C clamp. It has 40 t.p.i. (teeth per inch) on the screw, so one turn moves it $^{1}/_{40}$ in., or 0.025 in. The thimble is marked off in 25 equal parts, each of which is $^{1}/_{1000}$ in., or 0.001 in. On the hub, the divisions are marked off as on a rule. The numbers and the long marks below them

2. As you slowly back off the thimble, each mark on it that passes the horizontal line on the hub means 0.001 in. In one complete turn there are 25 of these, or 0.025 in. Notice that this one complete turn exposes the first short mark on the hub, or 0.025 in.

3. To read the mike, then, the reading on the hub is added to the reading on the thimble. In Fig. 163 the reading on the hub is $^{175}/_{1000}$, or 0.175. This is added to the $^{3}/_{1000}$ in. or 0.003

READING A MICROMETER

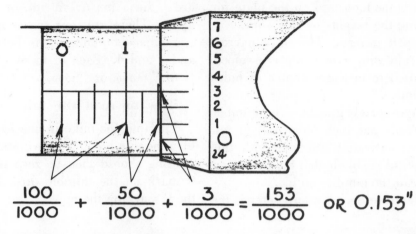

$$\frac{100}{1000} + \frac{50}{1000} + \frac{3}{1000} = \frac{153}{1000} \text{ OR } 0.153''$$

Fig. 4.71. Reading a micrometer.

in. on the thimble, for a total of 0.178 in.

4. To measure with the mike hold it in the left hand and screw the thimble down until it lightly touches the stock. Do not screw it down tight. Then carefully slide it off and read the setting. Never mike a piece of metal while it is turning, as in a lathe. If the micrometer is dropped, the accuracy may be destroyed.

Fig. 4.72. Grinding a knife on a tool grinder. The knife edge is up.

132

Grinding. Grinding is the process of cutting away material by means of abrasives. The abrasive may be in the form of a wheel which cuts as it revolves or it may be applied to a disc. *Surface grinders* cut flat surfaces and *cylindrical grinders* cut surfaces that are cylindrical or round. The *tool grinder* is the type with which you are probably most familiar.

Tool grinder. This machine is intended for sharpening tools and the light grinding of stock. It usually has two wheels, one coarse and one medium, or fine. Here are some tips to help you use the machine wisely and safely:

1. Always use goggles or a face shield when grinding if the machine does not have eye shields.

2. Support the tool on the rest, which should be about ⅛ in. from the wheel. Adjust the rest before you turn on the motor.

3. Press the tool lightly against the

wheel and keep moving over the surface to prevent the wearing of grooves in the wheel and the burning of the metal.

Limitations on the tool grinder. The grinder is not intended to take the place of a hack saw. If any appreciable amount of metal is to be removed, use the saw whenever possible. Soft metals such as copper, brass, aluminum, and lead should not be cut on the tool grinder. They clog the

abrasive and make it useless. When a tool gets dull it may need only honing. For every grinding there are probably six or eight honings. Ask your teacher when you are in doubt about which process to use.

Drilling. Holes in thick metal are usually drilled. In thinner stock they may be punched. Drilling is a process of cutting away chips or shavings; punching removes the metal in one piece the size of the hole (see p. 119). Industry uses many types of drilling machines, or drill presses. There are models which drill one hole at a time or a dozen holes. (See page 77 for instructions on the use of the drill press.)

Drill bits. The tool that cuts the hole is the drill bit. (See page 64 for details.) Drill bits for machine shop use should be of high-speed steel rather than ordinary carbon steel.

Fig. 4.73. Drilling a hole in a piece of metal on the drill press. Always use a drill press vise to hold small pieces.

Fig. 4.74. This heavy-duty machine lathe requires a 50-horsepower motor to drive it. *(Courtesy: American Tool Works Co.)*

The machine lathe. The machine lathe is the king of machine tools. It is the most versatile because so many processes can be performed on it, including facing, turning to diameter, cutting off, drilling, boring, and tapering. Some lathes are so small that watch parts can be made on them and some so large that locomotive drivers can be turned.

The principal parts of a small lathe are shown in Fig. 4.75. The motor turns the *headstock,* which supports one end of the stock to be machined; the *tailstock* supports the other. The *cutting tool* is clamped in the *tool holder* on top of the *carriage* which can be moved along the *bed* by the *hand wheel* or driven automatically by the *lead screw.* The cutting tool is moved into the stock by turning the handle on the *cross-slide* or on the *compound rest.* The tailstock can be moved back and forth and locked in position. Its *spindle* is moved in or out by the hand wheel.

Limitations of the machine lathe. The machine lathe is a precision machine and must be used carefully if it is to retain this accuracy. No hammering or other rough treatment is done on the stock in the lathe. Cutting metal is a slow process, so you must be patient. Take only as deep a cut as the lathe can adequately handle. For the most part, any adjustment and any setting on the lathe is either right or wrong. Be sure to have your teacher check you out on your setup before you turn on the motor; and ask him to watch you operate the machine now and then for the sake of your own learning and for the protection of the machine.

Fig. 4.75. A machine lathe of a size commonly found in school shops. (Courtesy: Atlas Press Co.)

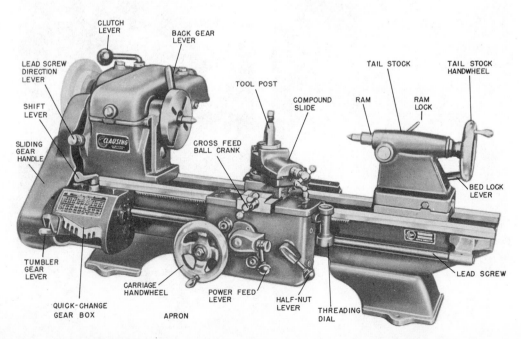

Speeds and feeds. Different speeds are required for different metals and for different sizes of stock. Soft metals can be cut faster than steel of the same size. Large-diameter stock requires slower speeds than small diameters. Speeds of the headstock spindle can be changed by shifting belts. Back gearing provides extra slow speeds. To obtain this, pull out the *bull pin* on the front of the headstock pulley and then gently engage the gears by means of the back gear lever.

Feed is the rate at which the carriage, carrying the cutting tool, travels along the bed. When the feed is automatic, the power is transmitted to the carriage by the gears on the end of the lathe and by the long *lead screw*. Some lathes have a *quick change gear box* by which several different feeds can be quickly obtained.

Chucks and chucking. Chucks are devices that screw on the headstock spindle and hold stock without the aid of centers. The 4-jaw chuck has jaws that are tightened independently. It is used to hold any shape of stock that is centered by trial and error. For a round piece, the jaws are screwed down so that they are spaced equally by the concentric rings on the face of the chuck. Then start the motor and hold a piece of chalk so that it marks the high side of the revolving metal. The high point is moved toward the center by adjusting the jaws.

The 3-jaw *universal chuck* holds round work. The jaws move at the same time when they are screwed in or out and automatically center the stock. Either type chuck holds either inside or outside as the stock permits. Drill chucks are used on the lathe for drilling holes and centers. They fit into the headstock spindle or tailstock by means of tapered *sleeves*.

Cutting tools and holders. Cutting tools, the small square-sectioned cutter bits, are ground to various shapes and angles to suit the cutting requirements. Tool holders are either left, right, or straight. The left-hand holder is most used. When you set up the lathe, the cutter bit should project not more than ⅜ in. from the tool holder. The holder should be back

Fig. 4.76. Chucking a piece in a 3-jaw chuck. It is locked securely with the chuck key.

in the tool post as far as possible. The point of the bit is set to the center height of the stock. To do this, align it with the point of the tailstock center.

Center drilling. When stock is to be turned between centers, it must have bearing surfaces cut into the ends to fit the lathe centers. These surfaces are provided by center drilling. Center the stock in the lathe chuck and hold the *center drill,* a special drill, in a

Fig. 4.78. Center drilling in a 3-jaw chuck. *(Courtesy: South Bend Lathe Works.)*

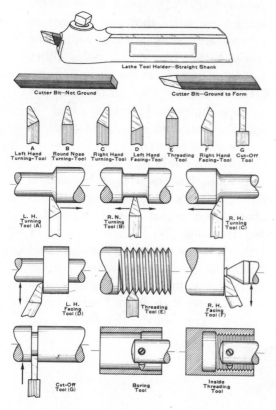

Fig. 4.77. Application of lathe tools. *(Courtesy: South Bend Lathe Works.)*

drill chuck that is inserted in the tailstock. Move the tailstock up close to the work and lock it on the bed. Lubricate the drill with cutting oil as you

screw it into the stock with the hand wheel. Drill to about three fourths of the taper.

Turning between centers. With centers drilled in both ends of the stock you are ready to turn it. These are the steps:

1. Screw a *face plate* on the headstock spindle. Wipe out the spindle hole and the tailstock hole and insert the centers.

2. Attach a lathe *dog* to one end of the stock (use the smallest dog that will fit).

3. Place a small amount of white lead lubricant in the center hole at the tailstock end. Insert the stock between the centers and screw up the tail center just snug enough to remove any play.

4. Tighten the tool bit and the straight tool holder in place with the bit on center.

5. The cut should be made from the tailstock end toward the headstock, so move the carriage to the right end of the work. Screw the cutter bit into the stock to take a light cut; start the

136

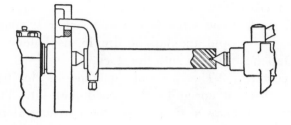

Fig. 4.79. Work properly set between the lathe centers is now ready for machining. (Courtesy: South Bend Lathe Works.)

lathe and move the carriage to the left for ¼ in. or so to try the cut. Reset the cut if necessary, then engage the power feed and let the machine do its work.

6. If the stock must be turned even smaller, disengage the carriage at the end of the cut, take a reading on the micrometer collar of the cross-feed knob, and then turn the knob counter-clockwise just enough to clear the stock. Return the carriage to the starting place and screw the tool bit to the same micrometer reading. Start the lathe, screw the cutter bit in for a new cut, and proceed as before.

Facing. Facing is the cutting of a flat surface on the ends or faces of stock. The work is held in a chuck while the cutting tool is moved across the surface. The tool should be at right angles to the direction of travel. Set it for the center height and cut from the center of the stock toward yourself. Lock the carriage to keep it from moving away. The stock should not project more than an inch or two from the jaws of the chuck.

Cutting off stock. This is done with the cut-off tool. The stock is held in a chuck and as close to the mark as possible. The tool point is set on the exact center and at 90 deg to the

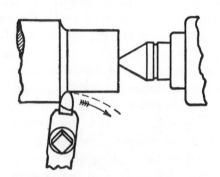

Fig. 4.80. This is a top view showing the correct position of the cutting tool for turning between centers. (Courtesy: South Bend Lathe Works.)

work. Run the lathe at the slowest speed and feed the tool into the metal by hand at a uniform rate. Use cutting

Fig. 4.81. The flapjack griddle is held in a 4-jaw chuck, ready for facing.

oil on it. Do not try to cut off stock held between centers.

Turning tapers. For short tapers, as on a center punch or lathe center, hold the stock in a chuck and turn the compound rest to the degree of taper required. The tool is set on center and the carriage locked in place. Turn the feed screw to make the cut.

Long tapers are cut by means of a taper attachment or by setting the tailstock over. The latter is done by means of the small set screws in the base of the tailstock. For straight turning, the tailstock and the headstock must be in perfect alignment as is indicated on the scale at the rear of the tailstock base. To find the amount of set-over for a taper, use this formula:

$$\text{Set-over} = \frac{\text{Taper per foot, in inches}}{2}$$
$$\times \frac{\text{length of piece}}{12}$$

Threading. The machine lathe cuts a great variety of threads. The simplest method, although not the most accurate, is to use a tap or die.

The lathe is run at its slowest speed and the tap or die in its holder is pushed into the stock.

The accurate method is to use a specially sharpened tool bit. The power feed moves the carriage along at a uniform rate. This is interesting to watch. Ask your teacher for a demonstration.

Knurling. Knurling is the process of rolling a raised, patterned texture on the surface of stock. It makes a good hand grip on tools and adds a decorative touch. The knurling tool is clamped in the tool holder at right angles to the work. Set the lathe for a slow speed and turn the knurls into the stock until they make a distinct pattern. Screw them in deeper until they make a deep pattern and then engage the carriage feed. Use plenty of oil. To make a deeper cut reverse the lathe spindle when the knurl has reached the left end of the work. The tool then automatically moves back to the start without removing the knurls from the pattern. Screw them in deeper and repeat the process.

Fig. 4.82. Measuring tailstock setover for taper turning. (Courtesy: South Bend Lathe Works.)

Fig. 4.83. Knurling between centers. (Courtesy: South Bend Lathe Works.)

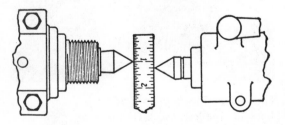

Lubricants. Machining metals always produces heat. Special lubricants and coolants are used when needed. Use *lubricating oil* for bearings, *cutting oil* for threading, and *white* or *red lead* for the tailstock center.

The shaper and the mill. The shaper uses a long, horizontal stroke in cutting similar to the stroke of a hand plane on wood. The mill uses a revolving gearlike cutter which moves across the face of the material either horizontally or vertically.

Safety sense. When you are ma-chining, be sure to observe these rules:

1. Take off your tie and roll up your sleeves.

2. Wear a face shield for turning, grinding, drilling, or any operation where chips may fly.

3. Never brush off chips with your hands. This is like brushing off razor blades.

4. Do not oil or adjust machines that are running.

Finishes for Metals

Many finishes may be used on

Fig. 4.84. A specialized type of machining. The operator traces the large plastic model of a watch face as the machine cuts an actual face. *(Courtesy: Elgin National Watch Co.)*

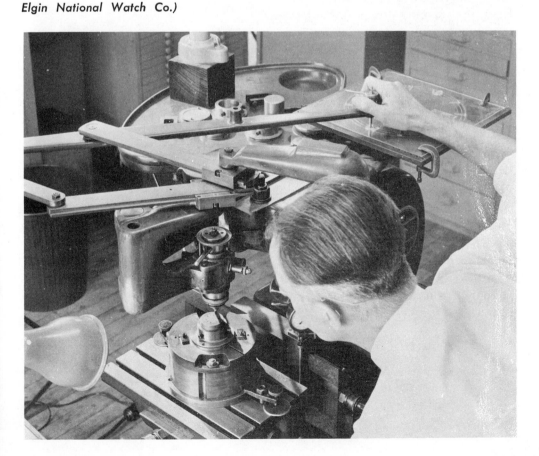

metals. Select one that best suits the use for which the product is intended.

Buffing. A high polish is obtained by buffing. Hold the metal against a revolving cloth wheel which is charged with a buffing compound, a fine abrasive. Hold it securely in both hands below the center of the wheel.

Scratch brush finish. A soft, satin finish is produced by holding a soft metal such as copper or aluminum against a revolving wire brush. Be sure to wear goggles when you do this.

Spot finish. This finish is for flat surfaces. Chuck a short piece of ½-in. dowel in the drill press. Spread a coat of fine abrasive powder and lubricating oil on the surface of the metal. Bring the spinning dowel down against the metal to make spots of shiny rings. Overlap them uniformly.

Copper finishes. Copper finishes require chemicals for antique effects. Many prepared finishes are available. Liver of sulphur mixed with water will do this, too.

Lacquers. To preserve the bright polish on copper and brass after buffing, brush or spray on a coating of clear lacquer. Transparent colored lacquers tint copper, brass, and aluminum.

Enamels. First use a metal primer over the bare clean metal. Flat black is appropriate on many iron and steel projects.

Some Things to Find Out

1. Why steel can be magnetized.
2. How thin gold can be hammered.
3. How metal spinning is done.
4. How uranium is refined.
5. Why metals become hard with hammering.
6. How a blacksmith fastens shoes on a horse.
7. How your bicycle frame is fastened together.
8. Why coins are made of silver.
9. Why a left-hand thread is used.
10. How copper and chrome plating are done.
11. How ball bearings are made.
12. Why oil makes a machine run easier.
13. Why copper wire is not suited for the element in your toaster.
14. The different metals used in an automobile.
15. What rust is.

Some Group Projects

Exhibits

1. From ore to steel. Make a model steel mill and rolling mill.
2. The story of aluminum. Include a display of common aluminum products found in the home.

Production Projects

1. Jewelry made of copper wire formed in jigs, such as first names or nicknames and animals, would be popular.
2. Small trays of aluminum can be pressed out in jigs constructed of hardwood.

Service projects

1. Make some planters or flower pots for the local hospital.
2. Make an outdoor fireplace grill for the park.

Welding Processes

Welding is the process of joining

Fig. 4.85. When you weld with an electric arc it looks like this.

metals by melting them together. In his day the village blacksmith was the local welder, too. He could heat two pieces of steel in his forge and then hammer them together on his anvil. Since then better methods of welding have been perfected so that now skyscrapers, ships, bridges, automobiles, airplanes, and many other products are held together by welding. Today there are two main types of welding. The oxyacetylene method uses heat resulting from the burning of acetylene gas with oxygen, producing temperatures as high as 6000°F. The other type uses electricity in various ways to produce heat; for example, there are electric arc welding, resistance welding, and induction welding. All types are done automatically in industry.

Oxyacetylene welding equipment. This equipment includes two metal cylinders or tanks, one of which contains oxygen, and the other, acetylene (a-*set*-e-lin). Since the tremendous pressure in these tanks would burst the hoses that pipe the gases to the *torch, regulators* are used to reduce the pressure and maintain an even flow. Each of these regulators has two *gauges.* One tells how much gas is in the tank, and the other shows the working pressure for welding. In the center of each regulator is a hand screw by which the working pressure is adjusted.

The green hose carries the oxygen, and the red hose, the acetylene. The torch has two valves for adjusting the flow of each gas. Different *tips* are

Fig. 4.86. The welding gauges and regulators on acetylene and oxygen tanks.

used on the torch, depending on the size of the flame needed. A cutting head may be attached to the torch for burning cuts through heavy metals. The *ignitor* is the lighter for the torch. Do not use a match. The flame is very bright, so special goggles must be worn when you weld or watch welding. Asbestos gloves will protect your hands.

How to weld with oxyacetylene. You should be able to make satisfactory welds after a few trials. The

will go. Turn the hand screw in until the low-pressure gauge shows the correct working pressure for the tip you will use. See your teacher about this.

2. Turn on the acetylene equipment in the same manner except that the tank valve should be opened only 1½ turns. When you open tank valves, stand on the side opposite the regulators as a safety precaution.

3. Slip the goggles on your head, put on the gloves, hold the ignitor in

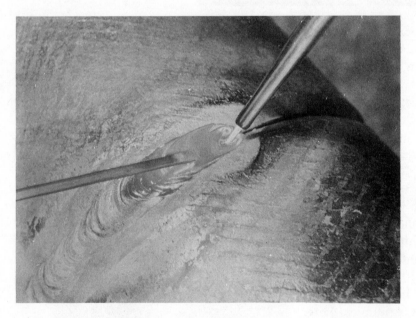

Fig. 4.87. Welding with the gas torch and filler rod. Try to make your weld look like this. (Courtesy: Linde Air Products Co.)

idea is simply to melt two pieces of metal together. Follow these steps:

1. First, make sure that the regulator hand screws are backed off so that no gas can get through. Close both valves on the torch. Open the oxygen tank valve slowly to allow pressure to build up gradually on the high-pressure gauge. When the hand stops, open the tank valve as far as it

one hand, and open the acetylene valve on the torch a part of a turn. Light the gas by holding the tip close to the ignitor and directed into the flash cup. Open the valve until you have a large, sooty flame, without blowing. The flame should touch the tip. Quickly turn on the oxygen until the flame is neutral. This is your welding flame.

To close down the equipment, first

shut off the acetylene, then the oxygen at the torch. Now turn off each tank valve. Open the torch valves and drain the hoses. Back off the regulator hand screws.

4. Making puddles is the first step in welding. Get a piece of ⅛-in. steel, a few inches long to practice on. Light the torch and hold it so that it balances easily in your hand. Bring the tip down to the steel with the flame at a 45-deg angle. Hold the cone of the flame about ⅛-in. from the metal. As soon as it begins to melt a puddle, move the torch slowly along, revolving the tip in small circles at the same time. These puddles should be about ³⁄₁₆ in. wide. Practice this several times, trying to keep the puddles uniform, with even ripples. When you move the torch too slowly, the metal burns through; when it moves too fast, there is no melting.

5. When you can run a good puddle on a flat surface, place two pieces of the metal edge to edge. Puddle each end together, then puddle the edges.

Laying beads. The next thing to try after puddling is the laying of a *bead* on a flat surface, using a welding rod for filler. Hold the torch as before, in one hand, and a piece of ³⁄₃₂-in. welding rod in the other. Keep the tip of the rod just inside the outer layer of the flame so that it will be almost melted. As the puddle forms, touch the rod to the puddle and deposit some metal there, then withdraw the rod slightly. Continue puddling

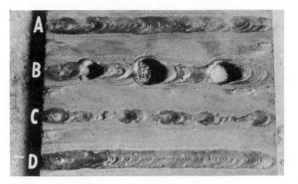

Fig. 4.88. Some good and poor welds. *(Courtesy: Linde Air Products Co.)*

A. Uneven ripples caused by uneven movement of the torch.

B. Too much heat burns through the metal.

C. Insufficient heat makes a poor weld, too.

D. A good weld. Note the uniform ripples and width of the bead.

and adding filler rod as needed to build up a bead. A bead should be similar to a puddle except that it is built up above the surface about ⅟₃₂ in.

Now place two pieces of stock edge to edge and tack each end as before, then weld them. This is a *butt weld* and it should penetrate to the other side of the metal. To make a *lap*

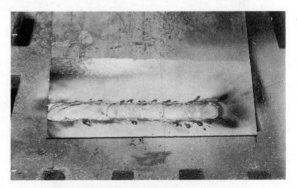

Fig. 4.89. A good braze weld. *(Courtesy: Linde Air Products Co.)*

weld lay one piece of stock overlapping the other. The heat must be directed to the lower piece to keep the other piece from burning.

Brazing. Brazing is a combination of welding and hard soldering. A bronze filler rod is used with a *flux*. You can more easily braze cast iron than you can weld it, and it will be fully as strong. The process is also used on steel, copper, brass, and bronze.

First grind or file the surfaces clean or the bronze will not stick. Bring them to a red heat, not a melting heat. Heat the end of the rod and dip it in the flux. Touch the rod to the hot metal and play the flame over the surfaces. When the metal is at the right heat the bronze will flow over it. If it is too hot, the bronze bubbles and burns off; if it is not hot enough, the bronze rolls

up into globs. Repeat this heating and filling to build up thickness and strength. Let the stock cool until the red has disappeared before moving it.

Electric arc welding. Arc welding uses the heat of an electric arc to melt the metal and the rod at the same time. It has the advantage of speed and economy and is especially suitable to the welding of thick metal.

Arc-welding equipment. There are two main types of arc welders, the alternating and the direct current. The first generally uses a transformer which steps down the voltage and steps up the amperage. The second uses a motor-driven generator to supply the welding current. Two heavy cables carry the current to the stock being welded. The electrode (welding rod) holder is attached to one of them. A special helmet with built-in filter glass

Fig. 4.90. Miniature electric spot welding. The watch bezel and the lug, which holds the wrist band, are clamped in the welder and are automatically fused together. (Courtesy: Gruen Watch Co.)

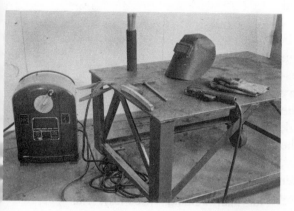

Fig. 4.91. An electric arc welding outfit suitable for school shops. *(Courtesy: The Lincoln Electric Co.)*

Fig. 4.92. A grinding and polishing head of welded construction.

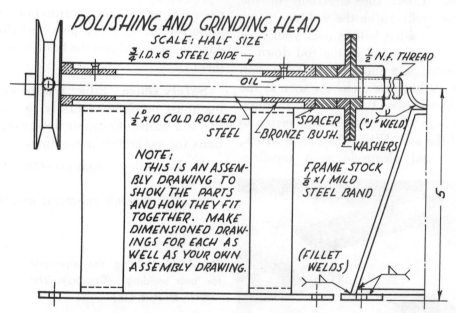

POLISHING AND GRINDING HEAD

SCALE: HALF SIZE

¾ I.D. x 6 STEEL PIPE

½ N.F. THREAD

OIL

½ D x 10 COLD ROLLED STEEL

SPACER

BRONZE BUSH.

("J" WELD)

WASHERS

FRAME STOCK ⅛ x 1 MILD STEEL BAND

NOTE:
THIS IS AN ASSEMBLY DRAWING TO SHOW THE PARTS AND HOW THEY FIT TOGETHER. MAKE DIMENSIONED DRAWINGS FOR EACH AS WELL AS YOUR OWN ASSEMBLY DRAWING.

(FILLET WELDS)

5

Fig. 4.93. Details of the grinding and polishing head.

is used for protection of the face and eyes.

How to arc weld. Arc welding is fascinating and is entirely safe when properly done. You will get accustomed to the flash which at first may cause you to jump. As you watch the flame closely through your shield, imagine that you are peering into the crater of a spewing volcano. Actually, arc-welding temperatures are hotter than the interior of a volcano; they exceed 6000°F. Here are the steps:

1. Use a piece of scrap metal not less than ⅛ in. thick and then check a welding chart to find the correct size of electrode. Your instructor will show you how to set the machine for the proper welding current.

2. Lay the metal on the welding table and clamp the ground cable to it or to the welding table. Adjust the helmet to fit, turn on the ventilating fan, and draw the curtains around the booth. Insert the electrode in the holder and turn on the welder.

3. Drop the helmet over your face and bring the end of the rod down to the metal in a short, sweeping motion as in striking a match. As soon as the arc forms, raise the electrode to about ⅛ in. to 3/16 in. from the metal to hold the arc. When the arc is struck, metal and electrode melt together.

Fig. 4.95. Holding the electrode for fillet welding. (Courtesy: The Lincoln Electric Co.)

4. Move the rod from side to side in small half-moons about ⅜ in. wide as you move it along the metal. The rod melts away, so you must keep moving it into the metal. When you have an inch or so of bead, stop and inspect it. Chip away the scale with the chipping hammer so that the weld is exposed, then show it to your teacher.

5. When you can run a bead that passes your teacher's inspection, try to butt-weld. Lay two pieces of stock edge to edge and run the bead between them.

Safety sense. Either type of welding must be done carefully to avoid fire and burns. Consider these suggestions for oxyacetylene welding:

1. Use only enough pressure to do the work.

2. If you smell unburned gas, turn

Fig. 4.94. Holding the electrode for butt welding. (Courtesy: The Lincoln Electric Co.)

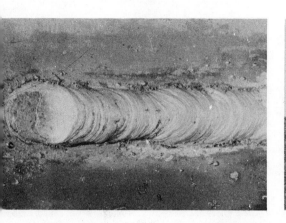 

Fig. 4.96 (left). A good arc-welded bead.

Fig. 4.97 (right). An enlarged section through this good bead. Note the penetration and the flat surface. *(Courtesy: The Lincoln Electric Co.)*

Fig. 4.98 (left). A section through a poor arc-welded bead, damaged by insufficient heat. *(Courtesy: The Lincoln Electric Co.)*

Fig. 4.99 (right). A poor weld with a high bead has little penetration. This is caused by insufficient welding current. *(Courtesy: The Lincoln Electric Co.)*

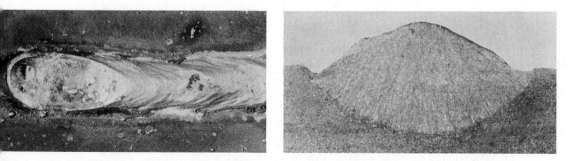

Fig. 4.100 (left). A bead formed when too much heat is used burns away the metal at the edges. *(Courtesy: The Lincoln Electric Co.)*

Fig. 4.101 (right). A section through a poor arc-welded bead, damaged by too much heat.

147

off the torch and call your instructor. The gas is not only inflammable but it is explosive if not controlled.

3. Always shut off the torch as soon as you are finished.

4. Don't watch the flame without welding goggles. However, these are not adequate for arc welding.

5. Be careful where you point a lighted torch.

6. Stand so that no molten metal can fall into your trouser cuffs or shoes. Isn't that an interesting thought? It has happened.

7. Remember that the metal may still be too hot to handle without gloves even though it is no longer red.

These suggestions are for arc welding:

1. The ultraviolet rays produced by the flash can burn just as the sun can. Wear gloves and keep your sleeves rolled down. Never watch the arc without a shield. Your eyes can sunburn too. You can imagine how it would feel to have your eyeballs peel. Shield your welding so that others won't watch it.

2. The welding fumes are very objectionable. Be sure there is adequate ventilation.

3. If your shoesoles are wet or if the concrete floor is damp, don't weld unless you can stand on a dry board or some other good insulator. You could get a shock.

Some Things to Find Out

1. Why annealing makes metals soft.
2. Why hammering makes them hard.
3. How your mother's aluminum pressure cooker was made.

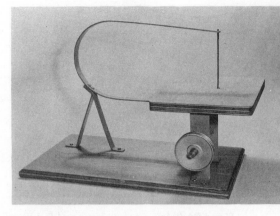

Fig. 4.102. A jig saw you can make.

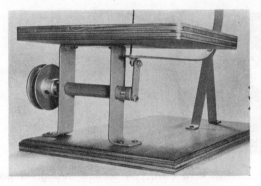

Fig. 4.103. A close-up of the jig saw mechanism.

4. How window screen is made.
5. How many different metals are known to man.
6. What kind of metal makes the flash in a photographic flash bulb.
7. Why titanium is the new "wonder" metal.
8. How tin-can metal (tin plate) is coated with tin.
9. Why some watches are nonmagnetic.
10. How your bicycle frame is fastened together.

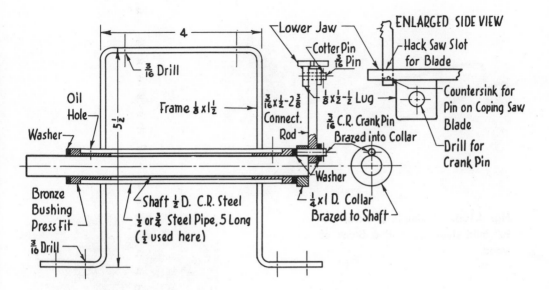

Fig. 4.104. Details of the jig saw mechanism.

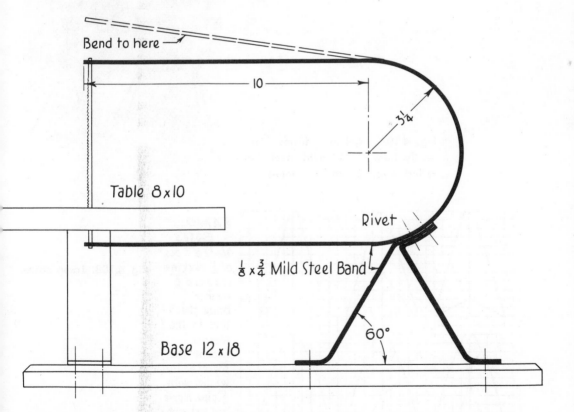

Fig. 4.105. The jig saw frame.

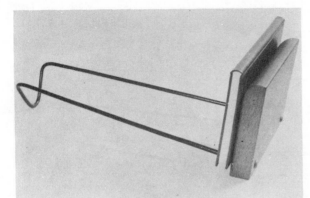

Fig. 4.106. A simple bookrack of
⅜" mild steel rod and a block of
wood.

Fig. 4.107. Animal forms are
easily bent of ⅛" mild steel, hot
rolled wire. Braze any points.

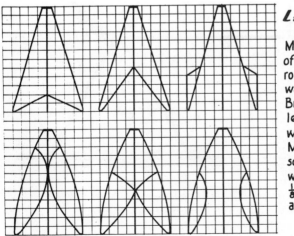

LAMP BASES

Made of 3 pcs.
of ¼" black iron
rod and a ⅜"
washer.
Braze the 3
legs to the
washer.
Mount the
socket on the
washer with
⅛" pipe nipple
and lock nut.

Fig. 4.108. Lamp bases.

Some Sources of Ideas and Information

Books

1. Barich, D. F. and Smith, L. C. *Metalwork for Industrial Arts Shops.* Chicago: American Technical Society, 1951.
2. Dragoo, A. W. and Reed, H. O. *General Shop Metalwork.* McKnight and McKnight, 1947.
3. Fraser, Roland R., and Bedell, Earl L. *General Metal.* New York: Prentice-Hall, Inc., 1955.
4. Glazener, Everett. *Modern Metalwork.* Austin, Texas: The Steck Company, 1954.
5. Smith, Robert E. *Bench Metal Work; Etching, Spinning, Raising and Tooling Metal; Machining of Metal; Sheet Metalwork; Units in Forging and Welding; Units in Patternmaking and Founding.* Bloomington, Ill.: McKnight and McKnight.

Booklets, Magazines

1. *ABC's of Hand Tools.* General Motors Corporation, Department of Public Relations, Detroit 2, Mich.
2. *Alcoa Library.* List of films and booklets. Aluminum Company of America, Pittsburgh, Pa.
3. *Contemporary Silversmithing.* Handy and Harmon, 82 Fulton Street, New York 38, N. Y.
4. *How to Run a Lathe.* South Bend Lathe Works, South Bend, Ind.
5. *Metallurgy and Wheels.* General Motors Corporation.
6. *Steel Making in America.* United States Steel Corporation, 71 Broadway, New York 6, N. Y.
7. *Steelways.* Bimonthly magazine, free. American Iron and Steel Institute, 350 Fifth Avenue, New York 1, N. Y.
8. *The Care and Operation of a Lathe.* Sheldon Machine Company, Chicago, Ill.
9. *The Picture Story of Steel.* American Iron and Steel Institute.

Films

1. *ABC's of Hand Tools.* See Booklets.
2. *Alcoa Library.* See Booklets.
3. *Motion Picture Films.* Bureau of Mines, United States Department of the Interior, Washington, D.C.
4. *Steel.* How steel is made. Modern Talking Picture Service, 9 Rockefeller Plaza, New York 20, N. Y.

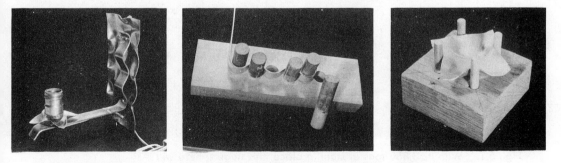

Fig. 4.109 (left). An aluminum pin-up lamp. The bracket is riveted to the back.
Fig. 4.110 (middle). The jig for bending the pin-up lamp bracket.
Fig. 4.111 (right). The jig in which the socket cut is formed.

Fig. 5.1.   With its 3,850 tons of steel in place, this huge sphere will house an atomic power plant similar to that used in U. S. Navy submarines. This is the power plant of the future. *(Courtesy: General Electric Company.)*

152

The 5 ELECTRICAL INDUSTRIES

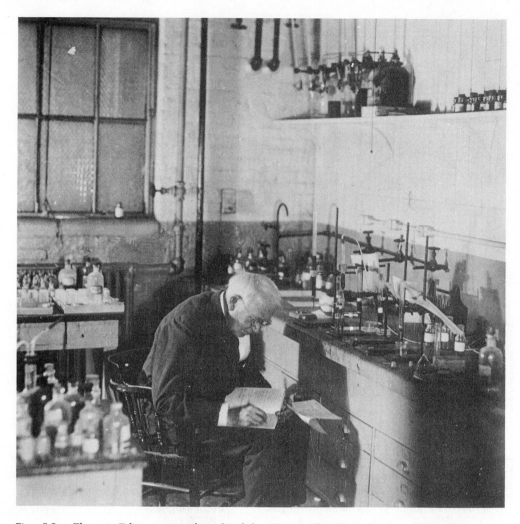

Fig. 5.2. Thomas Edison at work in his laboratory. This is a picture of a truly great American. (*Courtesy: General Electric Company.*)

Industry and Electricity

Electricity is the wonder worker in our homes and industries. It not only works wonders, but it is a wonder how well it can work for us. If the electricity were cut off from your home for a day, how many things would you have to do without? Imagine how inconvenient it would be if the current were off for a whole year. But worse than that would be the effects if electricity were not available to our industries. They would have to go back to steam, water, and wind power, which would throw millions of workers out of jobs. Electricity is indispensable in the United States.

154

Fig. 5.3. Man-made lightning is used in the study of electricity by scientists. (Courtesy: General Electric Company.)

A doctor uses electricity to treat his patients, but when it is used unwisely electricity can cause injury and death. It lights a tiny flashlight, and the whole sky in a storm. It makes your home cheery with light, but it can also set fire to a building. It can drive a mighty locomotive and guide a pilotless airplane. It can coat metal with plating less than a thousandth of an inch thick and it can melt tons of steel. Electricity is truly a wonder worker, so we should become well acquainted with it. All of the possible uses for it have not yet been found. It could be that you or one of your friends will someday find a new way to make it useful.

Primitive man cringed and hid when the lightning flashed. He was afraid of it because he could not understand it. Today we know about electricity and how to control it, so we need not fear it. As you study and work with electricity it is hoped that you will come to understand and appreciate it rather than fear it.

Occupations in the industry. Nearly every type of occupation known in American industry can be found in the electrical industries alone. Scientists, engineers, technicians, and skilled workers of all types are needed. You can work in a giant-size industry, or in a small plant, or in a one-man repair shop. If you like to experiment with electrical gadgets, take them seriously and go all out with them. You may find a clue to the job for you.

155

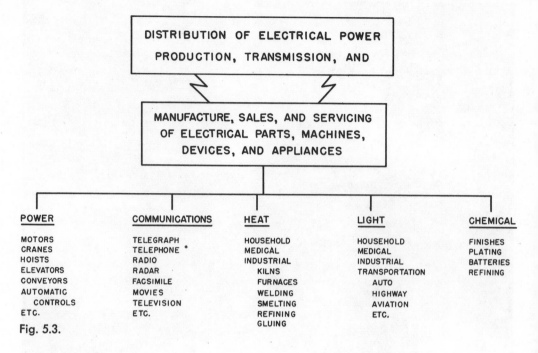

Fig. 5.3.

About Electricity

There are two kinds of electricity, *static* and *current*. When you comb your hair with a hard rubber comb and the comb attracts bits of paper, that is static. When you rub a cat's fur and you hear a snap and crackle, that too, is static. Shuffling across a thick wool rug will sometimes build up a charge of static that sparks when you touch metal or another person. The Greek wise man, Thales, is said to have discovered static electricity about six centuries B.C.

A lightning flash is a discharge of static electricity which we cannot control or put to use. Static is often more bothersome than useful. It creates radio and television interference and damages power lines and buildings. However, scientists are learning to

harness it to make it work for us. It is used in smoke eliminators in cities and to coat paper with abrasive grit in making sandpaper.

Electricity that flows along a conductor is called *current*. The scientist knows electricity as a flow of electrons along a conductor, which is usually a wire. Because electricity flows, it is useful to us. It is sent from the power station to your house and to industries over miles and miles of wires.

Kinds of current. There are two kinds of electric current. You probably have both in your home. One is *direct current* (D.C.) and the other is *alternating current* (A.C.) The current produced in your flashlight and auto batteries is D.C., that is, it flows in one direction only. The generator in your car generates direct current. Industry uses D.C. for such purposes as electroplating, battery charging, electric welding, electric locomotives, and street cars.

Alternating current flows forward and backward through the circuit. The current for your home is probably 110/120 volts, 60 cycle, A.C. The cycle tells us that the current flows 60 times forward and 60 times backward through the circuit in one second. Most of the electricity consumed today is A.C. It has an advantage in that its voltage can be stepped up or down by means of transformers. (See page 168.) This makes it possible for the power station to send it for hundreds of miles over wires. This cannot be done with D.C.

Why current flows. Water flows from a faucet only because pressure forces it through the pipes. Electricity flows too, because of pressure, but not of the water kind. It is called *voltage* (after Alessandro Volta). Voltage

pushes the electrons along the conductors, the wires. We are told that electrons are so tiny that it takes 25 trillion of them placed end to end to equal an inch.

Current flows from the terminal of a battery or of a generator having the most electrons to the one with the fewest. Because of this we say that it flows from the *negative* terminal (−) to the *positive* (+).

In your home you probably have a voltage of from 110 to 120 for lights and appliances. You may, however, have a motor on a saw or a pump which uses 220 to 230 v (volts). An appliance wired for the lower voltage will burn out when connected to the higher. A motor wired for 220/230 v will run slowly and with little power on the 110/220 v. You see, it is important that the correct voltage be used.

Voltage is measured with a *volt-*

Fig. 5.4.   A voltmeter is connected across the two wires; an ammeter, in one wire.

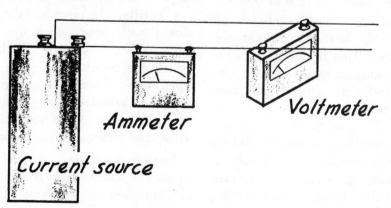

CONNECTING METERS

Ammeter

Voltmeter

Current source

meter which is connected across the two wires conducting the current in a circuit.

Current and amperage. To an electrician, current means *amperage*. The amount of current consumed by a light bulb or an appliance is given in *amperes* (after André Marie Ampère). Both voltage and amperage are usually indicated on a plate fastened to a motor or other appliance. See if you can find them on one of your shop motors. Both voltage and amperage are necessary for the flow of electricity. When the voltage is high and the amperage low, electricity easily jumps an air gap as in an automobile spark plug where 15,000 to 20,000 v are required. With low voltage and high amperage, great heat is possible as in electric welding. The combination may be about 40 v with 200 to 300 amp.

Amperage is measured by an *ammeter* which is connected in one wire of the circuit. An electric clock consumes about ⅟₃₀ amp; a ¼ hp (horse power) motor, about 4 amp; and a trolley bus, about 50 amp at 600 v.

Resistance. There is always opposition to the flow of a current over a conductor. This is called its *resistance*. The amount varies with the kind of material, its length, diameter (cross-sectional area), and its temperature. The greater the length of a wire, the smaller its diameter, and the higher its temperature, the greater is its resistance. Resistance is measured in *ohms* (after George Simon Ohm). Copper is most often used for wire

conductors because it has the least resistance of the plentiful metals. Silver has even less resistance, but it is too costly. Materials that conduct current with little resistance are called *conductors;* those that have great resistance are called *insulators,* for example, rubber, plastics, porcelain, and glass. In between these two groups of materials are those that are both poor conductors and poor insulators. Some of these are iron, steel, tungsten, and the alloys used for heating elements. Some high-temperature elements are nonmetallic. Resistance, you see, is not always objectionable.

Heat is given off in a wire when the voltage overcomes the resistance. The electrons resist moving and, in their being forced to move, heat is created.

Voltage, amperage, and resistance. These three qualities are always found together in a *circuit* (the path over which the current flows). They behave according to Ohm's Law:

$I = \frac{E}{R}$ This means Amperes $= \frac{\text{Volts}}{\text{Ohms}}$

If you know any two of the three you can find the third by arithmetic.

Circuits. An electrical circuit is a closed path over which the current flows. When you turn on the light switch, the circuit is complete and the light burns. Turning it off breaks the circuit. There are two common types of circuits with which you can easily work, the *series* and the *parallel.*

Series circuits. When several lights are connected in series they are all connected into the same wire. You have undoubtedly seen Christmas tree

DRY CELL HOOK-UPS

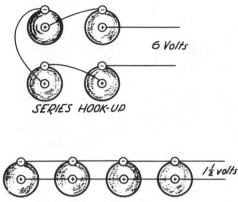

6 Volts

SERIES HOOK-UP

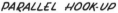

1½ volts

PARALLEL HOOK-UP

Fig. 5.5. Series and parallel hook-ups.

lights connected this way. When one burns out, they all go out. Connecting several batteries in series increases the voltage, but the amperage remains unchanged. Suppose you have four dry cells. Each has 1½ v. In series, the total voltage is 4 times 1½, or 6 v.

Parallel circuits. The other kind of Christmas tree lights are connected in parallel. Each light is connected to two wires. A bulb may burn out without affecting the rest. This is the type of circuit used in wiring your home and in the transmission lines that send electric power over the country. Four dry cells connected in parallel provide four times the amperage of one, but the voltage remains unchanged.

Short circuits. In any well-planned circuit there is just enough resistance among all the parts to balance the voltage and amperage. When the current is detoured over a shorter path, the current is too great for the resistance. Sparks fly, heat is formed, and a fuse burns out. Faulty insula-

tion on a lamp cord permits the wires to touch and build up excessive current.

Fuses. Fuses are silent sentries standing watch over the current flowing in a circuit. If too much flows, as it does when too many lights and appliances are turned on, the wiring becomes overheated. Instantly the fuse burns out, thus breaking the circuit and preventing a fire. When two bare wires touch, as they can when the insulation is broken, the current becomes excessive. Again the fuse instantly burns out, thus preventing further damage. New fuses will continue to burn out until the trouble is remedied.

The size of the fuse is determined by the size of the wiring in the circuit. A 15-amp fuse is proper in a circuit using 14-gauge wire, and a 20-amp fuse in one using 12-gauge wire. If the larger fuse is used in place of the smaller, it does not provide the necessary protection. Circuit breakers are commonly used instead of fuses. A switch is automatically shut off when the circuit is overloaded and can be reset after it has cooled.

Underwriters Laboratories. On some appliances, lamp cords, and other electrical goods you will find a tag bearing the label "U.L." This means that the product has passed the tests used on it by the Underwriters Laboratories, Inc., a testing company. It tells the consumer that the product will operate safely.

About Wire

Many sizes and shapes of wire are

159

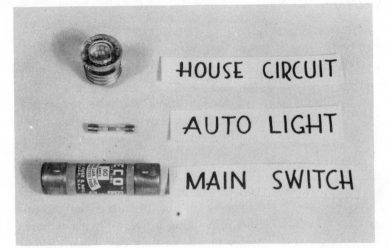

Fig. 5.6. Three common types of fuses.

used in conducting electricity. Copper is preferred for most wiring. Aluminum is often used in cross-country power lines. Its lightness makes possible the great spans between the steel towers. When ice forms on the wires the power is stepped up through them, warming the wire and melting the ice. High-tension lines are often bare rather than insulated.

Single cotton cover (S.C.C.)
Double cotton cover (D.C.C.)
Plain enamel (P.E.)
Enamel single cotton cover (E.S.C. C.)
Enamel double cotton cover (E.D. C.C.)

Special wire is used for radio and other electronic hookups. It is bare with a coating of tin. Insulation,

Fig. 5.7. Steel towers are replacing wood poles for carrying electrical power across country. (Courtesy: General Electric Company.)

COPPER WIRE TABLE

American Wire Gauge	Diameter in In.	Capacity in Amp.	Resistance in Ohms per 1000 Feet at 68°F.
1	0.289	100	0.123
10	0.102	25	0.998
12	0.081	20	1.588
14	0.064	15	2.525
16	0.051	6	4.016
18	0.040	3	6.385
20	0.032		10.15
22	0.025		16.14
24	0.020		25.67
26	0.016		40.81
28	0.013		64.90
30	0.010		103.2

Types of wire. The copper wire used for motors, transformers, magnets, and so on, is called *magnet wire*. It can be had with a variety of insulation. There are:

160

Fig. 5.8. Wire-drawing machines pull wire through a series of successively smaller dies to reduce its diameter. (Courtesy: Aluminum Company of America.)

Fig. 5.9. Small kiln.

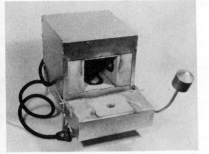

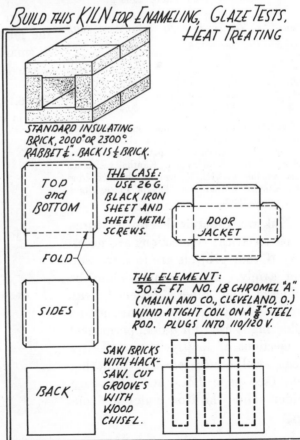

Build this KILN for Enameling, Glaze Tests, Heat Treating

STANDARD INSULATING BRICK, 2000° OR 2300°. RABBET ¼". BACK IS ½ BRICK.

TOP and BOTTOM

THE CASE: USE 26 G. BLACK IRON SHEET AND SHEET METAL SCREWS.

DOOR JACKET

FOLD

SIDES

THE ELEMENT: 30.5 FT. NO. 18 CHROMEL "A". (MALIN AND CO., CLEVELAND, O.) WIND A TIGHT COIL ON A ⅜" STEEL ROD. PLUGS INTO 110/120 V.

BACK

SAW BRICKS WITH HACK-SAW. CUT GROOVES WITH WOOD CHISEL.

called *spaghetti,* in various colors is slipped over it. Resistance wire is an alloy and a poor conductor. Because of this quality it is useful both in the home and in industry. It is used for heating purposes as in stoves, corn poppers, waffle irons, heat-treating furnaces, ceramic kilns, and the like. It is also used in rheostats and similar devices for the control of current flow in a circuit, such as the volume control on a radio.

Nichrome, Chromel, and Kanthal are brand names for resistance wire. Types are available for use at low temperatures as well as at those of 2200-2300°F.

Fig. 5.10. The wire must be put under a terminal screw, pointing clockwise so that it will draw down tight.

CHARACTERISTICS OF CHROMEL "A" RESISTANCE WIRE

Maximum Temperature 2200°F.

Watts	A. W. Gauge	Ohms/ft	No. of ft. Req'd.	Ft/lb
100	30	6.50	19.0	3495
200	28	4.09	15.1	2200
300	26	2.57	16.0	1380
500	22	1.017	24.3	545
700	20	0.635	27.8	341
1000	18	0.406	30.4	219

Note to instructor: complete information on Chromel resistance wire can be obtained from Hoskins Manufacturing Company, 4445 Lawton Avenue, Detroit 8, Michigan. Kanthal resistance wire, capable of 2462°F., can be obtained from The Kanthal Corporation, Amelia Place, Stamford, Connecticut.

Making electrical connections.

Good electrical connections are necessary if your projects are to work well and safely. Some joints should be soldered and others fastened with screws. In your radio construction, soldering is used for quick, permanent connections of low resistance. Use a clean, well-tinned electric soldering iron (see page 121) and rosin-core solder. Hold the iron under the con-

nection to heat the wires, then touch the joint with the solder and melt off a small drop. Very little solder is needed to make good connections.

Fig. 5.11. The underwriter's knot used in same attachment.

When a screw connection is made with wire, first make a hook to fit the screw. Then insert it under the head so that the end of the hook points in the direction that the screw will be turned for tightening. Can you figure out why? Try it the other way and you will have the answer.

Magnets and Magnetism

The discovery of magnets and magnetism was the first step in the long chain of discoveries and inventions that has made electricity commonplace today. The first magnets were lodestone, a natural rock. The early Chinese noticed the peculiar nature of this rock. It attracted iron. They used it for compasses probably 5000 years ago.

The best deposits of lodestone, an iron ore, were found near the city of Magnesia in Asia Minor. The ore was called *magnetite* and its quality of attracting and repelling was called *magnetism*. Early sailors used lodestone for compasses until it was found that a piece of iron could be magnetized by rubbing it with the ore.

Your compass has a needle in it that is a *permanent* magnet, and as you have noticed, one end always seeks

Fig. 5.12. One of the world's most powerful motors, producing 83,000 horsepower, is used in a U. S. Air Force wind tunnel. *(Courtesy: Westinghouse Electric Corp.)*

the North and the other, the South. If you suspend a bar magnet by a string so that it is free to move, it will point North and South by itself unless it is attracted by other magnetic material. Here are some facts about magnets:

1. Magnets attract many materials, especially those bearing iron.

2. Each magnet, no matter how tiny or large, has two *poles:* the North-seeking, or North pole and the South-seeking, or South pole.

3. Iron and steel can be magnetized by rubbing with a magnet. Stroke it several times in the same direction.

4. Soft iron does not retain magnetism long; hard steel retains it permanently.

5. Among magnets the unlike poles attract and the like poles repel each other. North attracts South and repels North.

6. Each magnet has a *field of force,* or a magnetic field. You can prove this. Lay a piece of clear plastic (glass or cardboard will do, too) over a permanent magnet. On this sift some iron filings. Tap the plastic lightly and watch the particles arrange themselves between the poles.

Permanent magnets are used in

Fig. 5.13. The magnetic field between two magnetic poles forms a distinct pattern with iron filings.

Fig. 5.14. A nail wrapped with magnet wire becomes a strong magnet when current is passed through it.

such devices as scientific instruments, motors, radio speakers, telephones, and generators. New magnetic alloys have been developed which make tiny magnets very powerful.

Electromagnets. Electromagnets are magnets produced by electric current. Connect one end of a 2-ft length of No. 24 or 26 copper wire to a dry cell. Hold a compass below the wire. Touch the other end of the wire to the other terminal and watch the compass needle. The closer the compass is to the wire the stronger the attraction. This experiment proves that there is a magnetic field about a current-carrying wire. Coil this wire like a spring and it will be a stronger magnet; coil it about an 8d nail and it will be even stronger. With this nail as the core it will pick up another nail.

Make the iron-filings test with this magnet. Hold a compass near each end of the nail. One will be the North pole and the other the South. Reverse the battery connections and watch the compass. This shows that changing the direction of the current changes the *polarity*. The more turns of wire you put on the core, the stronger the magnet.

Electromagnets have more uses than has the permanent type. They are the hearts of electric motors and generators. Because of them the generation of electricity as we have it today is possible.

The Generation of Electricity

Faraday discovered that when a wire conductor is moved through a

Fig. 5.15. An electric motor you can build.

AN ELECTRIC MOTOR
YOU CAN BUILD

ARMATURE SUPPORT (2)

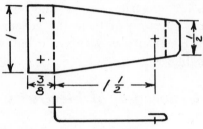

MAGNET TEST

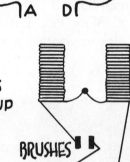

ARMATURE CORE

ARMATURE ASSEMBLY

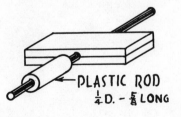

PLASTIC ROD
$\frac{1}{4}$ D. - $\frac{5}{8}$ LONG

SERIES HOOK-UP

BRUSHES

SHUNT HOOK-UP

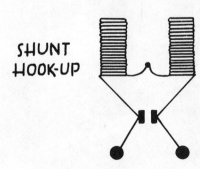

Fig. 5.16 The motor.

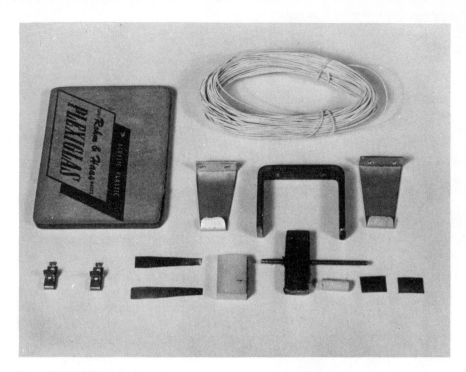

Fig. 5.17. The parts.

Fig. 5.18. Balancing the armature.

167

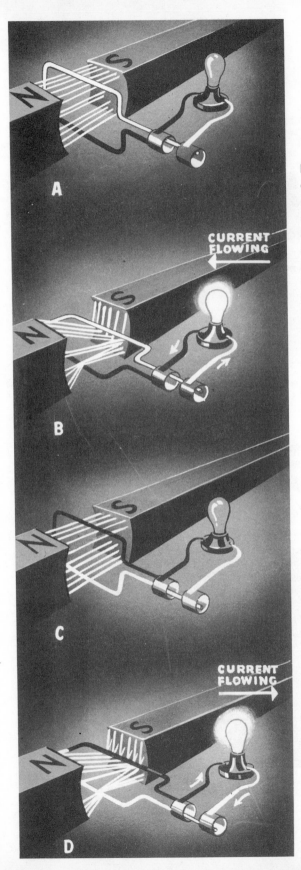

CURRENT FLOWING

CURRENT FLOWING

A

B

C

D

Fig. 5.19. How a generator produces electric current. In A, no current is flowing, because the magnetic field between the North and South Poles is not cut by the revolving wire. In B, the wire cuts the lines of force as it turns, and generates a current. In C, no current is flowing. In D, current is flowing, but in the opposite direction. The revolving wire is called an armature. In a real generator the armature has a great number of wires. The more wires, the greater the current. (Courtesy: Ohio Edison Company.)

magnetic field (see page 164) a current is *induced* in the wire. This current will flow only if the ends of the wire are connected into a circuit. Hook them to a galvanometer, a very sensitive meter, as in Fig. 5.19.

The device for generating an electric current is a *generator*. There is one on your auto engine. It supplies the current to run the engine, radio, heater, and so on. At the power station, which supplies the homes and

Fig. 5.20. A powerhouse at Grand Coulee Dam contains nine water-wheel generators. Each is rated at 108,000 kilowatts. *(Courtesy: Westinghouse Electric Corp.)*

W ELECTRICITY IS MADE AND DELIVERED

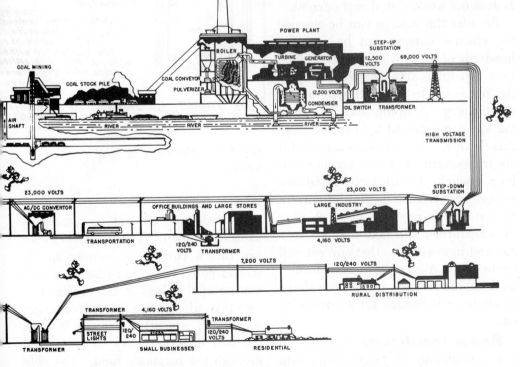

Fig. 5.21. How electricity is made and delivered. *(Courtesy: Ohio Edison Co.)*

industries in your area, are huge generators driven by either steam turbines or water power. When water power is used the station is called a *hydroelectric* plant. In the near future it is expected that atomic power will be used in one way or another to drive generators. Study the diagram on page 169 to see how a power station produces and transmits electric power.

The Transformer

In Fig. 5.21, as you trace the power lines from the station to the house, you find that whenever the voltage is stepped up or down there is a transformer. This device works automatically, using alternating current. It does not work with direct current.

Because the voltage can be stepped up, electric current can be sent for hundreds of miles with very little loss. In a pipeline carrying gasoline from the oil fields to bulk stations across the country, pumping stations along the way are required to keep the gasoline flowing. Transformers do this for electric current. If a wire conductor is long enough it will have resistance enough to overcome the flow of current so that hardly any will flow. A step-up transformer can take a small voltage and increase it so that current will again flow. A step-down transformer works in the reverse; it reduces voltage to whatever is needed for a particular use.

How a transformer works. In our explanation of electromagnetism it was pointed out that a coil of wire carrying a current has a magnetic field set up about it. When another coil of

170

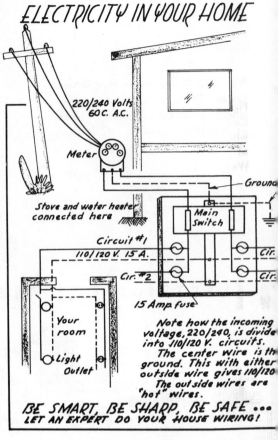

ELECTRICITY IN YOUR HOME

220/240 Volts
60 C. A.C.

Meter

Ground

Stove and water heater connected here

Main Switch

Circuit #1
110/120 V. 15 A.

Cir.

Cir. #2

Cir.

15 Amp fuse

Your room

Light Outlet

Note how the incoming voltage, 220/240, is divided into 110/120 V. circuits.
The center wire is the ground. This with either outside wire gives 110/120. The outside wires are "hot" wires.

BE SMART, BE SHARP, BE SAFE ...
LET AN EXPERT DO YOUR HOUSE WIRING!

Fig. 5.22. Electricity in your home.

wire is brought close to it, the magnetic field is cut and a current is caused to flow in the second coil. We say that a current is *induced* in the second coil. There must be an actual cutting of the lines of force. Remember that alternating current changes direction frequently. Because it does, the coil does not have to be moved through the magnetic field. The ebbing and flowing of the current takes care of the cutting and causes the field to build up and then collapse. This

Fig. 5.23. A giant high-voltage transformer. It is rated at 230,000 volts, contains 77 miles of copper wire and 22,000 gallons of insulating and cooling oil. It is located at Joppa, Illinois. *(Courtesy: Westinghouse Electric Corp.)*

THE TRANSFORMER

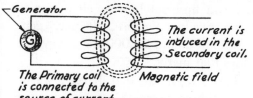

Generator

The current is induced in the Secondary coil.

The Primary coil is connected to the source of current.   *Magnetic field*

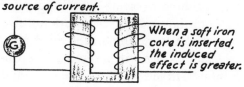

When a soft iron core is inserted, the induced effect is greater.

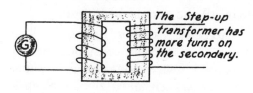

The Step-up transformer has more turns on the secondary.

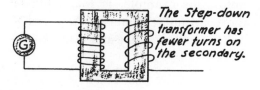

The Step-down transformer has fewer turns on the secondary.

Fig. 5.24. How a transformer works.

171

provides the necessary cutting of the field by the wire.

Step-up and step-down. A step-up transformer has more turns of wire in the second coil than in the first. We say more in the *secondary* than in the *primary*. If the secondary has one hundred times as many turns as the primary, it will have one hundred times as many volts.

In the step-down transformer the primary has the more turns. If the secondary has only one tenth as many turns, it will have only a tenth as many volts. An electric train set is operated from a transformer. When you plug it in, 110/120 v go into the primary winding and from 10 to 20 v come out of the secondary to operate the train. The various voltages are obtained as you move the control dial. The secondary coil was tapped and connections made at different numbers of turns so that it operates as though there were several different coils.

Transforming direct current. Direct current, when it is made to start and stop rapidly, can be transformed. The timer on a model airplane engine does this. As the current starts and stops, the magnetic field in the primary winding of the ignition coil is cut and a high voltage current is induced in the secondary.

Electricity and Power

It has been pointed out that an electric current is a flow of electrons along a conductor, usually a wire. As the electrons flow, work is done; for ex-ample, resistance is overcome, heat is given off, and a magnetic field is set up. How rapidly work is done by the moving electrons depends on how many there are (amperage) and how much pressure is pushing them along (voltage). We know that

$$\text{Power} = \text{Current} \times \text{Voltage}$$

and since the unit of electrical power is the *watt*, the formula becomes

$$\text{Watts} = \text{Amperes} \times \text{Volts}$$

This means that 1 amp times 1 v equals 1 w.

The ton as a unit of weight is more convenient to use than the pound when large quantities are being weighed. Likewise, the *kilowatt*, a thousand watts, is the more convenient unit of electrical measure for large quantities. When you visit your local power plant you can find out how much power is being produced there. It may generate only about 25,000 kw or several times that many.

The ¼ hp motor that drives a washing machine or some other appliance in your home does the work of five men and a boy. One of the giant electric motors used in irrigating the Columbia River Basin from Grand Coulee Dam does more physical work than all the people in Detroit.

Current consumption. The amount of current consumed by an electrical device is measured in watts. The power consumed by an electric motor, for example, is found by the above formula: Watts = Amperes × Volts. On light bulbs and many household appliances the wattage is indicated. Check a toaster and an electric iron.

In figuring your electric bill the power company uses *kilowatt hours* (KWH) instead of watts. For example, if your rate is 5¢ per KWH you could use one thousand watts for one hour for a nickel. In actual practice this would permit you to burn, say, ten 100-watt lamps for an hour, or five of them for two hours, and so on.

You can figure the cost of operating an electrical device by this formula:

$\text{Cost} = \frac{\text{Watts used}}{1000} \times \text{Rate per KWH}$
What, then, does it cost to use your radio if it consumes 100 watts and the rate is 5¢ per KWH? The answer is $\frac{100}{1000} \times 5¢$, or ½¢ per hour.

When the wattage is not given, as is common with motors, use this formula:

$\text{Cost} = \frac{\text{Volts x Amperes}}{1000} \times \text{Rate per KWH}$

Reading the kilowatt hour meter. A meter keeps record of the number of kilowatt hours used in your home, just as the speedometer on an auto records the number of miles traveled. It is a clever instrument, since it multiplies volts by amperes, divides this by 1000, and multiplies the result by the hours. Here's how to read the meter (see Fig. 5.25).

1. Start at the right and read each dial in order.

2. Find the last number passed by the pointer in each dial.

Fig. 5.25. Reading an electric house meter.

3. Jot down each number from right to left.

Ignition Systems for Engines

Current from the battery flows through the primary winding of the coil when the *timer* closes. When the timer is opened the flow of current is interrupted, thus causing a current of high voltage to be induced in the secondary winding. This current flows to the *spark plug* where it jumps the gap at the *points* making a spark which ignites the fuel. The *condenser* is placed across the timer points to keep them from becoming burned and pitted.

Fig. 5.26. An ignition system for a model airplane engine.

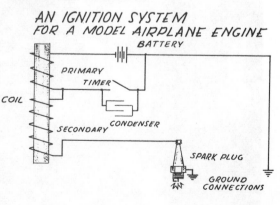

The ignition system for an automobile engine is about the same as this one. But because it has several cylinders and spark plugs there is a rotary switch, called a *distributor*, which directs the high voltage current to the correct plugs. When 6 v go into the primary, 15,000 to 20,000 leave the secondary.

Some internal combustion engines, such as those on lawn mowers and motor bikes, use a *magneto ignition system* instead of a battery. A magneto is really a generator; it uses permanent magnets instead of electromagnets to set up the magnetic field.

Electricity and Communication

Take electricity out of our methods of communicating with one another and there would be nothing left but handwriting and speaking. Ships and airplanes would have to carry our messages across the oceans, and trains, trucks, and airplanes, across the country. There was a time, as you know, when the pony express system tried to keep one side of our country in touch with the other. Think what the old timers missed in not having the telegraph, telephone, radio, television, and facsimile (fac-*sim*-i-lee). Nowadays you can know what is happening anywhere in the world almost as soon as it happens. Do you take advantage of this opportunity to keep up with the news?

The telegraph. The telegraph was the first successful electrical device for sending communications over great distances. Invented by Samuel Morse in 1840, it spurred the searching for better means of electrical communications. On December 17, 1953, regular broadcasting of color television began

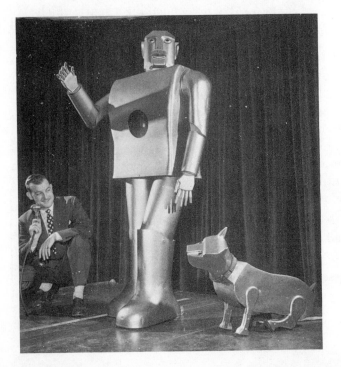

Fig. 5.27. By speaking into a microphone, the engineer can direct the actions of Elektro, the seven-foot, 260-pound mechanical man. He does tricks, makes a speech, and smokes cigarettes. His dog, Sparko, has a somewhat more limited repertory. (*Courtesy: Westinghouse Electric Corp.*)

in the United States. Mr. Morse probably never dreamed that his invention might lead to such a marvel.

In the early telegraph systems wire was used to carry the current between stations. Marconi's wireless telegraph, called *radio*, eliminated the need for connecting wire.

A code system of dots and dashes is used in sending messages. It is necessary for an operator to memorize the code so that he can send as well as receive. The story is told that when Steinmetz, the great electrical wizard, and Edison would meet, they would use the code in place of talking. Edison was deaf and Steinmetz would tap out his message on his friend's knee.

If you have listened to short-wave radio you have probably heard the high-pitched tones of dots and dashes being transmitted by a "ham." The amateur radio operator is known as a ham by other operators. He uses the Continental International Code. (See Fig. 5.28.) The letter A sounds like "dit-dah," and C like "dah-dit-dah-dit." A ham must have a federal license to broadcast.

The telephone. It was on October 9, 1876, that Alexander Graham Bell carried on the first successful two-way telephone conversation. This was between Boston and Cambridgeport, Massachusetts, two miles away. Since then the telephone has become a most important industry.

Today it is possible to talk around the world by radio telephone (a combination of wire and wireless tele-

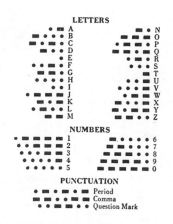

Fig. 5.28. Continental International Code. (Courtesy: Allied Radio Corp.)

phone). Two-way telephones are used in automobiles. Ship-to-shore telephones have been used for years. The telephone wires and cables laid across the nation are also used to carry telegraph messages and radio and television programs.

How a telephone transmitter works. The mouthpiece of a telephone has a tiny transmitter in it. There is the same kind of device in a radio microphone. It changes sound waves into electrical current.

Sound waves from the mouth strike a sensitive steel diaphragm which is a thin, circular disc. It springs in, packing the tiny carbon particles together. Since carbon is a conductor, current from the battery can then flow around the circuit. The louder the voice, the more the particles are compressed and the more current flows. Actually the diaphragm vibrates with the variations of the voice thus causing a vibrating current to flow.

A TELEGRAPH SYSTEM

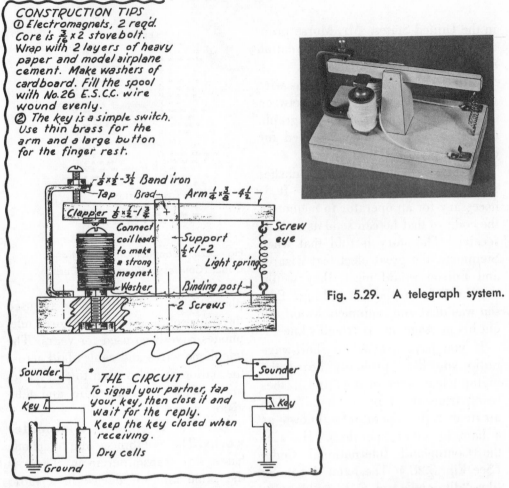

CONSTRUCTION TIPS
① Electromagnets, 2 reqd.
Core is $\frac{3}{16}$ x2 stovebolt.
Wrap with 2 layers of heavy
paper and model airplane
cement. Make washers of
cardboard. Fill the spool
with No.26 E.S.C.C. wire
wound evenly.
② The key is a simple switch.
Use thin brass for the
arm and a large button
for the finger rest.

$\frac{1}{8}$ x $\frac{1}{2}$ -3$\frac{1}{2}$ Band iron
Tap   Brad   Arm $\frac{1}{4}$ x $\frac{3}{8}$ -4$\frac{1}{2}$
Clapper $\frac{1}{8}$ x $\frac{1}{2}$ -1$\frac{3}{4}$
Connect
coil leads   Support   Screw
to make $\frac{1}{2}$ x1-2   eye
a strong
magnet.   Light spring
Washer   Binding post
2 Screws

Sounder   Sounder
     THE CIRCUIT
To signal your partner, tap
Key   your key, then close it and   Key
wait for the reply.
Keep the key closed when
receiving.
Dry cells
Ground

Fig. 5.29. A telegraph system.

In the earpiece of the receiver at the other end of the line, is an electromagnet operated by this current. A diaphragm springs in and out as the vibrating current causes the electromagnet to attract and release it. As this diaphragm vibrates, it sets the air in front of the ear in motion and creates sound waves like those spoken into the mouthpiece.

When you dial a number. Between your telephone and another is the telephone company's central office. It is here that your call is connected to the telephone of the party to whom you

wish to speak. As you lift the receiver, a switch in your telephone closes and permits a current from the batteries in the central office to flow.

This flow of current sets a switching mechanism at the office to work, hunting for your line. When it finds the line with the current in it, it stops and makes a connection. Then you hear the dial tone which means, "Number, please."

When you dial the number, each click as the dial returns to its starting place sends a pulse of current to the switchboard in the office. The board

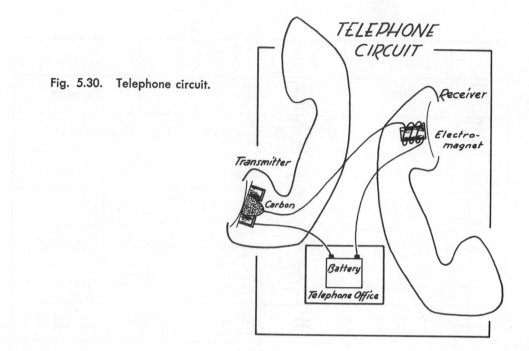

Fig. 5.30. Telephone circuit.

RADIO TRANSMITTING AND RECEIVING

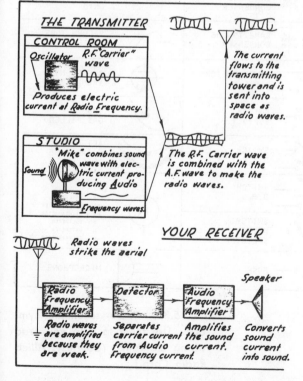

THE TRANSMITTER

CONTROL ROOM

Oscillator

R.F. "Carrier" wave

Produces electric current at *Radio Frequency*.

The current flows to the transmitting tower and is sent into space as radio waves.

STUDIO

Sound

"Mike" combines sound wave with electric current producing *Audio*

Frequency waves.

The R.F. Carrier wave is combined with the A.F. wave to make the radio waves.

YOUR RECEIVER

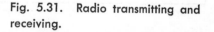
Radio waves strike the aerial

Radio Frequency Amplifier → Detector → Audio Frequency Amplifier → Speaker

Radio waves are amplified because they are weak.

Separates carrier current from Audio Frequency current.

Amplifies the sound current.

Converts sound current into sound.

Fig. 5.31. Radio transmitting and receiving.

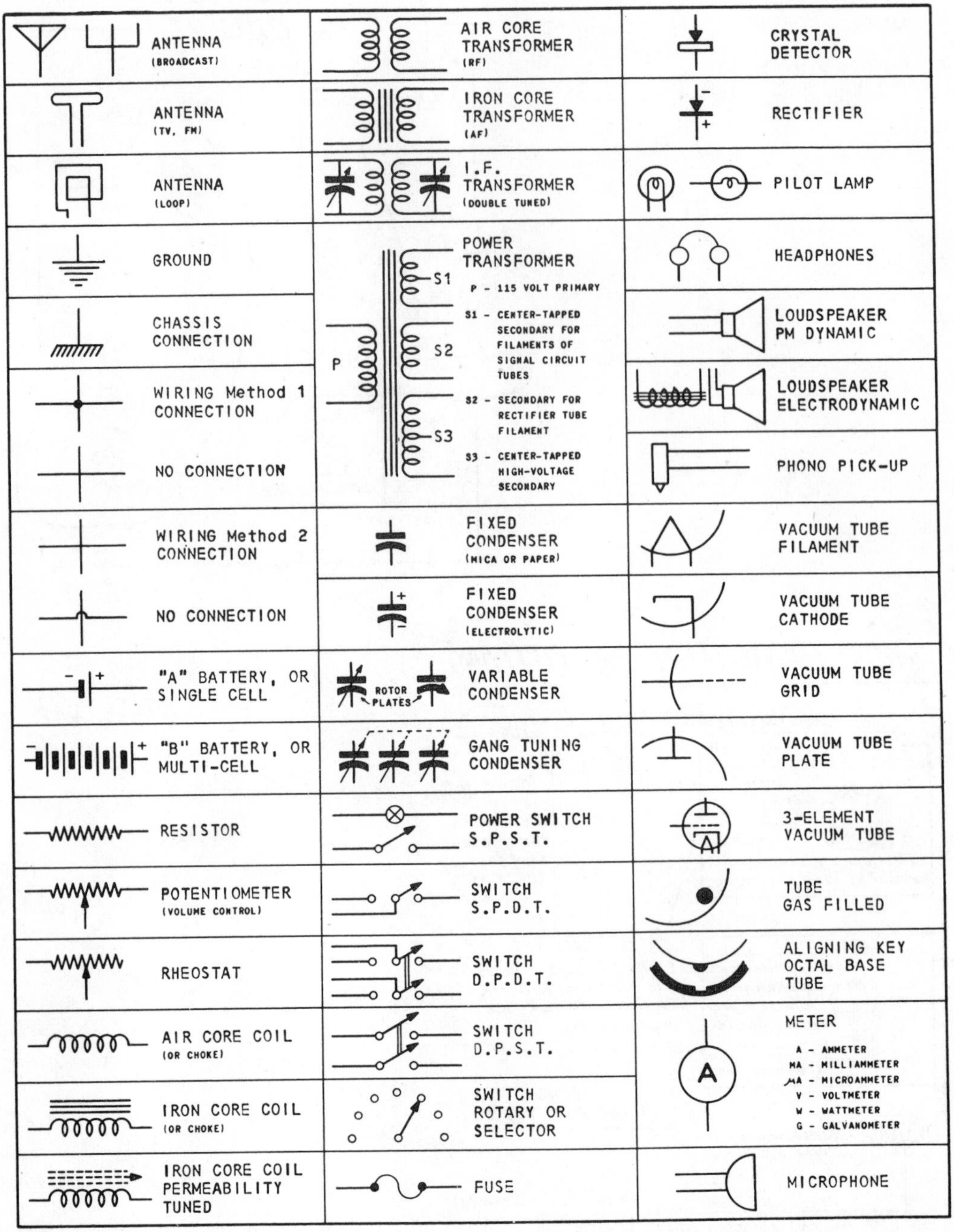

	ANTENNA (BROADCAST)		AIR CORE TRANSFORMER (RF)			CRYSTAL DETECTOR
	ANTENNA (TV, FM)		IRON CORE TRANSFORMER (AF)			RECTIFIER
	ANTENNA (LOOP)		I.F. TRANSFORMER (DOUBLE TUNED)			PILOT LAMP
	GROUND		POWER TRANSFORMER	S1	P – 115 VOLT PRIMARY	HEADPHONES
	CHASSIS CONNECTION	P		S2	S1 – CENTER-TAPPED SECONDARY FOR FILAMENTS OF SIGNAL CIRCUIT TUBES	LOUDSPEAKER PM DYNAMIC
	WIRING Method 1 CONNECTION				S2 – SECONDARY FOR RECTIFIER TUBE FILAMENT	LOUDSPEAKER ELECTRODYNAMIC
	NO CONNECTION			S3	S3 – CENTER-TAPPED HIGH-VOLTAGE SECONDARY	PHONO PICK-UP
	WIRING Method 2 CONNECTION		FIXED CONDENSER (MICA OR PAPER)			VACUUM TUBE FILAMENT
	NO CONNECTION		FIXED CONDENSER (ELECTROLYTIC)			VACUUM TUBE CATHODE
	"A" BATTERY, OR SINGLE CELL		VARIABLE CONDENSER	ROTOR PLATES		VACUUM TUBE GRID
	"B" BATTERY, OR MULTI-CELL		GANG TUNING CONDENSER			VACUUM TUBE PLATE
	RESISTOR		POWER SWITCH S.P.S.T.			3-ELEMENT VACUUM TUBE
	POTENTIOMETER (VOLUME CONTROL)		SWITCH S.P.D.T.			TUBE GAS FILLED
	RHEOSTAT		SWITCH D.P.D.T.			ALIGNING KEY OCTAL BASE TUBE
	AIR CORE COIL (OR CHOKE)		SWITCH D.P.S.T.			METER
	IRON CORE COIL (OR CHOKE)		SWITCH ROTARY OR SELECTOR			A – AMMETER, MA – MILLIAMMETER, μA – MICROAMMETER, V – VOLTMETER, W – WATTMETER, G – GALVANOMETER
	IRON CORE COIL PERMEABILITY TUNED		FUSE			MICROPHONE

Fig. 5.32. Radio schematic symbols. Use them to help you read wiring diagrams. (Courtesy: Allied Radio Corp.)

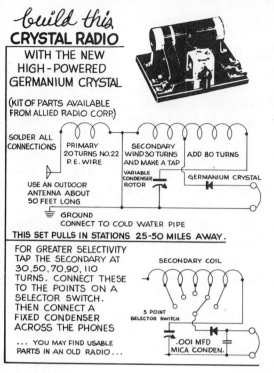

build this
CRYSTAL RADIO
WITH THE NEW
HIGH-POWERED
GERMANIUM CRYSTAL

(KIT OF PARTS AVAILABLE
FROM ALLIED RADIO CORP.)

SOLDER ALL
CONNECTIONS

PRIMARY
20 TURNS NO.22
P.E. WIRE

SECONDARY
WIND 30 TURNS
AND MAKE A TAP

ADD 80 TURNS

VARIABLE
CONDENSER
ROTOR

GERMANIUM CRYSTAL

USE AN OUTDOOR
ANTENNA ABOUT
50 FEET LONG

GROUND
CONNECT TO COLD WATER PIPE

THIS SET PULLS IN STATIONS 25-50 MILES AWAY.

FOR GREATER SELECTIVITY
TAP THE SECONDARY AT
30,50,70,90,110
TURNS. CONNECT THESE
TO THE POINTS ON A
SELECTOR SWITCH.
THEN CONNECT A
FIXED CONDENSER
ACROSS THE PHONES

... YOU MAY FIND USABLE
PARTS IN AN OLD RADIO ...

SECONDARY COIL

5 POINT
SELECTOR SWITCH

.001 MFD
MICA CONDEN.

Fig. 5.33. Crystal radio. (Courtesy: Allied Radio Corp.)

Fig. 5.34. 1-tube and rectifier AC-DC receiver. (Courtesy: Philmore Manufacturing Co.)

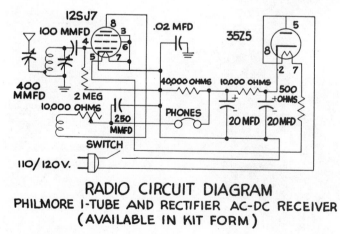

12SJ7
100 MMFD
.02 MFD
35Z5

400
MMFD
2 MEG
10,000 OHMS
250
MMFD

40,000 OHMS
10,000 OHMS
500
+OHMS

PHONES

20 MFD 20 MFD

SWITCH

110/120 V.

RADIO CIRCUIT DIAGRAM
PHILMORE 1-TUBE AND RECTIFIER AC-DC RECEIVER
(AVAILABLE IN KIT FORM)

Fig. 5.35. 1 Circuit diagram for 1-tube and rectifier AC-DC receiver. (Courtesy: Philmore Manufacturing Co.)

keeps track of the number of clicks and connects your party. Then the current from your telephone makes a circuit with the other telephone as you talk with the person there. This is all done automatically, without the aid of a telephone girl as was formerly necessary.

Teletype. The newest form of the telegraph is the *teletype.* The operator copies the message on a special typewriter which transmits it over wire to its destination. There the receiving typewriter types the message automatically on paper, ready for delivery.

Radar. The term RADAR is an abbreviation of *Radio Detection And Ranging.* It is a device which, by means of radio waves, locates objects and tells how far away they are and how fast they are moving. The newest

form of Radar is PPI Radar (Plan Position Indicator). A ship or airplane having this equipment can "see" in the dark and through fog and clouds. A rotating antenna sends out the radar beam in all directions. When an object is struck by the beam, it is reflected back to the radar receiver. This shows the object on a screen similar to a television screen.

Facsimile. With *fascimile* a photograph can be converted into an electric current and radioed or wired to a receiver which reverses the process and reproduces the photo. This process is used by newspapers in covering events around the world. Police in one city can work closely with police in another on the trail of a wanted person if they have his photo.

Television. When you take a

Fig. 5.36. Monitoring a telecast. The operator watching the small screens directs each cameraman. *(Courtesy: Station WAKR-TV.)*

Fig. 5.37. Televising a program. The cameras are moved and controlled by the cameramen and are cut in and out by the monitor. (*Courtesy: Station WAKR-TV.*)

photograph, the film records the variations of light and dark, and in the print you have shades from white through grays to black. A photoelectric cell, such as is used in a light meter (see page 233) for finding the correct exposure, changes the light the object reflects into electric current. The more light, the more current.

A television camera uses a photoelectric cell. The cell is continually moving over the picture, picking up the reflected light, and converting it into current. The amount of current varies with the light. This process is called *scanning*. This current is combined with a radio wave and is sent out into space from the huge antenna towers.

Your television antenna collects the waves and in the receiver they are changed back to electrical current like that produced in the scanning process. In a manner just the reverse of that used in the television camera, the current is converted into the picture on the screen. This entire process happens at almost the same time, since electricity travels at the speed of 186,-000 miles per second.

Electricity and Heat

Electricity makes heat in various ways. The heat in a stove, toaster, corn popper, and the like, is caused by a resistance to the flow of the current. The heating element is a poor

181

Automatic HOT DOG ROASTER

CLOSE THE COVER
TO TURN ON THE CURRENT. /
WATCH 'EM SIZZZZZZLE!

CONSTRUCTION TIPS

① Form the cover of
¼" acrylic plastic sheet
over a block of wood
shaped to fit.
② Use aluminum nails.
Drill holes in plastic
for a tight fit so that
the heads will hold the
wrapped wire securely.
③ The wire is rubber-covered
lamp cord, split.
④ Guard falls over prongs.
Use a plastic disc, fit loosely.

Fig. 5.38.   Hot dog roaster.

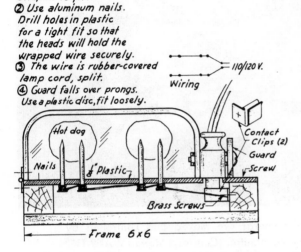

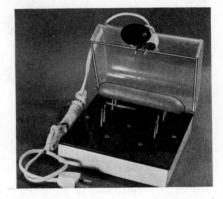

conductor. When the current is forced through it in spite of its wishes, it gets hot. The more it is forced, the hotter it gets. (See page 158.) Such appliances consume considerable power, so be sure not to connect too many into the same circuit.

Infrared rays are used to provide a deeply penetrating heat. They dry the paint on automobiles from the inside out. A doctor uses them to relieve pain. A farmer uses this heat for baby chicks and pigs. Infrared rays are called *heat rays.* You can purchase infrared lamps at the store to use at home.

Heat from an *electric arc* is used in welding metals. A current of very heavy amperage and low voltage melts the metal and fuses it together. (See pages 144-146.)

182

Carbon arc melting furnaces are used in the smelting of high-grade steel, such as stainless. One electrode is of heavy carbon; the metal to be melted is the other. The carbon is moved close to the metal to make contact and is then withdrawn a bit to keep the electric arc flowing. Temperatures of 6000° F. are common.

Thermostatic controls. Most electric heating devices for home use have thermostatic controls to regulate the heat. The heart of a thermostat is a *bimetallic strip.* It has two different kinds of metals fastened together. When the strip is heated, one of the metals expands more than the other, causing the strip to bend. This opens the contact points, shutting off the current. Upon cooling, the strip straight-

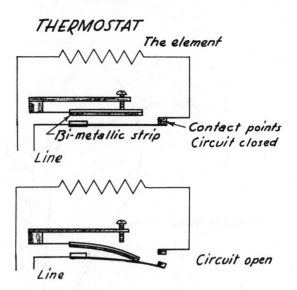

THERMOSTAT

The element

Bi-metallic strip

Contact points
Circuit closed

Line

Circuit open

Line

Fig. 5.39. Thermostat.

ens and closes the circuit, allowing current to again flow. If there is a heat adjustment on the appliance, turning the screw changes the distance between the contact points so that more or less heat is required to bend the strip and control the current.

Electricity and Lighting

Man-made light today is almost entirely electrical. Candles and oil lamps are used mostly for decorative purposes now. Edison's incandescent lamp showed the possibilities of electric illumination. Since then many types of lighting have been developed.

The incandescent lamp. We have learned that when a current flows through a resistance wire heat is formed. When enough current flows, the wire gets white hot and glows; it becomes *incandescent*. This piece of resistance wire in a lamp is called the *filament*. It is made of the metal *tungsten,* also called *wolfram,* which has a

very high melting temperature. To keep the filament from burning up, the air is removed from the bulb and replaced with either nitrogen or argon gas. (See Fig. 5.40.)

The fluorescent lamp. The fluorescent lamp makes a new type of lighting possible. It is soft, glareless, cooler, and less costly to operate than is the incandescent lamp. It gives about three times as much light on the same amount of current. Inside the tube at each end is a small heating coil coated with chemicals. When the switch is turned on, these coils heat up and send out electrons which react with the mercury vapor. Ultraviolet rays given off cause the phosphor coating on the inside of the tube to glow.

How light is measured. The lamp bulbs you use at home are stamped with the number of watts they consume. Since the consumer pays for electric power according to watts per hour (kwh, see page 172), this marking is convenient. The intensity

183

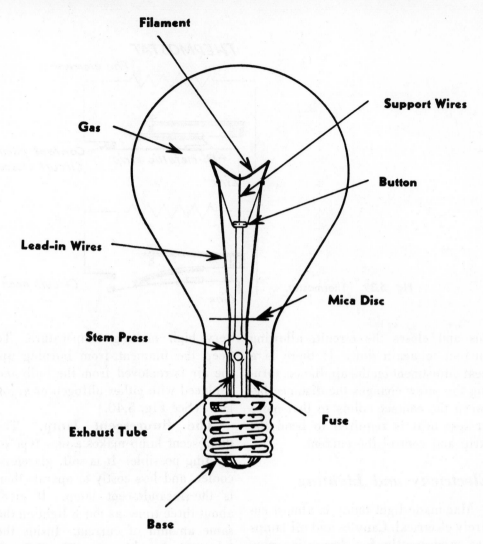

Filament

Gas

Support Wires

Button

Lead-in Wires

Mica Disc

Stem Press

Fuse

Exhaust Tube

Base

Fig. 5.40. The parts of an incandescent lamp. *(Courtesy: General Electric Co.)*

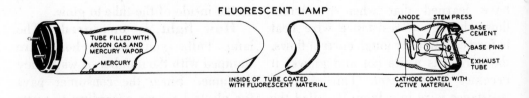

FLUORESCENT LAMP

TUBE FILLED WITH
ARGON GAS AND
MERCURY VAPOR

MERCURY

INSIDE OF TUBE COATED
WITH FLUORESCENT MATERIAL

ANODE   STEM PRESS

BASE
CEMENT

BASE PINS

EXHAUST
TUBE

CATHODE COATED WITH
ACTIVE MATERIAL

Fig. 5.41. The parts of a fluorescent lamp. *(Courtesy: General Electric Co.)*

184

of electric light is not measured in watts but in *candlepower*. A standard candle which burns according to certain specifications is used as the measure, just as a pound is used in measuring weight. A headlight lamp on an auto may be 32 cp (candlepower). This means it is 32 times as powerful as the standard candle. The great beacons and searchlights at airports may have a million or more candlepower.

Light meters such as those used by photographers use photoelectric cells to measure the intensity of reflected light.

Use good lighting. Adequate lighting in your school shop means lighting that permits you to work accurately and safely without glare and eyestrain. You need better lighting when you are drawing or working on fine details than when you are planing a board. Your teacher can get a lighting specialist from the local power company to check your shop lighting. Ask him about good lighting in the home, too. Remember, you will have but one pair of eyes all your life. Treat them well and they will serve you well.

Electricity and Chemistry

When electricity and chemistry are combined, new uses and products result. Two common uses are batteries and electroplating.

The dry cell. A dry cell, such as is in your flashlight, is a portable source of electric current produced by a chemical action. (Study Fig. 5.42.) The center terminal is positive (+)

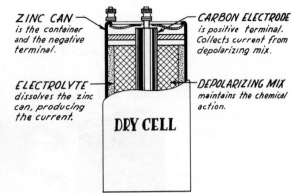

ZINC CAN
is the container and the negative terminal.

CARBON ELECTRODE
is positive terminal. Collects current from depolarizing mix.

ELECTROLYTE
dissolves the zinc can, producing the current.

DEPOLARIZING MIX
maintains the chemical action.

DRY CELL

Fig. 5.42. A section through a dry cell.

and the outer, negative (−). When these are connected with a wire, current flows. A dry cell no matter how large or small always has 1.5 v. The larger the cell, the greater the amperage and the longer it will last. A *battery* is a group of cells. In a 45-v radio B battery there are 45 divided by 1.5, or 30 dry cells.

Cells connected in series multiply the voltage, 1.5, by the number of cells. When in parallel the voltage remains the same, but the amperage is increased. In a flashlight the cells are in series because the extra voltage is needed to make a bright light. For electroplating, low voltage and high amperage is needed.

Dry cells are often stamped with a date to insure freshness when you buy them. They lose their power with age as well as with use.

The storage battery. A storage battery is a group of *wet cells* connected together. An auto battery has 3 or 6 cells depending on whether 6 v or 12 v are required. Each cell, large or small, has 2 v. (See Fig. 5.43.) A

185

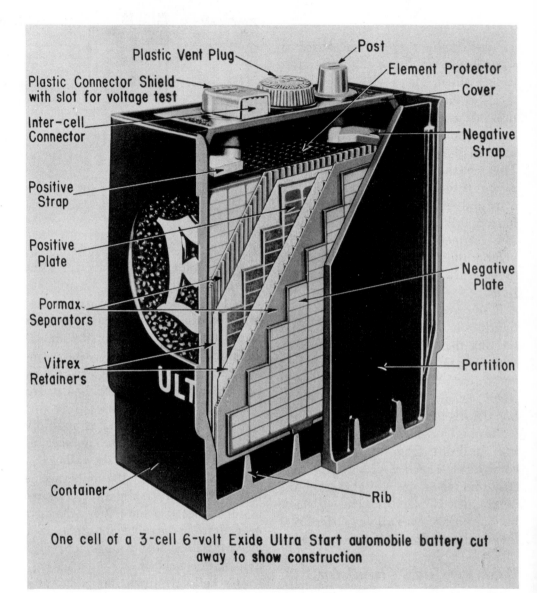

Plastic Vent Plug

Post

Element Protector

Cover

Plastic Connector Shield with slot for voltage test

Inter-cell Connector

Negative Strap

Positive Strap

Positive Plate

Negative Plate

Pormax Separators

Vitrex Retainers

Partition

Container

Rib

One cell of a 3-cell 6-volt Exide Ultra Start automobile battery cut away to show construction

Fig. 5.43. A section through a storage cell. *(Courtesy: Electric Storage Battery Co.)*

storage cell does not produce its own current as does a dry cell. It must be *charged* before it can be used. Electric current is passed through it until its capacity is reached. Then the battery is fully charged and ready for use. The automobile generator keeps the battery charged. Watch the ammeter on the instrument panel. It tells whether the battery is charging or discharging.

The sulfuric acid will eat holes in

186

ELECTROPLATING WITH COPPER

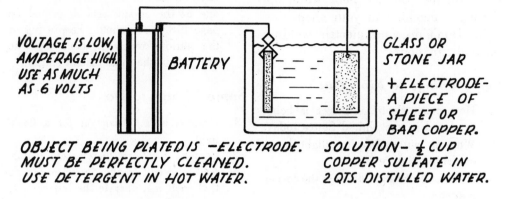

VOLTAGE IS LOW, AMPERAGE HIGH. USE AS MUCH AS 6 VOLTS

BATTERY

GLASS OR STONE JAR

+ ELECTRODE- A PIECE OF SHEET OR BAR COPPER.

OBJECT BEING PLATED IS −ELECTRODE. MUST BE PERFECTLY CLEANED. USE DETERGENT IN HOT WATER.

SOLUTION- $\frac{1}{2}$ CUP COPPER SULFATE IN 2 QTS. DISTILLED WATER.

Fig. 5.44. Copper plating.

clothes, except woolens, so when you work around a storage battery, remember how to keep your mother happy.

Electroplating. Electroplating is a process of removing metal from one object and depositing it on another. Plating is used to protect the object, which is usually of steel, and to make it more attractive. The common types are brass, copper, cadmium, nickel, and chrome. Bicycle wheel rims are usually cadmium plated; handle bars are chrome plated.

Direct current of low voltage and high amperage is used. You can easily copper-plate a tool that you have made on the machine lathe. Clean it thoroughly in a strong detergent to remove all grease or oil. Rinse in water. Pick it up with tongs or pliers, not fingers, and place it in the solution as shown in Fig. 5.44.

Safety Sense

Electrical current is not particularly dangerous unless both voltage and amperage are high. You can get a jolt from a spark plug on an automobile engine, but you don't get burned, because the amperage is very low. The "wise guy" who sticks his finger into a house-lamp socket to show how tough he is, is just asking for trouble. That's like shaking hands with an octopus. Study these suggestions. Can you add others?

1. Do not try to do your own house wiring. This is for an expert electrician. Cities have laws which prohibit anyone but a licensed electrician from doing wiring.

2. Replace a blown fuse only with the same size fuse (no pennies, please). If it continues to blow, the trouble is still there.

3. Why doesn't it make safety sense to touch an electrical appliance or switch while you are taking a bath in the tub or shower? (This will really burn you up.)

4. If your shoes are wet, do not

187

stand on the concrete floor while operating a machine in your shop.

5. Don't do your electric welding on a damp floor.

Some Things to Find Out

1. How much electrical power is being produced in the United States today.
2. Why an automobile headlight beam can shine high or low.
3. How the traffic light down at the corner operates.
4. How many devices there are in your home which use electricity.
5. How many volts are used in a bicycle headlight.
6. How many volts there are in an airplane battery.
7. How aluminum is made with electricity.
8. How a doorbell works.
9. How much more does it cost to operate your mother's electric iron than her washing machine.
10. Why you should not be in swimming during an electrical storm.

Some Group Projects

1. Visit your local power station and then construct a model power station and distribution system that can be put on display. Label the important parts so that everyone will get the story.
2. Arrange to visit your local fire station to watch some demonstrations on rescue and first aid for electrical accidents. Find out how to fight electrical fires.
3. Visit a ham radio operator's station, a commercial radio station, or a television station to see what goes on in a broadcast.

4. Each student in the group might build one of the crystal sets described on page 178. Each should keep a log of the stations received. Let's see who can pull in the most distant station.

Some Things to Do

1. Draw a wiring diagram for a flashlight.
2. Connect a battery, buzzer, and switch.
3. Add a switch to the above circuit so that each will operate the buzzer.
4. Copper-plate a tool that you have made.
5. Hook up the ignition system for a model airplane engine.
6. Learn the radio code.
7. Charge a storage battery.
8. Cut open an old dry cell and locate the parts. (See Fig. 5.42.)
9. Repair a faulty lamp cord.
10. Wire a lamp which you have made.

Sources of Ideas and Information

Books

1. Bendick, Jeanne. *Electronics for Young People.* New York: McGraw-Hill Book Company, 1947.
2. Collins, Frederick. *Fun With Electricity.* New York: D. Appleton Century Company, 1936.
3. Cook, Sherman R. *Electrical Things Boys Like to Make.* Milwaukee, Wis.: Bruce Publishing Company, 1943.
4. Cornetet, Wendell H. *Principles of Electricity.* Bloomington, Ill.: McKnight and McKnight, 1952.
5. Dragoo, A. W. and K. L. *General Shop Electricity.* Bloomington, Ill.: McKnight and McKnight, 1946.
6. Morgan, Alfred. *A First Electrical Book for Boys.* New York: Charles Scribner and Sons, 1952.

7. Morgan, Alfred. *First Radio Book for Boys.* New York: D. Appleton Century Company, 1941.

8. Perry, Josephine. *The Electrical Industry.* New York: Longmans, Green and Co., 1945.

9. *Radio Builders Handbook.* Chicago: Allied Radio Corporation.

Booklets, pamphlets

1. *Crystal Diode Circuit Kinks.* Sylvania Electric Products, Inc., 254 Rano Street, Buffalo 77, N. Y.

2. *Electricity and Wheels.* General Motors Corporation, Department of Public Relations, Detroit, Mich.

3. *Gorge Power Plant.* The Ohio Edison Company, Akron, Ohio.

4. *Motors Make the World Go Around. The Romance of Electricity. The Story of the Turbine.* These are listed in the *Catalog of Publications* available from General Electric Company, Publications, Department 2-119, Schenectady, N. Y.

5. *The Magic of Communication. The Telephone in America.* Ask for these at your local Bell Telephone Company.

Films

1. *Electronics at Work.*

2. *On the Air.* Broadcasting explained.

3. *What is Electricity?* These films are available free from Modern Talking Picture Service, 9 Rockefeller Plaza, New York 20, N. Y., or 14 E. Ontario St., Chicago, Ill.

Fig. 6.1. Pressmen examine the cover of a magazine being printed in one of the world's largest plants. (Courtesy: Popular Science Publishing Co.)

The GRAPHIC ARTS INDUSTRIES

6

People had been writing and drawing for several thousands of years before anyone figured out how copies could be made quickly and easily. Until this was discovered, each copy was written or lettered by hand, letter by letter. Imagine how long it would take you to make a hand-lettered copy of the Bible. Back in the Middle Ages, copies of the Bible were made this way by monks who spent their lifetimes at copying with quill, ink, and parchment of their own making. You know the Bible story of Moses and the Ten Commandments which were cut into stone tablets. The Ark of the Covenant was built to house these tablets because they were the only copies of the law by which the people lived. Only a few people could write in those days. They were called scribes because they could write. Scribes kept records and made copies of the laws.

The first use made of printing seems to have been on government seals in Egypt, Syria, and Babylonia, probably about 5000 years ago. The designs were cut into stones which when inked made impressions on other material. The Chinese found out how to carve their language characters into wood blocks and to print from them as early as A.D. 700–800. They actually printed paper money at about the year 807 and were manufacturing paper a thousand years before other peoples.

Printing from movable type. Somehow Johann Gutenberg, a German silversmith, got the idea that each letter of the alphabet could be made separately on a block. He first made them of wood, but being a metal worker, he soon made them of metal. This was *movable type*, which could be

191

Fig. 6.2. Babylonian VI-V century B.C. tablets of baked clay with cuneiform inscriptions recording business transactions. *(Courtesy: Metropolitan Museum of Art.)*

set up, printed from, and then taken down to be used again. Gutenberg is credited with being the first European to use movable type.

With movable type it was now possible to print unlimited copies. In 1452 Gutenberg produced the first book printed from movable type. It was the Bible, which now could be had by many more people than ever before. For you stamp collectors, a stamp commemorating the five hundredth anniversary of the Gutenberg Bible was issued in 1952. It was necessary for Gutenberg to design a press in which the actual printing could be done. His was a very simple device: the paper was pressed down on the inked type with the aid of a screw and a lever. For the next three and a half centuries this kind of press was standard.

Paper and ink. Paper and ink are as important in printing as the type and the press. The early scribes used papyrus (pap-*eye*-rus), a plant that grew in the Nile valley. The long fibers of the leaves were soaked and pressed into sheets. Parchment and vellum made from the skins of sheep, goats, and cattle were more durable. The skins were scraped thin and cut into sections which were used as scrolls. Paper as we know it was first made by the Chinese and Japanese from bamboo, silk, and linen. In Europe by the time that Gutenberg made his movable type, paper was being made from rags. Today most of our paper is manufactured from wood pulp.

The graphic arts industries. From such simple beginnings the graphic arts industries have grown. They are the industries that produce our newspapers, magazines, books, pamphlets, comic books, and the like, and reproduce in quantities drawings, pictures, photographs, paintings, and all such illustrations.

192

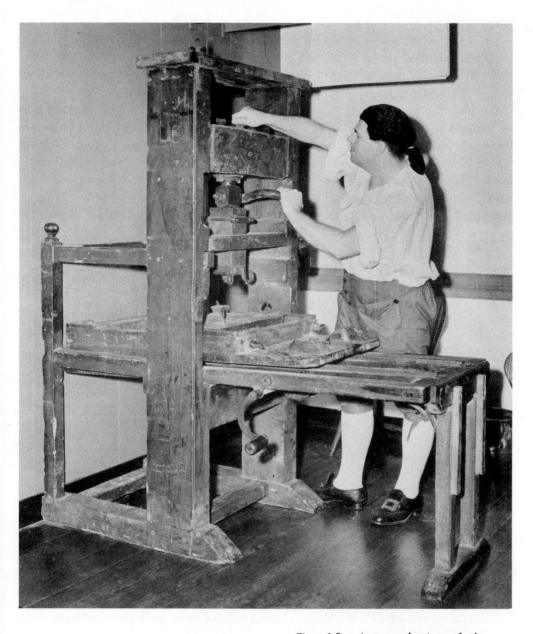

Fig. 6.3. A reproduction of the printing press used by William Parks, pioneer American printer, when he began publication of the *Virginia Gazette* in Williamsburg in 1736. (Courtesy: Colonial Williamsburg.)

Occupational possibilities. Very little printing is done by hand nowadays. Automatic, high-speed presses make possible tremendous production of printed materials and at the same time provide thousands of jobs which would not exist if hand methods were used. Even the smallest community usually has a printing shop; it is often combined with the local newspaper. of the type in which one can start at the bottom and advance to the top without special education or training.

The processes used in printing pictures are more complicated than are those used in printing words. Pictures are printed from *plates* and *cuts;* words, from *type* and *plates.* A separate color plate is required for each color used in an illustration. A natural

Kind of Printing	Method	Uses	Kind of Plates
Letterpress	Printing from a *raised* surface.	Newspapers Magazines Books Letterheads	Block cuts Line etchings Halftone etchings Stereotypes Electrotypes Rubber plates and stamps
Planography	Printing from a *flat* surface.	Magazines Books Advertisements Billboards Posters	Crayon-stone lithography Photolithography Photogelatin
Intaglio	Printing from a *sunken* surface.	Art prints Wallpaper Stamps Paper Money Gravure section of Sunday paper	*For lines:* Line etchings Line engravings Dry point Steel engraving Copper plates *For tones:* Soft ground etching Aquatint Mezzotint *Photographic:* Photogravure Rotogravure
Other	Silk screen Duplicating Blueprinting		

Many of the jobs in printing are available only through apprenticeship. Formerly a boy who served an apprenticeship to learn the trade was called a printer's devil. He started out by doing many of the "chores," such as cleaning and sorting type and sweeping floors. Many of the occupations are color photograph, for example, can be reproduced with three color plates, a yellow, a red, and a blue.

Plates are metal forms, flat or curved, from which whole pages or parts of pages are printed. Different printing processes and presses use different kinds of plates. In newspaper printing

the plate for a page is one solid metal casting. It includes type as well as the cuts for illustrations. For each kind of printing described here you will find an explanation of the plate-making process.

Letterpress Printing

Letterpress printing means printing from *raised* surfaces. It is sometimes called *relief* printing. As in the case of a type *character,* all the material has been cut away except that which is to make the impression on the paper. See Fig. 6.7. The raised surfaces are inked with a roller and then pressed against the paper to make the impression. This is done in a *press* into which paper may be fed by hand or automatically, a sheet at a time, or automatically from a roll.

The presses at the New York *Daily News* plant print 52,000,000 pages of newspaper each hour. As a matter of fact, this same company uses 5000 tons of *newsprint* (newspaper paper) per week. This amounts to 33,144 miles of paper, five feet wide. Let's see, it is only 25,000 miles around the world, isn't it? It figures out that these presses print a mile of this paper every 3⅓ minutes. This production makes the *Daily News* the world's largest newspaper. In fact, it has the largest circulation of any newspaper.

Type. In letterpress printing the printing is done from type, plates and cuts. Type is the individual characters, cast in small blocks of metal, and entire words and sentences cast in *slugs.* Type metal is an alloy of lead, tin, antimony, and copper.

195

Fig. 6.5. A small hand press is easy for a beginner to operate. *(Courtesy: The Kelsey Co.)*

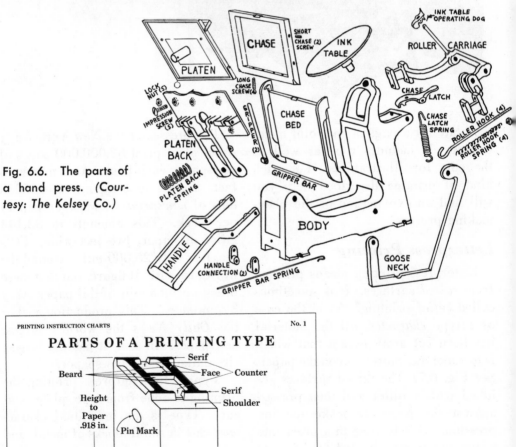

Fig. 6.6. The parts of a hand press. *(Courtesy: The Kelsey Co.)*

PRINTING INSTRUCTION CHARTS No. 1

PARTS OF A PRINTING TYPE

Serif
Beard
Face — Counter
Serif
Shoulder
Height to Paper .918 in.
Pin Mark
Feet — Groove
Nick

Prepared and Distributed by the Department of Education
AMERICAN TYPE FOUNDERS SALES CORPORATION
200 Elmora Avenue, Elizabeth N. J.

Fig. 6.7. Parts of a printing type. *(Courtesy: American Type Founders.)*

How type is made. The type metal is melted and cast in molds to form the characters. *Foundry* type is cast in single characters. Slug castings are whole words and lines in single blocks. These are made in Linotype and Intertype machines. The operator sits at a keyboard tapping out the story, or *copy*. The machine makes the molds, melts the metal, and casts and discharges it automatically as slugs. It does typesetting too, you see. The Monotype machine operates similarly except for the fact that it casts individual characters.

Sizes of type. Type is made in several sizes according to a *point* system:

72 points equal 1 inch

12 points equal 1 pica (*py*-ca)

6 points equal 1 nonpareil (non-pa-*rel*)

6 picas equal 1 inch

Common sizes of type for school use are 6, 8, 10, 12, 14, 16, 18, 24, 30 and 36 point. In a printing shop, additional sizes to 120 point are used. Larger sizes are cut in wood or linoleum block. The standard height of type is 0.918 inches.

Type fonts. Type is purchased by the pound and by the *font*. A font in-

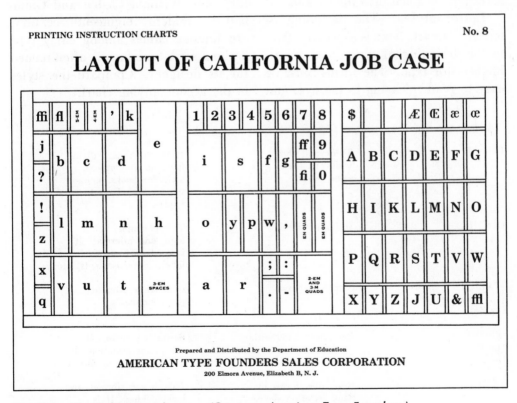

Fig. 6.8.   The California job case. *(Courtesy: American Type Founders.)*

CHARACTERS DIFFICULT TO DISTINGUISH

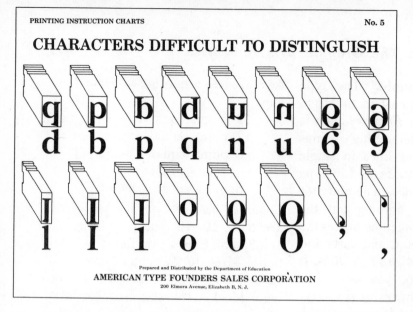

Fig. 6.9. Type charac-
ters difficult to identify.
(Courtesy: American
Type Founders.)

Prepared and Distributed by the Department of Education
AMERICAN TYPE FOUNDERS SALES CORPORATION
200 Elmora Avenue, Elizabeth 3, N. J.

cludes a complete assortment of one size and style of type. For the letters used most often, such as *a*, *e*, and *i*, more type is given than for *x*'s and *z*'s.

Letter styles. The designing of letters is an art. This is especially true in the designing of type faces, or alphabets for type. The forms must be easy to read, pleasing to the eye, and have a feeling of fitness for certain uses. Nicholas Jensen, fifteenth century, Claude Garamond, sixteenth century, and William Caslon and Giambattista Bodoni, eighteenth century, are famous names among early type designers. A type face is often named for its designer. Compare the styles in the accompanying chart.

Style	*Characteristics*	*Use*
ROMAN	Thick and thin widths in the same letter.	It is formal and digni-fied; an all purpose style for books, news-papers, etc. Easy to read.
GOTHIC	Uniform width.	This is simple, bold, loud, and informal. It is used on posters, labels, advertisements, etc.
ITALICS (In Roman or Gothic)	Slanted letters.	Commands attention, gives emphasis.
SCRIPT (in Roman or Gothic)	Resembles handwriting.	Script is graceful; it commands attention. It can be formal or informal.
TEXT	Resembles forms of hand lettering done by scribes centuries ago.	This is very formal, and legal-looking. It is difficult to read, so use it sparingly.

198

This is Roman, thick and thin.

This is Gothic, uniform thickness.

This is Italic, inclined.

This is Script, similar to writing.

𝕿𝖍𝖎𝖘 𝖎𝖘 𝕿ext, original hand lettering.

Fig. 6.10.   Letter styles: Roman, Gothic, Italic, Script, Text.

Serifs. The cross bars on the ends of the stems of letters are *serifs*, or spurs. A *sans-serif* type face is one without serifs.

Spacing devices. Spaces are needed between words, between lines, and sometimes between letters to make the printing easy to read and easy to look at. *Quads, spaces, leads*, and *slugs* are used for these purposes.

Quads and spaces. These are blocks of type metal of the same size as the font of type. They also have the nicks. The *em* quad is square and the others are wider or thinner than it.

Leads and slugs. Spacers in thin, long strips are *leads* and *slugs*. Sometimes they are called coppers and brasses because they are made of those metals. Leads are commonly 2 point and slugs, 6 point. They can be cut to desired lengths.

Furniture and reglets. *Furniture* is filler material of wood or metal. It is used to fill the space around the type in the chase so that the type can be locked in securely.

Reglets are thin strips of wood used for furniture as well as for spacing in type setting.

Printing inks. There are many kinds of printing inks. Each is intended for particular printing jobs. For example, there is *news ink* for printing newspapers, *job ink* for general purposes, *lithograph ink*, and the like. Inks are made for printing on metal, glass, plastics, and other materials. You will probably use job ink, lino-block ink, and silk screen ink.

BROAD PEN DISPLAY FACES

Kaleidoscopic New Patterns	*Bernhard Tango*
PERMANENT SERVICE	*Cartoon Light*
INCORPORATION	*Cartoon Bold*
Exigencies of the job in hand	*Gloria*
All the great printers	*Grayda*
Men of few words are the best men	*Legend*
Printing has been called mother of the arts.	*Lydian Cursive*
I Am the Leaden Army tha	*Stylescript*

GOTHIC DISPLAY FACES

RIGHTEOUS Headstrong	*Alternate Gothic #3*
QUARTZ Borough	*Franklin Gothic*
REPRODUCED Neat Pamphlet	*News Gothic*

THICK-AND-THIN SERIFED DISPLAY FACES

CAMBRIDGE Resources of Central	*Corvinus Light*
BE EQUIPPED to satisfy the special	*Eve*
TROPHY original design	*Ultra Bodoni*

Fig. 6.11. Some type faces.

SPACING DEVICES

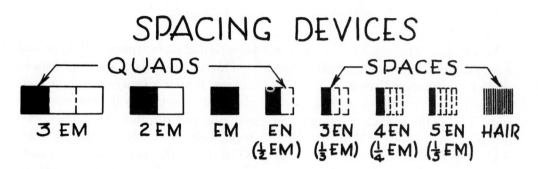

Fig. 6.12. Spacing devices.

Plate Making for Letterpress Printing

Relief line etching. This is a plate-making process for use with illustrations or copy that is in solid black or white, with no middle tones or grays. The design is photographed and the negative developed. A contact print (see page 234) is made on a sensitized zinc plate which is then developed, fixed, and washed as though it were a snapshot.

Powdered rosin, called *dragon's blood*, is dusted over the plate. It sticks only to the printed areas and protects them. This rosin is melted

Fig. 6.13. A zinc cut for a book plate (upper left) made from the drawing (right) and the print.

over a flame. The plate is then put in a weak nitric acid bath which etches away the bare metal areas. The rosin-covered areas are left high and in *relief*. The plate is then trimmed and mounted on a block so that it is type-high. The finished plate is often called a *cut*.

Halftone etchings. This process is similar to that for relief line etching except that the middle tones, known as *halftones*, are reproduced.

The design is photographed through a very fine *screen* which breaks it up into tiny dots. With a magnifying glass look at a photograph in a newspaper and in a magazine. The dots in the paper are larger than those in a magazine.

Stereotypes. Stereotypes are plates for printing newspapers. The type and cuts for an entire page are locked up in a chase. A matrix (*may*-tricks), or mat, of moist paper is laid over the type and cuts and run through a press. An impression is squeezed into the mat. When dried, the mat is put into a casting box and molten metal is poured in. Upon cooling, the impression is formed in the metal. This plate may be flat or curved, depending on the printing press in which it will be used.

Electrotypes. Electrotype plates, or electrotypes, as they are called, are made with an electroplating process. They are more durable, give better impressions than do stereotypes, and are used chiefly for book and magazine printing.

A thin metal plate is coated with

Fig. 6.14.   An operator at the keyboard of a slug-casting machine. *(From Karch: How to Plan and Buy Printing, New York: Prentice-Hall, Inc.)*

Fig. 6.15. The product is a slug. This is type cast on a production basis. *(From Karch:* How to Plan and Buy Printing, *New York: Prentice-Hall, Inc.)*

Fig. 6.16. Stereotype caster. The mat is in place on the bed which the operator is holding; when this is locked against the vertical bed, molten type metal flows over the mat, registering all the details. *(Courtesy: Hammond Machinery Builders.)*

beeswax and the type or cut is pressed into it to leave the impression. The wax is then coated with graphite, which is a conductor of electricity. Then the plate is put into a tank and copper plated. When the plating is thick enough it is removed from the wax as a thin metal sheet bearing the impression. A layer of lead is poured over the back to give support to the thin metal. The printing is done from the copper.

Rubber plates and stamps. Rubber plates and stamps can be used to print not only on flat surfaces but on curved as well. Intricate designs on dishes, for example, are often printed with rubber stamps. They can be made from type, linoleum block cuts, electrotypes, and the like.

A mold is first made, using a special molding compound. The type is pressed into the compound and when removed the impression remains, just like tire tracks in the snow or mud. A rubber compound is placed over the mold and, in a heated molding press, it is forced into the impression where it is vulcanized. The press and process are similar to those used in service stations for patching inner tubes. The rubber is then removed, trimmed, and mounted on a block. You can easily make rubber stamps. To start out, get a kit of materials from one of the many companies supplying them. Follow their instructions.

Linoleum Block Printing

Linoleum block printing is printing from a raised surface with the design cut into heavy linoleum. Thousands of prints can be made from such a block.

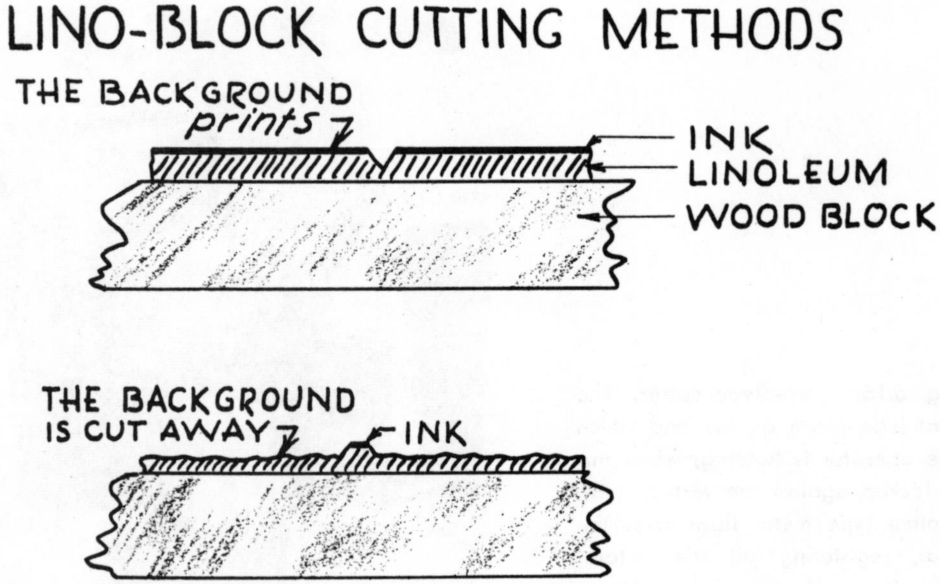

LINO-BLOCK CUTTING METHODS

Fig. 6.17. Linoleum block cutting methods.

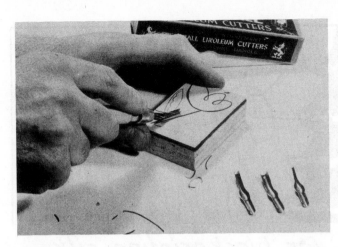

Fig. 6.18. Cutting a linoleum block.

Equipment needed. Use ready-made blocks which have heavy linoleum glued to thick plywood blocks. Some are type high. Either water-mixed block printing inks or regular printing ink can be used. Special cutting tools are preferred—either the push type or the pull type. The latter is the safer. A brayer of soft rubber or plastic is needed for inking the block. The ink is rolled out on a heavy glass slab.

How it works. Take your choice of two techniques. For your first trials use the first method.

1. Trace the pattern with the veining tool, making a narrow V cut about $\frac{1}{16}$ in. wide and deep. The ink prints on each side of the cut, leaving a line on a colored background.

2. This method leaves a raised line with the background cut away.

Making a block print. 1. First make a suitable design in ink on tracing paper. Ink those areas where you want the printing ink to be. Transfer this design *in reverse* with carbon paper on to the block.

2. With the veining tool cut the outline into the linoleum. Cut away any unwanted background with a wide tool.

3. Squeeze about a half inch of ink onto the glass and roll it out uniformly thin with the brayer. When evenly coated, roll the brayer over the design until it is well inked.

4. Lay your printing paper on a thick pad of newspapers and place the block where you want it. Step on the block to make the impression. From this proof you can tell whether any changes are needed in the design. Printing can also be done in a printing press or a vise.

Safety sense. When using a push type cutting tool, keep your fingers behind it, never in front. Sometimes the tool skids.

How to Set Type

Follow these steps for setting your name and address. Perhaps you could use them on some stationery.

1. Select the size and type face to suit the purpose you have in mind.

205

Fig. 6.19.   Some ideas.

HOW TO READ COMPOSED TYPE

Type is read from left to right as are the lines on the printed page, but the characters are upside down. With a little practice the reading of type will become easy. Do not read type in any other manner than upside down, from left to right.

Type is read from left to right as are the lines on the printed page, but the characters are upside down. With a little practice the reading of type will become easy. Do not read type in any other manner than upside down, from left to right.

Prepared and Distributed by the Department of Education

AMERICAN TYPE FOUNDERS SALES CORPORATION

200 Elmora Avenue, Elizabeth B, N. J.

Fig. 6.20. How to read composed type. *(Courtesy: American Type Founders.)*

2. Holding the composing stick as shown, insert a 6-point slug, as long as or longer than the longest line of type.

3. Set the type for the first line on the slug. Start at the left end of the stick and make sure the nicks are all up. The words should read from left to right, with the letters upside down.

4. Place a lead over the first line to provide a space between the lines. Use more space if you wish.

5. Add the next lines in the same manner.

6. *Justify* the lines. This means to tighten the line in the composing stick by adding ems, and ens, and thin spaces.

7. Add spacing material to even

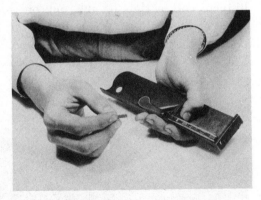

Fig. 6.21. The first line of type is set against a 6-point slug in the composing stick.

the ends of the lines so that the type forms a block.

8. Carefully slide the whole block,

207

Fig. 6.22. When the type has been set it is tied to hold it temporarily. It is now called a *form* and is placed in a galley.

now called a *form,* into a galley and tie it securely with a string. Wrap the first turn over the loose end to hold it so that you can hold the form with one hand. Wrap the form with five or six snug turns. After you have just passed a corner, tuck the end under several strands. Spread the strands up and down over the height of the type.

9. Make a proof print. With a brayer, roll a dab of ink out on a piece of plate glass. When the brayer is evenly covered, roll it over the type. Put the type and galley in a proof press for the impression. If you have

no proof press, lay the paper on the type and press down on it with a piece of cardboard.

10. Check the proof for accuracy; if corrections are necessary, move the form or the line back into the composing stick.

11. Now clean the type with a cloth pad, a type brush, and some type cleaner. Clean the brayer and glass too.

12. Lock the type near the center of, and as high in, the chase as possible. Use whatever furniture is necessary. With the *quoins* or set screws in

Fig. 6.23. The type is locked up in the chase. Then it is planed, or is tapped down with a block and a mallet. This sets each piece of type to the same height.

the hand press chase, wedge the type and furniture in securely. No piece of type should be loose.

13. *Plane* the type with the planing block and mallet. The form should be placed on the imposing table or stone and tapped lightly, the planing block being moved here and there over the type. Place the chase and type on the imposing stone. Move the planing block over the type, tapping it lightly. This should make the type surface even so that all letters will print.

How to Print

With the type locked in the chase, the press must be made ready to print.

1. Place a small dab of printing ink on the lower left corner of the inking plate. Operate the press a few times so that the rollers can spread the ink evenly over themselves and the plate.

2. Insert the chase—be sure it is locked in place—and make an impression on the *tympan* paper.

3. Insert the *gauge pins* in the tympan paper. These will hold your paper in the proper position for printing. Three are usually needed. Adjust the *grippers*—the long slender fingers that keep the paper from sticking to the type—to clear the type and the pins. If the form does not have much inked surface, the grippers are not needed.

4. Make a print and check it for position and inking. If it appears that more pressure is needed, slip a sheet or two of paper under the tympan paper.

5. Now print as many copies as you want. Add ink when needed, but remember that beginners tend to use too much.

6. When the run is complete remove the chase and clean the type.

7. Remove the ink rolls and clean them. Put them in their special rack. Rolls can be spoiled by leaving them on the plate or on the type. They flatten out and stay that way.

8. Clean the inking plate. Put used rags in a fire-safe container.

Fig. 6.24. Gauge pins for holding the paper are inserted in the tympan sheet, after the chase has been inserted in the press. Make a print on the tympan paper to help you locate the gauge pins.

9. Distribute the type. Slip the form back into the composing stick or the galley and, one letter at a time, return them to their proper compartments in the proper case. There is one person whom we can get along without in a printing shop. He is the one who leaves his type for someone else to distribute, or who mixes up the type in the case. When you meet this person you'll feel this way, too.

Safety sense. Your experiences with graphic arts can be more enjoyable if you use *safety sense*. Remember:

1. The cleaner you use on type and on the presses is inflammable. Keep the used rags in a fireproof container.

2. There isn't room for your hand between the type and the paper in the press. Keep it out of there or you will spoil the printing (and what else?).

3. If you use power presses in your shop make sure the belts and gears are well guarded.

4. Don't talk with a person who is feeding a power press. Give him a chance to enjoy his work.

5. A paper cutter will cut fingers, too. Keep your eyes on them at all times.

Planography

There are several types of planographic, or lithographic, printing, but all are possible because grease attracts grease and repels water. The illustration and the copy is drawn or photographed on a plate of metal with a greasy ink. These inked areas pick up ink from the roller; but the other areas, being wet, do not. The image is then printed on the paper under pressure.

Crayon-stone lithography. Stone lithography was the first of these processes. It was invented in Germany by Alois Senefelder in the eighteenth century. A slab of limestone is ground perfectly flat with another stone and some abrasive. The design is then drawn on the surface with the grease pencil or crayon. The background is etched with nitric acid. The surface, moistened with water, resists the ink

210

Fig. 6.26. The type is distributed when the job is completed. Each piece must be returned to its proper place in the case. Mixed up type is called *pied* type.

on the roller while the drawn lines attract it. A dampened paper is laid over it and the impression is printed in a press. The stone is reground each time a new design is needed. Beautiful tones are obtained by this method.

Offset lithography. The design is drawn, typed, or photographed on a flexible metal or paper plate. Special crayons and typewriter ribbon are used. Then the plate is fastened on the cylinder press. Two sets of rollers contact the plate; the wetting rollers first, and then the ink rollers. As the cylinder revolves, the image is printed on a rubber blanket covering the offset cylinder. The paper is printed from the blanket. This process is used in competition with letterpress printing as well as on jobs which it alone can handle. It can be arranged to print on metal toys, nameplates, milk bottles, and the like.

Photolithography. This process is used to reproduce illustrations by lithographic plate. The layout is photographed on sensitized metal plate and a halftone screen is used, just as is done in letterpress plate making.

Photo-gelatin process. The design is photographed on sensitized gelatin without the use of a screen. The areas of gelatin exposed to the most light become hardened and quite waterproof. Those with little or no exposure remain absorptive of water. In printing, the most absorptive ink areas pick up the most water and the least ink. The hard areas take the ink. This process reproduces photographs most beautifully because little detail is lost.

Intaglio Printing

Intaglio printing is done from a surface below the face of the plate. The image is cut into the plate with a tool or bitten in with acid. When a tool is used, that is *engraving*. The acid process is *etching*. The plates can be made by hand or by photographic methods. You can easily make some of the types of intaglio plates and print from them.

For printing, the ink is down in the hollows and not on the top of the

The Spirit of Liberty

"Liberty lies in the hearts of men and women. When it dies there, no constitution, no law, no court can save it. No constitution, no law, no court can 'even do much to help it . . . The spirit of liberty is the spirit which is not too sure that it is right. The spirit of liberty is the spirit which seeks to understand the minds of other men and women. The spirit of liberty is the spirit which weighs their inter-

ests alongside its own without bia
of liberty remembers that not eve
falls to earth unheeded. The spir
is the spirit of Him who, near tw
years ago, taught mankind that l
never learned, but has never qui
that there may be a kingdom wh
shall be heard and considered
with the greatest."
—Judge

★

George Washington
First President
Of The United States

"If a nation values anything more than freedom, it will lose its freedom: and the irony of it is tha
if it is comfort or money that it values more, it will lose that too." —Somerset Maughar

ℬooks are keys to wisdom's treasure;

Books are gates to lands of pleasure;

Books are paths that upward lead;

let us read.

EMI
ana Public Library, He

WV

Annual All Sports Banquet

West View High School

May 20, 1953

Nº 505

SOPHOMORE
"Heart Beat Leap"

Friday, February 29, 1952

West View High School

8:30 P.M.—11:30 P.M

Refreshments .35

Nº 508

𝒯HE PRINTER is the friend

of intelligence, of thought;

He is the friend of liberty

nd freedom in law; in truth,

The printer is the friend of

every man who is the friend

Of order, the real friend of

every man who can read.

--Charles Dickens--

MOTHER'S DAY

SUNDAY
MAY 11

AMERICAN
ℰDUCATION
WEEK

Mother O' Mine
Rudyard Kipling

God took the sunshine from the skies
And made the lovelight in your eyes;
From honeyed flowers he took the dew
And made your tears,- unselfish, true;
Upon a rock He built your faith,
With angel prayers He gave you breath
And with His love, made yours divine
But best of all—He made you mine

Printed by Jerome Kranach, Student, Hamilton Jr. High School

Visit
Your Schools

Fig. 6.27. Letterpress printing by students of Don Remaley at the Hamilton Junior High School, Pittsburgh, Pennsylvania.

plate. Plates are made flat for platten presses and curved for rotary presses.

Line methods for plate making. Certain methods are used to make plates when the illustrations are drawn in lines, with no halftones as there are in photographs or paintings. Shades and shadows are made by varying the width, depth, and spacing of lines.

Line engravings. The design is drawn in reverse on a metal plate. With a tool called a *graver*, the lines are cut into it. Various shapes of gravers make varying lines. This process is about the same as that for cutting a linoleum block.

Zinc, copper, and steel are used for plates. Steel, being the hardest, reproduces the finest detail and lasts the longest. Our paper money is printed from steel engravings. Magnifying lenses are used by the engraver as he works on fine detail. Engraved plates are also made by machine. An original is placed in the machine and is used as a guide for the cutting of others.

Line etchings. This method depends on acid biting down into the plate to make the lines. A plate of copper is cleaned and polished on one side. This is coated with an acid-resisting *ground* which is a mixture of asphalt paint, beeswax, and gum mastic. The design is transferred in reverse on this ground and is cut through it with a hard metal point called a *stylus*. The point cuts through to the bare metal.

The back and edges of the plate are also coated with the ground. The acid eats into the copper wherever it is not covered by the ground. When the bite is deep enough, the plate is cleaned, trimmed, and tacked to a block of wood, making it type-high.

Dry points. This is an interesting process for plate making, and you can use it for making greeting cards and sketches. Finest results are obtained with a plate of copper, although you can use aluminum or celluloid. Transfer the design in reverse with carbon paper. With a hard, sharp stylus slowly pull the point over the marks, pressing firmly. This procedure raises a burr along the marks. Ink is applied with a dauber and wiped off the surface of the plate. Use a soft paper and make the print in a hand press. The lines will be fuzzy wherever the burrs print. This fuzziness identifies a drypoint print. The plate lasts for only a few prints because the burrs break down.

Tone methods for plate making. These methods reproduce the shades and shadows in an illustration by means of dots. Those described here are *soft ground, aquatint,* and *mezzotint.*

Soft-ground etching. This technique can be easily done in the school shop. A polished plate of copper is coated with an etching ground. The drawing is made on thin rough paper, dampened and laid over the plate. As the drawing is traced with a pencil, some of the ground sticks to the back of the paper. The pressure used and the kind of pencil point determine how much ground is picked up. When the paper is removed, bare copper shows here

COMPARISON CHART OF THE GRAPHIC ARTS PROCESSES

	LETTERPRESS	OFFSET-LITHOGRAPHY	GRAVURE
Rotary Methods of each Process	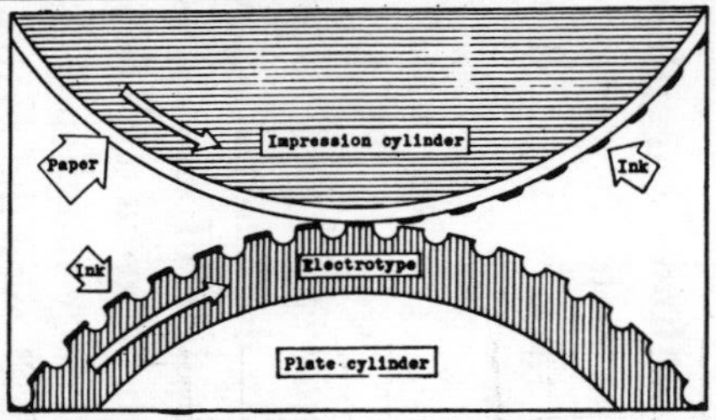 *(diagram: Ink, Impression cylinder, Electrotype, Plate cylinder, Paper)*	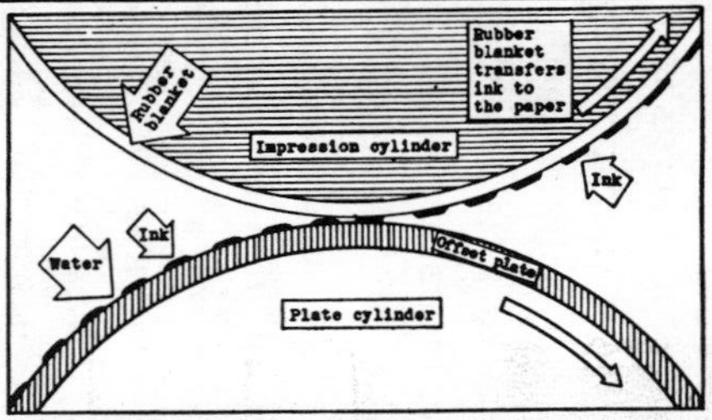 *(diagram: Ink, Rubber blanket transfers ink to the paper, Impression cylinder, Offset blanket, Plate cylinder, Rubber blanket, Water)*	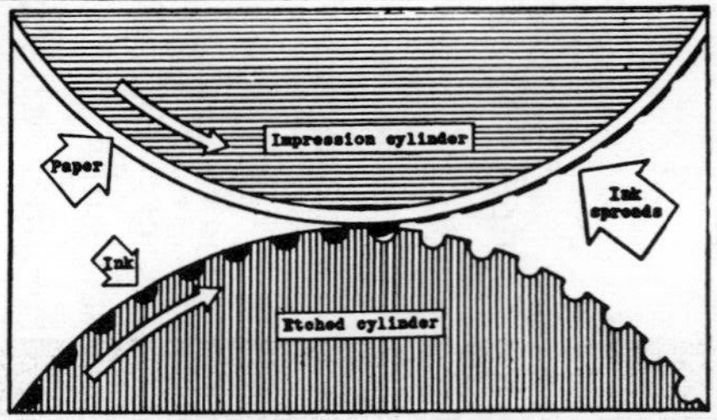 *(diagram: Ink scraped, Impression cylinder, Etched cylinder, Paper, Ink)*
Examine Type	Often shows a slight impression on back of sheet — hold at an angle to light	Never shows an impression on the back of sheet — hold at an angle to light	All type is screened the same as illustrations — examine with a magnifying glass
Examine Line Engravings	Impression may show on back of sheet — hold at an angle to light	Never shows impression on back of sheet	Illustrations which appear as line are actually screened
Examine Ink	Usually appears as an intense black Detail is sharp	Solid blacks usually appear gray when compared with letterpress Detail usually less sharp than letterpress	Smooth, blending tones Detail not as good as in letterpress or lithography
Examine Halftone Dots	Highlight dot / Shadow dot  Usually 120–133 line	Highlight dot / Shadow dot  Usually 80–133 line	Highlight and shadow screen  Usually 150 line; ink tends to fuse and obliterate screen
	Because of the extreme differences in quality of work done in letterpress and offset-lithography,	it is often difficult to distinguish one process from another. Offset often looks like letterpress.	

Fig. 6.28. Comparison chart of graphic arts processes. *(From Karch:* How to Plan and Buy Printing, *New York: Prentice-Hall, Inc.)*

214

and there. These are then etched in the nitric acid.

Aquatint. This is a process for reproducing paintings. Rosin powder is dusted on the copper plate for the ground. This is heated to melt it onto the plate. The etcher works with different areas, cutting them as deeply as desired. The deeper the etching, the darker the printing.

Mezzotint. The mezzotint process is used for portraits. The copper plate is coated with an etching ground and then, with a special tool that pricks holes through the ground, the drawing is laid out. These holes expose the bare metal, which is then etched.

Photographic methods. Photogravure and rotogravure are commercial methods for producing tones on plates. The picture section of the Sunday paper, which is sometimes in brown tones, was probably printed by rotogravure. Wall paper, oilcloth, cloth, and books are printed by these processes. Photogravure plates are flat; rotogravure plates are curved to fit rotary presses used for fast production.

The photogravure plate is dusted with rosin and heated to melt the particles. These tiny bubbles serve as the photographic screen. A photographic positive is printed and developed on a sensitized glass plate. From this a print is made on a sensitized sheet of special gelatin tissue. This is pressed onto the plate, which is then etched.

In rotogravure the illustration is photographed through a very fine screen with as many as 20,000 dots to the square inch. The rest of the process is the same as for photogravure.

How Magazines Are Published

The next time you pass a newsstand try to count all the different magazines. Some are weekly, some monthly, others quarterly, and a few are annuals. They all go through the same processes in publication. After the advertising space is sold and the articles or stories are on hand, the editorial and art staffs go to work. These are the main steps:

1. *The dummy.* Rough page layouts are made so that the available space can be best used.

2. *Illustrations.* The drawings, sketches, and so on, for the ads and the articles are made. The cover is designed and the photographs are selected.

3. *The page layouts.* All type is set and prints are made. These and the illustrations are pasted on sheets of cardboard to make the page layouts as they are to appear in the magazine. (See Fig. 6.29.)

4. *The plate making.* Magazines are usually printed from stereotype or electrotype plates (see page 202). One plate prints a pair of pages.

5. *The printing.*

6. *The binding and trimming.* Magazines are either stapled or stitched with wire.

How Newspapers Are Published

The printing of a newspaper is a

Fig. 6.29. Editors examine the page layouts for an issue of *Popular Science Monthly*. (Courtesy: Popular Science Publishing Co.)

race against time. Just imagine how well planned the entire operation must be at the New York *Daily News* plant when 2,200,000 copies are printed daily and nearly 4,000,000 on Sunday. Before one edition is ready for the street the next edition is ready to run. Such terrific production shows what industry in our country is capable of. No matter where you live in the United States you can get a newspaper. In rural communities the paper may sometimes be a day late, but it does get there.

Modern newspapers go through the

following steps before they are ready for circulation:

1. *The news is gathered.* Teletype systems bring in national and world news from such sources as A.P. and U.P. (Associated Press and United Press). Reporters cover local news. Advertising is sold.

2. *The pages are laid out.* Advertising art work is done. The compositors set the type and the engravers make the cuts.

3. *Full-page mats are made.* (See page 218.) From them, the plates are cut.

Fig. 6.30. News arrives by wire at the teletype machine which automatically types the message. *(Courtesy: Forest City Publishing Co.)*

Fig. 6.31. The type form for page 29 of the *Cleveland Plain Dealer* is being checked. Notice the cuts which print illustrations. *(Courtesy: Forest City Publishing Co.)*

Fig. 6.32. Making a matrix, or mat. The hard, dense moist mat paper is laid over the page of type and rolled through the press. This forces the impressions of the type into the mat. *(Courtesy: Forest City Publishing Co.)*

Fig. 6.33. The operator has just removed the mat from the stereotype. The plate was cast from the mat. The plate at the lower right in the photo is curved to fit the rotary press. *(Courtesy: Forest City Publishing Co.)*

Fig. 6.34. The newspaper rolls off the presses, folded and ready for the newsboys to deliver. *(Courtesy: Forest City Publishing Co.)*

4. *The paper is printed.* The plates are installed in the presses. The paper is fed from rolls. The pages are cut, assembled, and folded automatically, and the paper is ready for delivery.

How Books Are Made

The printing and publishing of books today is a huge business. With most of the processes done by machine, there is little resemblance to those processes used centuries ago when books were printed letter by letter with a pen on handmade paper or vellum.

A publisher undertakes a book only if he feels that there is a good market for it. Let us assume that an author sends him a *manuscript,* a typewritten copy, for his examination. It is turned over to an editor who sends it out to several critics who pass judgment on it. When the decision is made to proceed with the publishing, the book is given a thorough editing. This includes checking for misspelled words, poor sentence structure, errors in punctuation, and the like.

Book designers plan page layouts,

Fig. 6.35. Plate making is the first step in printing a comic book. Here the original drawing for Walt Disney's *Goofy* is being photographed on a sensitized metal plate. (Courtesy: Western Printing and Lithographing Co.)

Fig. 6.36. The exposed plate is developed to bring out the image. (Courtesy: Western Printing and Lithographing Co.)

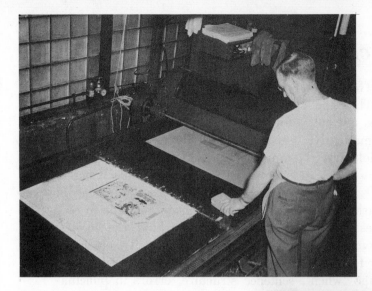

Fig. 6.37. On this proof press a print is made from the cover plate to check it for accuracy. (Courtesy: Western Printing and Lithographing Co.)

Fig. 6.38. The comic books are printed on this two-color offset press. (Courtesy: Western Printing and Lithographing Co.)

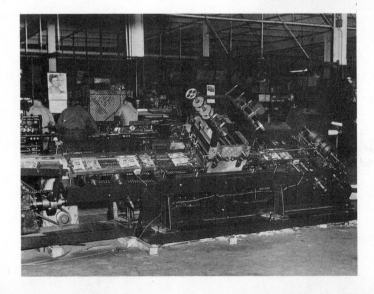

Fig. 6.39 The comic books are stitched and folded automatically. (Courtesy: Western Printing and Lithographing Co.)

select type faces and paper, and design the cover. Then type is set, *galley proofs* are made, and errors are corrected. *Page proofs* are then printed and are checked carefully by the editor and the author. Soon electrotype plates are made and the book is printed. After the pages are bound, the cover is attached and the book is ready for the market. Publishing a book requires from six to nine months.

Types of book binding. Bookbinding is the process of making a book from the loose pages. They are folded in groups called *signatures,* which are bound together by any one of several means.

Padding. This is the method for making tablets and scratch pads. The sheets are clamped securely to a cardboard back and a glue, the padding compound, is applied to one edge. The hinge of a cover is pressed into the glue, which dries in a few minutes. Trimming is done after the pads are dry.

Wire stitching. Fastening the pages with wire is a fast, economical method. *Side wire stapling* is used when the book is thick. *Saddle wire stitching* is done through the fold when the book is thin.

Mechanical binders. Your loose-leaf notebook cover is a type of binder. So is the wire or plastic spiral on a pocket notebook. There are many of such devices. All require that holes be punched in the pages. Special paper drills are available for use in a drill press.

Case binding. The book you are now reading was bound by this method, as were most of the books in your library. Many variations are used by different binderies, but the actual sewing together of the signatures is the usual method.

Paper and Paper Making

Most of today's printing is done on paper; without paper, there would be no graphic arts industries. We know that in the early days paper was made by hand. Today it is made by machine. Old paper, wood pulp, and rags are the raw materials. The highest quality paper is made from rags or has a lot of rag in it.

How paper is made. The raw material is cooked in great vats and then put in huge beaters, which stir it into a thick, heavy mass. Bleaching and dyeing follow. The material is now pulp and is washed and thinned with water and flowed out over wide copper screens. The screen is an endless belt that constantly shakes. This causes the pulp fibers to criss-cross one another and to settle down. The water drains through the screen, leaving a rough mat of pulp fibers. This mat is conveyed between rollers, which squeeze out more water and press the mat thin. The surface finish is pressed on by further rolling, after which the paper is dried and wound on rolls or cut into sheets.

Kinds of paper. Papers are made for many purposes. You find them in paper money, laminated plastics, insulation for homes, picnic plates, as well as in hundreds of other uses.

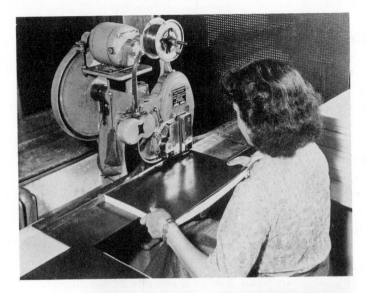

Fig. 6.40. Some books are stitched with wire. (*Courtesy: Acme Steel Co.*)

Fig. 6.41. Dried pulp in sheet form is placed in a vat, called a beater, which adds water and breaks the pulp into fibers. (*Courtesy: Strathmore Paper Co.*)

Fig. 6.42. A mixture of ½ per cent fiber and 99½ per cent water is poured onto a moving wire screen, called a Fourdrinier papermaking machine. The fibers are held on the screen as the water falls through, forming a sheet of paper. (*Courtesy: Champion Paper and Fibre Co.*)

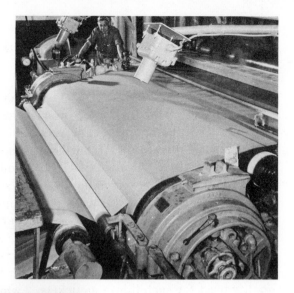

Fig. 6.43. The paper now leaves the screen and is carried on continuous rolls of felt, where more water is squeezed out and the paper becomes increasingly stronger. (Courtesy: Champion Paper and Fibre Co.)

Fig. 6.44. After the paper is ironed smooth on huge, hot calender rolls, it is wound into rolls. This one is 156 inches wide and three miles long. (Courtesy: Champion Paper and Fibre Co.)

Newsprint is made from wood pulp. (See Fig. 3.10.) More of this is made than any other paper. It tears easily but serves its purpose well.

Kraft paper is wrapping paper made from wood and paper pulp. It is commonly brown in color. You see it in paper bags and in rolls at the store.

Writing paper is made of wood pulp and rags. Better grades are *water-marked*. The manufacturer's name or mark is in the paper, not on it. Hold a piece to the light to read it. The more rag in writing paper, the stronger it is.

The standard size of writing paper supplied by the mill is 17 by 22 in. A package contains a ream of 500 sheets and weighs from 13 to 36 or 40 lb. This size is cut in four 8½ by 11 inch reams, which is the standard size for writing and typing. If you buy a ream of this paper in the 20-lb. weight, it means that four of them weighed 20 lb. The heavier the paper the more costly it is.

Book papers are usually of wood pulp. Many different finishes are used, depending on the nature of the book and the methods of printing. A finely grained, smooth paper is used when the greatest detail in the illustrations is wanted.

Cardboard stock comes in many grades, weights, and finishes. *Bristol board* is a light-weight board of good quality used for such things as tickets, cards, and announcements. *Railroad board* is a heavier card for printed posters and signs. *Showcard board* is a very heavy card with a dull surface, or *tooth,* used especially for hand-lettered posters.

The standard sizes for cardboard vary, but most of them are 22 by 28 in. or close to it.

How you can make paper. You can make some very attractive paper from old paper or white rags. Make several sheets and print on them. They will look very rich.

Making the pulp. Cut the paper or rags, or both, into small narrow strips. Soak them in water and cook until they become a thick, heavy mass. Beat this smooth in a kitchen mixer. Then pour it into a pan of clean cold water and stir until the pulp is well thinned.

Forming a sheet. A wooden frame covered with a piece of copper fly screen is the *mold.* It is placed inside another frame, the *deckle.* Together these are used to dip the pulp. Be sure the mixture is well stirred.

The deposit of pulp held on the screen will be the sheet of paper. Remove the deckle and lay a sheet of heavy felt over the pulp and press out the water. The pulp now clings to the felt and can be lifted off. Several of these paper and felt sheets are stacked and pressed until almost dry. They can be sandwiched between pieces of cardboard and run through a clothes wringer to press out water.

Sizing. Sizing is applied to the sheets when they are intended for writing with ink. Otherwise they will behave like blotters. Get a box of gelatin at the grocery store and dissolve it in hot water according to the instructions. To a pint of it add a half ounce of alum as a hardener. Now spray or dip the sheets.

Finishing. Different surfaces for the sheets are possible. Lay one between coarsely woven cloths, press it dry with a hot iron and you will get a coarsely textured paper. Pressing directly with the iron gives a smooth surface.

Deckle edge. The edge of a sheet when left rough and ragged as it comes from the deckle is called *deckle edge.* It is very attractive for some uses.

Duplicating Processes

Duplicators are office type machines which can print copies of typewritten material and drawings. You will see one or more of such machines in your school.

One group of the processes use *stencils.* These are thin, waxy, fibrous sheets on which the original is typed or drawn. Lines are actually cut through the stencil. It is placed on an inked cylinder which rotates. Ink is squeezed through the stencil cuts into the paper.

Another group uses a gelatin plate. The original is typed or drawn with a special ink. This ink is absorbed by the gelatin. When paper is pressed upon the gelatin by hand or by a revolving cylinder, it picks up the impression.

Blueprints

Originally this was a process for making blue copies of drawings. Today the term includes several processes for making prints of drawings. The prints may be blue with white lines, white with black, white with brown, or other color combinations. Blueprinting is a contact printing process. (See page 13.) A sensitized paper is exposed and developed.

These prints are usually made by automatic machines. The sensitized paper and drawing are fed together into the printer, where electric lights make the exposure. Developer in liquid or fumes brings out the image. Washing and drying follow, with the finished print ready for use in a few minutes. Look for such machines when you visit industries. They are usually found in the drafting departments.

How to make a blueprint. A sun frame is the simplest device for making blueprints. It is made like a picture frame with glass and an easily removable back. A layer of felt lines the back. Cut a piece of blueprint paper a little larger than the tracing of the drawing. Lay the tracing in the frame, face down on the glass. Place the printing paper on the tracing, sensitized side down. Clamp the back in place and expose the drawing to the sun for two or three minutes. Remove the printing paper and quickly wet it all over in water. Sponge with a dilute solution of potassium bichromate dissolved in water.

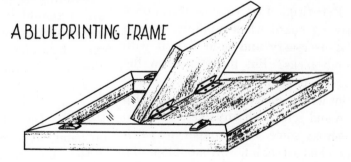

A BLUEPRINTING FRAME

ENLARGED SECTION

Fig. 6.45. A simple blueprinting frame.

COVER

FELT
BLUEPRINT PAPER
DRAWING
GLASS

This brings out the image. Wash well and hang up to dry. You may have to try different exposures to get the best print. Exposure to a bright sun requires less time than to a dull one.

Stenciling

Stenciling is a simple production process for making many identical prints. It can be used on flat or curved surfaces of paper, cloth, wood, metal, leather, clay, and other materials. Tempera colors are used on paper and sometimes wood; special textile paints on cloth and leather; enamels on metals and woods; and glazes, underglaze colors, or *engobes* on unfired clay pieces.

Cutting a stencil. Lay a piece of transparent stencil paper over your design and with a sharp knife cut out the openings where you want them. It is a good idea to spread the parts out over the sheet so that there are no narrow sections between openings. These usually tear out.

Printing. Lay your material on a drawing board when possible. Stretch it if necessary and hold it taut with thumb tacks. Put the stencil in the correct position. Use thick, heavy paint with a special stencil brush. Dip it in and scrape off any excess. Swipe it across some waste paper to catch any clots of paint. Stroke from the edge to the center of the opening. Use a very dry brush and let the brush marks show for interesting results, or fill the openings solidly with color.

Silk Screen Stencil Printing

Silk-screen printing is a fast form of stenciling that can produce identical prints with considerable detail. It has many commercial uses from billboard advertisements to labels on milk bottles. Several variations in the method are possible. The lacquer-film method is the commercial process and is described here. Use it for signs, posters, Christmas cards, T-shirt emblems, and so on.

Equipment needed. Make the frame of soft wood as shown, with mitered corners and a chamfer for tacking the silk. It should be not less than four inches larger each way than the design to be printed.

Use silk that is made for screen printing. Organdy can be used, but it doesn't print as sharply. Moisten the silk with water before tacking it on the frame. Drive a tack at the center of each side. Tack toward the corners, stretching the silk as you go. It must have no wrinkles.

Printing is done with a *squeegee* which should be slightly longer than the width of the design. Take good care of the sharp rubber edges. When nicked, they make streaks on the print.

The lacquer film is sold under several names, for example, Nufilm and Profilm. Do not keep a large supply on hand. It deteriorates with age.

Get the adhering liquid recommended for the film you will use. This is very volatile and inflammable, so keep the lid on the container when not in use.

Fig. 6.46.   A hand-cut stencil and a print.

If you want water-soluble paints, use a good grade of tempera colors. For signs and posters to be hung out of doors, use the regular oil-base silk-screen printing colors. Textile paints should be used on cloth. In all cases the paints should be thick, like gravy, so that they do not seep under the edges of the stencil.

How to print:

1. To cut the stencil, thumbtack the lacquer film over the drawing with the wax paper side down. With a sharp knife cut through the film, not through the wax paper, and carefully peel off the film from the areas which are to print.

2. Lay this film at the center of the board under the silk. Fold a soft absorbent cloth into a pad about two inches square. Dip this into the adhering liquid and rub it over the silk, pressing against the film. Cover only a small area at a time and immediately rub it dry with another cloth. Continue until all the white patches between the silk and the film have disappeared. If you use too much liquid and the film dissolves away (this happens so easily), coat the area with some thin lacquer. After a few minutes for drying, lift the frame and carefully peel the wax paper off the back.

3. With masking tape and some wrapping paper, seal off the screen around the film so that the ink cannot leak out.

4. Position a sheet of printing paper under the screen and mark the upper and left edges. Stick two strips

227

Fig. 6.47. Cutting a silk screen stencil in lacquer film.

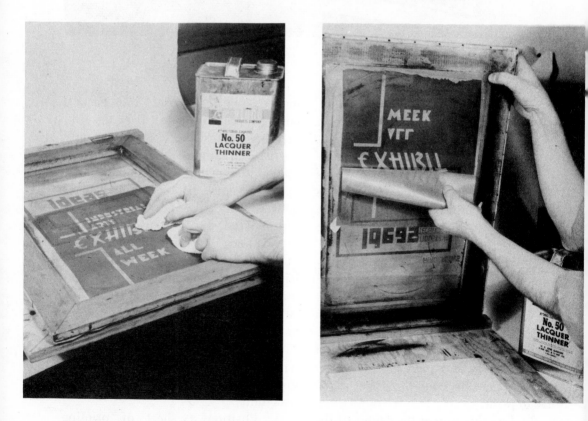

Fig. 6.48 (left). Adhering the film to the screen with adhering liquid.

Fig. 6.49 (right). The wax paper backing is carefully pulled from the film.

Fig. 6.50. In printing, ink is forced through the openings in the stencil by the squeegee.

Fig. 6.51. The print.

of light cardboard along these marks with rubber cement. These are guides to hold the paper in place.

5. Spread a spoonful of paint along the upper edges above the design. Hold the squeegee in both hands and pull it through the paint over the stencil. Try to cover it all in one stroke. Now lift the screen and remove the print.

6. Wash out the paint when you are finished, otherwise the screen will be clogged. To remove the film so that the screen can be used again, dissolve the film in the adhering liquid and soak it up with cloth.

Safety sense. The cloths you have been using are inflammable. Be sure they are safely disposed of.

Photography and Its Industries

The simplest camera is a light-tight box in which a light-sensitive film is held at one end and a lens at the other, with a shutter for admitting light. This is a box camera. Louis Daguerre made the first such camera in 1839. Since then it has been so improved that a photographic industry has grown up around it and its uses. It was not until 1885 that roll film became available. This invention, by George Eastman,

229

ABCDEF
GHIJKLM
NOPQRS
TUVWXY
Zabcdefg
hijklmnopq
rstuvwxyz

Fig. 6.52. An alphabet for stencil use.

made it possible for anyone to take pictures. It promoted the discovery of dozens of uses for photography which had not existed because up to this time film was on glass plates. For example, as soon as Thomas Edison bought one of the rolls of film he was able to make a motion picture camera, out of which has grown the movie industry. Since World War I, color photography has been perfected, and recently theaters have shown the movies in three dimensions for true-to-life realism. With the giant mirror of Mount Palomar, photo-

graphs are made of planets millions of miles away; and with the electron microscope scientists can make enlargements of 100,000 diameters of matter so tiny that it is invisible under a regular microscope. New uses are constantly being found for photography: the process of recording lifelike images of objects on film and paper.

About Cameras

A camera is designed according to its intended use. Both a box camera

Fig. 6.53. A camera of the 1880's. Sold ready-loaded with film, it was returned to the factory for film processing.

Fig. 6.54. Inspecting cameras before packing for shipment.

and an aerial camera take pictures, but they have little in common except the principle by which they work. The box-type camera is intended for the person who wants to take snapshots occasionally and with the simplest of cameras. No adjustment and no figuring is needed; just aim and shoot.

The amateur photographer wants to take pictures for which the box camera is unsuited. He needs one that can be *focused* and that has variable *shutter speeds* and *diaphragm openings*. He may use film in rolls or sheets.

The news photographer needs a *flash camera* which can be set up and adjusted quickly. He uses an assortment of lenses.

The commercial photographer who makes the kind of photos in this book uses a *studio camera* with a large negative and *ground glass* focusing.

Movie cameras are in a class by themselves. The home movie size is usually 8 mm (the width of the film). The professional photographer uses 35-mm cameras. 16 mm is in between. With a "still" camera you take one picture at a time, then move the film. The movie camera takes one at a time, too, but at the usual rate of 16, 24, or 32 pictures per second. When the film has been developed (it is then positive), it is projected on a screen at the same rate.

Camera Features. The camera is a machine that must be operated skill-

fully to get good pictures. You need to know the purpose of the following features:

View finder. This is a device in which you see the picture as it will be taken. On some cameras focusing is done through the finder; on others, however, it is done on a ground-glass back.

Focusing. The distance from the lens to the film is adjusted until the image in the view finder or on the ground glass is sharpest. Sometimes the focusing is done by setting the distance in feet.

Diaphragm. The amount of light entering the camera is controlled by the size of the diaphragm opening. The *stops* or "sizes" are found on the

Fig. 6.55.   How a simple camera works.

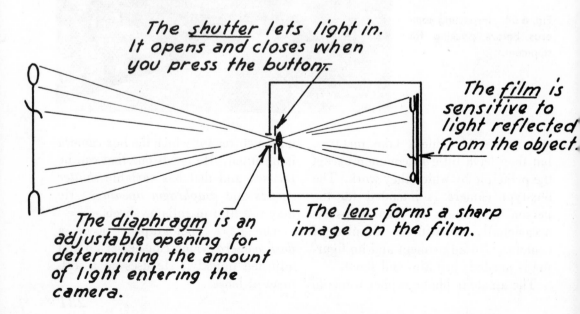

HOW A CAMERA TAKES A PICTURE

The <u>shutter</u> lets light in. It opens and closes when you press the button.

The <u>film</u> is sensitive to light reflected from the object.

The <u>diaphragm</u> is an adjustable opening for determining the amount of light entering the camera.

The <u>lens</u> forms a sharp image on the film.

THE DIAPHRAGM OPENING
determines the depth of focus in a picture.
The depth of focus is the distance from
the nearest to the farthest objects which
are in focus.

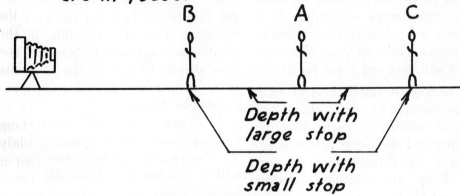

Fig. 6.56.   Depth of field and diaphragm openings.

lens mount. For a camera with an F. 4.5 lens the stops will usually be 4.5; 5.6; 8; 11; 16; and 22. The 4.5 opening admits twice as much light as does the 5.6, and the 5.6, twice as much as the 8, and so on. The smaller the opening the more of the picture will be in sharp focus.

Shutter. This is the device that determines for how long the light is permitted to enter the camera. Common shutter speeds are ⅟25, ⅟50, and ⅟100 second. More expensive cameras have both higher and lower speeds.

Exposure. Exposure is a combination of diaphragm opening and shutter speed. For example, using these given above, F. 4.5 at ⅟100 second gives the same exposure as 5.6 at ⅟50 second, and 8 at ⅟25 second. The first setting would stop fast action in the picture; the last would not. The first would have little depth of focus; the latter, much more.

Film

Many types of film are available for the same camera. If you are starting out in photography, use *orthochromatic* film (common brands are Verichrome and Plenachrome). It is an all-purpose film not sensitive to red light. *Panchromatic* film is sensitive to all colors and must be developed in total darkness.

How an image is formed on the film. The side of the film that is exposed to the light is coated with a light-sensitive *emulsion* which contains a compound of silver. When the light strikes the emulsion, the silver is affected. The image formed is not visible to the eye until the film has been treated with chemicals, a process called *developing*. This process changes the silver compound to metallic silver. Then the film is fixed in a fixing solution to make it insensitive

233

to light. The result is a negative which has its light and dark areas in reverse of the object photographed.

How to develop a roll of film. Follow these steps carefully. It is very easy to spoil a roll anywhere in the process. Use an *orthochromatic* film (it will have red paper on it).

1. Arrange 4 small trays of solutions as shown in Fig. 6.57. Use 12 to 16 oz of solution in each. Mix the developer and the fixing solutions according to the directions on the cartons. Keep all solutions between 65°F. and 68°F.

2. Turn on the red safelight and close the darkroom door. Unroll the paper on the film until the film appears. Grasp this end of the film and pull the paper until the other end of the film appears. Tear off the paper and hold the film firmly by each end in a large U so that it can't twist.

3. Dip one end in tray no. 1 and see-saw the film up and down, holding the U until it is wet all over. Drain and repeat this process in the developer tray. Note the time when you start. Work the film up and down just slowly enough to keep from slopping the developer, and for the time recommended. Drain and rinse several times in bath no. 2.

4. With the same technique treat the film in the fixer for two or three minutes. Then lay the film in the solution and agitate it frequently. The film should be left in the fixer for twice as long as it takes for the white coating to disappear.

5. Drain, then wash in a tray of running water for 30 minutes. Hang the film up and wipe both sides lightly with a wet sponge. When dry cut it up into negatives.

How to make a contact print. A contact print is a picture printed directly from and in contact with the negative. It is the same size as the negative. If your negatives are bright and clear, use a No. 2, or normal paper, preferably single weight, glossy. When the negatives are thin and pale, use a No. 3 or contrast paper; and when real black and thick, a No. 1 or soft paper. Mix the developer according to the directions and arrange the trays as shown in Fig. 6.57. Use a yellow-orange or yellow-green safelight.

Fig. 6.57. Arrange your solutions for developing like this.

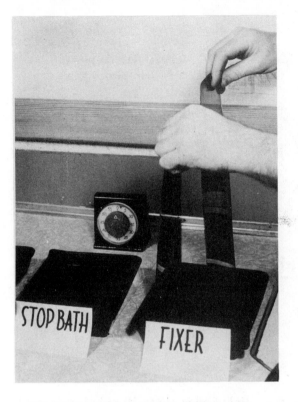

Fig. 6.58. The film removed from the spool is worked up and down in each tray. Grasp each end firmly.

1. Insert the negative, shiny side down, into the guide on the printer, with the mask adjusted to fit. Insert the paper, close the lid, and turn on the printing light. Time the first exposure by counting "one-thousand-one," "one-thousand-two," to "one-thousand-five," then turn off the light.

2. Slip the paper into the developer, wetting it all over quickly. Use developing tongs to keep it moving for the recommended time. Lift out, drain, and rinse it in tray no. 2 for a few seconds.

3. Immerse it in the fixer and keep it moving for a few seconds. After 15 minutes of fixing, prints should be washed in running water for 30 minutes. To dry a print, place it face down on a wet ferrotype plate, cover with a newspaper, and squeeze the water out with a *print* roller. When the print is dry, it comes loose by itself.

4. If, however, after the first few seconds in the fixer this particular print is too light, take another piece of paper and expose it twice as long. Develop this and then you can tell whether to change the time again. The longer the exposure the darker the print. If the first one was too dark, cut the time in half for the next print. Developing time is kept constant; the printing time is varied to produce the right contrast.

How to make an enlargement. Prints can be made larger than the negative by a process called *enlarging*. For your first attempts use a single weight, glossy paper, 5 by 7 in. and of normal contrast. Pick out a nega-

235

Fig. 6.59. Contact paper is placed glossy side down on the negative in the printer.

tive that is neither too light nor too black. Mix the developer for enlarging according to directions. Use trays just large enough to take the paper. A yellow-orange or yellow-green safelight is needed.

1. Place the negative, shiny side up, in the carrier in the enlarger. Adjust the easel to fit the paper, allowing ¼-in. margins. Insert a piece of plain white paper for focusing. In the dark darkroom turn on the enlarger light and bring the image into focus on the paper in the easel. Adjust the image for size and position and refocus it until it is as sharp as possible.

2. Cut some test strips of enlarging paper about an inch wide. Place one of these diagonally across the opening in the easel and put the rest back in the envelope. Turn on the enlarger

light and count to 10 as before, quickly placing a coin on the strip. Count to 20 and place another coin. Continue counting to 50 and turn off the light. This gives a series of exposures.

3. Develop this strip for the specified time, rinse, and fix as for contact prints. Examine the spots; the lightest is for an exposure of 10. Pick the spot that shows the most detail as the correct exposure time. Insert the sheet of enlarging paper and make that exposure. Develop, fix, wash, and dry as before.

Getting Started in Photography

The best way to get started is through your industrial arts program. If this is not possible, try to find a camera club and attend meetings. If

236

Fig. 6.60. The negative holder is inserted into the enlarger.

neither is possible, get a developing and printing kit from a camera store. The instructions are easy to follow. You can build much of your equipment. Any small room which you can completely black out will serve as the darkroom. See Fig. 6.63 for details on a printer and Fig. 6.65 for a safelight.

What is a good photo? Consider these measures of a good photograph each time you make one:

1. The print has good quality. It has a range of tones from white to black. It is not muddy. There are no stains from improper handling.

2. The subject has been well selected so that the picture includes only what is needed to tell the story. Make every picture tell a story. The background should not detract from it.

3. Those objects in the picture that should be sharp, are; the others are soft and fuzzy.

Some Things to Find Out

1. The early history of your local newspaper in your community. Talk to some old-timers.
2. Why antimony is used in type metal.
3. Why the letters on typewriter keys are arranged as they are.
4. Why "the pen is mightier than the sword."
5. How automobile license plates are printed.
6. How long you would have to serve as an apprentice before you could become a printer in your town.
7. How roll films are developed and printed in commercial processing plants.
8. How to read a photoelectric exposure meter.

Fig. 6.61. The enlarged print is made permanent in the fixing solution.

DEVELOPER   STOP BATH   FIXER

Fig. 6.62. A print made on glossy paper is washed and then rolled face down onto a wet ferrotype plate. When dry, the print lifts off and has a glossy surface.

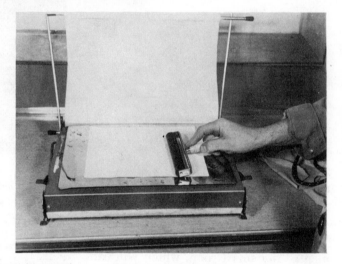

Fig. 6.63. A contact printer you can make.

CONTACT PRINTER

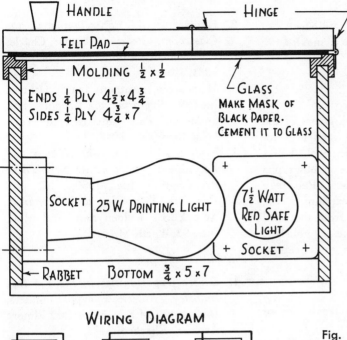

HANDLE   HINGE

FELT PAD

MOLDING ½ x ½

ENDS ¼ PLY 4½ x 4¾
SIDES ¼ PLY 4¾ x 7

GLASS
MAKE MASK OF
BLACK PAPER.
CEMENT IT TO GLASS

SOCKET   25 W. PRINTING LIGHT

7½ WATT
RED SAFE
LIGHT

SOCKET

RABBET   BOTTOM ¾ x 5 x 7

WIRING DIAGRAM

DOORBELL
BUTTON

PRINTING
LIGHT

SAFE
LIGHT

Fig. 6.64. Details of the contact printer.

Fig. 6.65. Make your own safe-light from a fruit juice can. The light filter of orange cellophane is cemented between two pieces of card. Use four to six thicknesses of the cellophane. The filter slides in a groove of sheet metal made by bending a narrow channel on a bar folder, as in Fig. 4.48. Solder the grooves to the bottom and sides of the opening. Use a 7½-watt red lamp.

9. How an aerial camera works.

10. What makes slow-motion movies.

Some Group Projects

Exhibits and displays

Tell the story of the development of the printing industry. Make a model of an old-time print shop. Find some old books and newspapers. Get some photographs of modern high-speed presses. Put these all together, with cards explaining the story. You might get help from the local printers' union and the local publisher, or write to newspapers in your capital city.

Production projects

1. Design and print a souvenir school calendar.
2. Print some posters announcing an industrial arts exhibit or a community hobby show.
3. Do a production job for the school board. Be sure to invite the members to attend your class so that you can explain the processes to them.

Service projects

1. Print a pamphlet about the library, about a historic site, or some other feature of your town.
2. Print a small handbook to be given to each new freshman student in your school. Your principal will probably take care of the writing.

Sources of Ideas and Information

Books

1. *Eastern Printers Guide.* This is an annual free to teachers. George Fein and Company, Inc., 509-519 Vine Street, Philadelphia, Pa.

2. Hunter, Dard. *Papermaking in the Classroom.* Peoria, Illinois: Charles E. Bennett Publishing Company, 1931.
3. Marinaccio, Anthony and Osburn, Burl N. *Exploring the Graphic Arts.* Scranton, Pa.: International Textbook Company, 1948.
4. Nesbitt, Alexander. *The History and Techniques of Lettering.* New York: Prentice-Hall, Inc., 1950.
5. *Printing Yearbook and Almanac.* New York: Walden Sons and Mott, Inc., 93 Worth St.

Pamphlets

1. *Career Opportunities in the Printing Industry.* American Type Founders, Department of Education, 200 Elmore Avenue, Elizabeth, N.J.
2. *From Forest to Writing Paper.* Hammermill Paper Company, 1579 E. Lake Road, Erie, Pa.
3. *Forestry and Paper.* P. H. Glatfeller Company, Spring Grove, Pa.
4. *How to Choose the Right Ink.* IPI Division, Interchemical Corporation, 67 W. 44th St., New York, N.Y.
5. *Modern Trends in Lithography.* IPI, see above.
6. *Processes That Made Printing History.* Samuel Bingham's Son Manufacturing Company, Chicago, Ill.
7. *Proof Readers' Marks.* The Mergenthaler Linotype Company, Brooklyn, N.Y.

Magazines

1. *Graphic Arts Index.* Free. International Graphic Arts Association, 412 National Savings and Trust Building, 719 Fifteenth St., N.W., Washington, D.C.

2. *The Graphic Arts Monthly*. Free. The Graphic Arts Monthly, 608 S. Dearborn St., Chicago, Ill.

Teaching Aids

1. *California Job Case*. A chart. Free. Hamilton Manufacturing Company, Two Rivers, Wis.
2. *Diagram of Paper Cutter*. Free. The Chandler Price Company, Cleveland, Ohio. Also, from the same source:
   Diagram of Platen Press.
   Oiling and Instruction Chart for Platen Presses.
3. *Fourdrinier Paper Making Machine*. Free. Hammermill Paper Company.
4. *Great Names, Great Designers, Great Papers*. Free. Eastern Corporation, Bangor, Maine.

5. *Printing Project Idea File*. American Type Founders.
6. *Printing Processes*. Free. International Paper Co., 220 East 42nd Street, New York, N. Y.

Free Films

1. *From Trees to Tribune*. Chicago *Tribune*, Public Service Office, Chicago, Illinois.
2. *Great White Trackway*. Hammermill Paper Company, Erie, Pennsylvania.
3. *Paper Work*. Modern Talking Picture Service, Inc., 45 Rockefeller Plaza, New York, N.Y.
4. *Park Row. Invention of the Linotype*. Mergenthaler Linotype Company, Brooklyn, New York.
5. *The Paper Made for You*. Gilbert Paper Company, Menasha, Wis.

Fig. 7.1.   The first factory in America was a glass plant, established in 1608 at Jamestown, Virginia. *(Courtesy: J. C. Harrington.)*

7 The CERAMIC INDUSTRIES

Clay and rock were among the first materials that prehistoric man used with hands as his only tools. He threw rocks in self-defense before he found that a club was better. He found that he could line the insides of baskets with clay to make them hold water. With his discovery of fire he could heat rocks and drop them into these baskets to heat the water. Some of these baskets were probably set too close to the fire, which burned away the reed but left hardened clay shells. When early man observed that clay became hard and strong by burning, the ceramic (se-*ram*-ik) industry was born. Begun as pottery making, the industry today includes the manufacturing of products from inorganic (nonvegetable), nonmetallic minerals, using high temperature heat, called *firing*. These products include those of clay, glass, enameled metals, cements, and plasters.

Occupations in the ceramic industries. Occupations in these industries are as varied as the products that are made. Different plants make dinnerware, art pottery, sanitary ware, refractories, brick, tile, insulators, glass and glass products, cements and plasters, and different processes are used in each. Many of the skilled and unskilled jobs are rapidly being replaced by automatic machinery. Since the 1930's, the clay products industries have probably done more of this converting than in all of their past history. In certain of the industries many of the skilled jobs can be had only through the process of apprenticeship; for example, mold makers, jiggermen, and decorators. An apprentice spends several years working

243

Fig. 7.2. A primitive potter lines a basket with clay.

with a skilled craftsman to learn the trade. The key man in a ceramic plant is the ceramic engineer who controls the materials and the processes used with them. His is a very technical job. Mechanical engineers and chemists are needed, too.

Centers of production. Brick, tile, and cement plants are found in every state. Potteries and glass plants are not so widely scattered. The pottery center of the world is in the East Liverpool, Ohio, area. The glass and glass products industries are centered chiefly in Ohio, West Virginia, and Pennsylvania.

The Clay Products Industries

Clay was the first of the ceramic materials used by man. It is one of the most abundant materials in the earth's crust. The Chinese were using it for pottery 7,500 to 10,000 years ago. They were the first to find a clay

that fired white, and from it they made the first *porcelain* (*por*-se-lin). They discovered that this clay, called *kaolin* (*kay*-o-lin), could be fired high enough to make it translucent and glasslike.

The *potter's wheel* was invented by the early Egyptians and, until the turn of this century, was a basic production process. It has been displaced by the *jigger*, which today automatically forms most of our plates, platters, cups, and saucers.

Early man placed his clay pots in the fire to become hard. Today ware is fired automatically in *kilns* (pronounced either "kils" or "kilns"), which move it continuously from cold, to hot, to cool.

PRODUCTS OF THE CLAY INDUSTRIES

Products used in houses, buildings, bridges, highways	Brick—common, face, fire, insulation
	Block—hollow building tile
	Conduits—large tile for carrying water, sewage, etc.

Drain tile—porous tile for draining swamps, lowlands, etc.
Flue liners—for chimneys
Tile—for floors, walls, roofs
Terra cotta—architectural decoration

Products used by industry
Abrasives—for grinding, cutting polishing, i.e., grinding wheels, abrasive cloth, and paper
Filters—for liquids
Insulation—against heat and cold, and electrical insulators
Laboratory equipment—chemical vats, apparatus
Refractories—heat resistant linings for furnaces, kilns, crucibles

Products used in the home
Art pottery
Dinnerware
Kitchenware
Sanitary ware
Stoneware

Personal products
Jewelry—man-made gems, ornaments
Pencil lead—made of clay and graphite
Medicines, dentures

A guide for the study of clay products manufacturing. The following steps represent basic processes used in the manufacture of clay products, listed in the usual order of application.

Basic steps in the preparation of clay

1. Mining—digging clays from the earth.
2. Crushing—breaking up lumps.
3. Grinding—breaking clay down into fine particles.
4. Blending—measuring and adding various ingredients to obtain the desired qualities of the clay.
5. Blunging—mixing with water in a large tank called a blunger (*blun*-jer).
6. Filtering—sieving to remove foreign matter. Iron is caught by magnets; other matter, by lawns (cloth sieves).

Fig. 7.3. Quarrying clay at the United States Quarry Tile Company. It will be used for wall and floor tile.

7. Pressing—squeezing out excess water, in a filter press.
8. Pugging—kneading to make the clay plastic, in a pug mill.
9. De-airing—removing air to make the clay dense. This is usually combined with pugging.

Basic methods for forming clay into products

10. Hand building—this is used only in small potteries.
11. Throwing—the potter's wheel is used when quantity production is not essential.
12. Jiggering—clay is shaped on a revolving mold by a stationary template (*temp*-lat) or pattern.
13. Dry pressing—clay powder is formed into objects in steel dies under tremendous pressure, for example, floor tile.

14. Ramming—moist clay is pressed into shape between the two halves of a plaster mold, to form such products as plates and saucers.
15. Extruding—Moist clay is forced through a die and emerges in the desired shape, for example, brick and tile.
16. Slip casting—liquid clay is poured into plaster molds and a thin layer adheres to the cavity. Then the excess is poured out, leaving vases, lamp bases, and the like.
17. Turning—semidry clay is turned to shape on a lathe to form electrical insulators, precision parts, and the like.
18. Molding—soft clay is pressed into molds, just as is done for brick.

Fig. 7.4. A potter throws a pot on the potters wheel.

Fig. 7.5. Forming cups by the hand jiggering method. The plaster mold shapes the outside; the metal template shapes the inside. The operator is the jiggerman. (*Courtesy: Onondaga Pottery Corp.*)

Fig. 7.6. An automatic jigger forms dinnerware. The man at the right is placing rolls of clay on the conveyor which feeds it to the jiggers at the lower center. (*Courtesy: Miller Pottery Equipment Co.*)

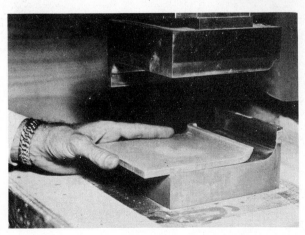

Fig. 7.7. Removing a wall tile from the steel dies which have pressed it into shape. Clay powder is used for floor and wall tile. (*Courtesy: United States Quarry Tile Co.*)

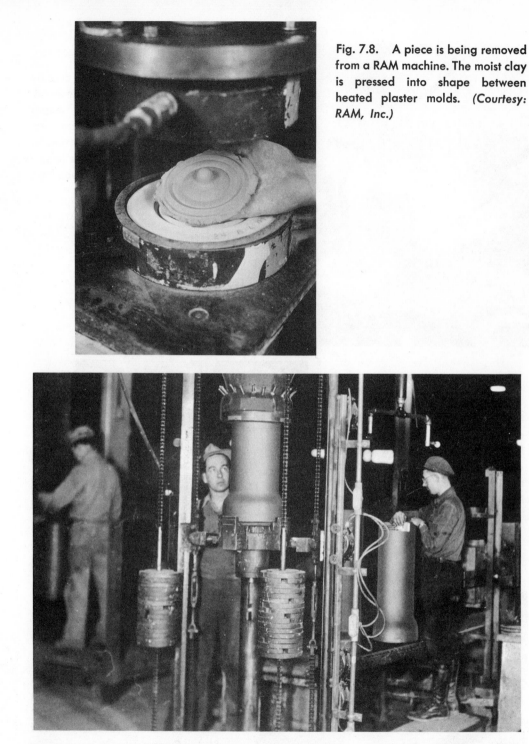

Fig. 7.8. A piece is being removed from a RAM machine. The moist clay is pressed into shape between heated plaster molds. *(Courtesy: RAM, Inc.)*

Fig. 7.9. Sewer tile is made by extrusion. The moist clay is forced through dies which give it shape. *(Courtesy: Robinson Clay Products Co.)*

248

Fig. 7.10. Cup handles are formed in gang molds. Liquid clay, called slip, is poured into the molds which absorb the water leaving the clay hard and shaped. *(Courtesy: Onondaga Pottery Co.)*

Basic processes used on the formed ware

19. Decorating—decals (decalcomanias), which are designs printed on paper in ceramic colors, are applied over or under the glaze.

    Lining, or banding—this is the application of border lines, done by hand and machine.

    Hand painting—this is done with underglaze and overglaze colors.

    Rubber stamping of designs is done by hand and machine.

    Silk screen printing is done by machine.

20. Glazing—the ware is covered with a coating which, when fired, becomes glasslike.

21. Firing—this is the key process common to all clay products. They are heated until the particles are fused together. Tunnel kilns are commonly used. The ware moves continuously, day and night. It goes around the circle in about 48 to 60 hours.

How dinnerware is made

The clay usually goes through the processes 1-9, inclusive and 12, 14, 16, 19, 20, and 21.

How brick is made

Brick, an entirely different product from dinnerware, goes through processes 1, 2, 3, 8, 9, 15 or 18, 20 (for some types), and 21.

Planning Your Projects. Until you have had considerable experience with clay building there isn't much point in spending a lot of time in planning a project. For example, dimensions will not be the same before and after firing because clay shrinks as much as 10 to 15 per cent. To work accurately to dimensions you would have to know the exact amount of shrinkage so that you could allow for it. The clay may take a form different from the one you intended, as you build, or as it dries. Effective plan-

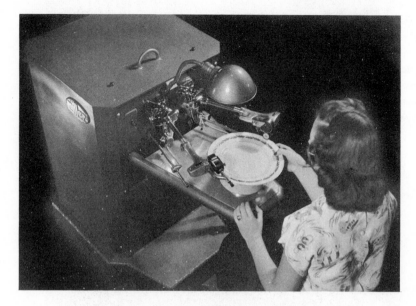

Fig. 7.11. Lines of color are applied automatically by this banding machine. *(Courtesy: Miller Pottery Equipment Co.)*

Fig. 7.12.   A large circular tunnel kiln. Green (unfired) ware goes in on the right, is fired, cooled, and then emerges at the left for unloading. *(Courtesy: Ferro Enamel Corp.)*

ning for clay products requires a knowledge of the material and what can be done with it, as well as the skill to make it behave.

It is better for you as a beginner to start with an idea for a simple project, make a pattern or sketch if necessary, and then proceed at once to build it, without worrying about whether it comes out exactly as intended. When you have made several pieces, you will be able to plan others more wisely.

Contemporary Ceramists. The list of expert ceramists grows rapidly with today's increasing interest in clay work. Look for pieces by Don Shreckengost, designer for the Homer Laughlin China Company; Viktor Shreckengost, Cleveland; Eugene Deutch, Chicago; Charles Lakofsky, Bowling Green, Ohio; Edwin and Mary Schier, Durham, New Hampshire; Lee R. Rosen, New York; Paul Bogatay, Columbus; Carleton Ball, Carbondale, Illinois; Bernard Leach, foremost English potter; to name but a few.

Designing your projects. If a clay product does well the job it was intended to do, it is well designed whether it is a bowl for your puppy or a brick. It is as easy to make pottery of good design as to make it otherwise. Use the simple curves and shapes which grow out of the function of the piece. They are more pleasing than fancy ones unrelated to the function. Be rather critical of your designs; compare them with those done by experts. "Cook up" your own

ideas rather than copy what you see in stores or in magazines. It is much more fun. Ask your friends and your teacher to help you decide which of your ideas is best.

Mother Nature has a huge assortment of examples of interesting shapes. Gourds and smooth rocks suggest bowls; flat stones suggest dishes and trays. Leaf shapes can be used for trays as well as for decoration; for example, willow and white oak leaves. Whenever you decorate a piece try to make it a part of the pot, rather than something extra added for effect. If the piece looks as well without the decoration, don't add it.

Look for pictures of pieces exhibited at the annual Syracuse National Ceramic Show sponsored by the Syracuse Museum of Fine Arts. They are outstanding in beauty and craftsmanship.

How to make things of clay. Clay is one of the easiest of all materials for you to use. It requires the fewest tools. With your hands you are free to express your ideas in clay as you are in no other material, so take advantage of this freedom and see what you can create.

What clay is. Clay is really rock. This rock was formed ages ago by the intense heat of volcanic action, and since then it has decomposed into clay. When mixed with water, clay becomes soft, plastic, and easily shaped; when fired, it becomes hard, strong, and permanent. There are many kinds of clay, each suited to different purposes. The

Fig. 7.13. A set of dinnerware made by F. Carleton Ball.

common clay that you may find along a creek or in an excavation is the kind that is used for brick, tile, and some art pottery. The purest of clays is kaolin, or china clay. It is used in porcelain dinnerware and such clay products as fire white. Clay used in manufacturing is often blended from several different ingredients. In a pottery you will see, for example, large bins of kaolin, probably from Georgia or Florida; *ball clay* from Tennessee; *feldspar* from South Dakota; and *flint* from Michigan.

Selecting a clay. The clay for pottery, such as is suggested here, should be suited to modeling and should not fire higher than your kiln allows. An

underfired clay has little strength and takes *glazes* poorly. A clay that fires between *cones* 07–04 is recommended. (See page 266.)

Keeping clay moist. The easiest way to keep clay moist is to store it in a plastic bag such as can be purchased at the dime store. To keep your project moist from one period to the next, slip it into a plastic bag.

Preparing clay for use. If your clay is a powder, mix it with water according to the recommendations of the manufacturer. If it is moist, it may be ready for use. Cut a chunk in two on the *wedging wire.* If there are no holes, the clay has probably been pugged and is ready to use. If there are

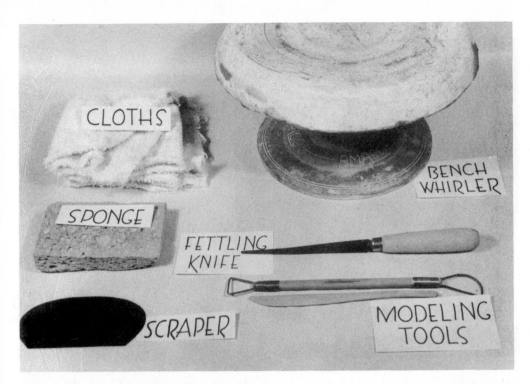

Fig. 7.14. Some of the tools used by a potter.

Fig. 7.15. To keep your pottery moist, slip it into a plastic bag.

Fig. 7.16. A wedging bench on which clay is made more plastic and from which air is driven.

holes or lumps, you should wedge the clay. As you cut the chunk in two, slam one piece down hard on the other. Repeating this a dozen times or so drives out the air and makes the clay dense and plastic. In industry this is done to clay in a pugmill and de-airing machine.

Welding clay. To stick two pieces of clay together permanently they must be equally moist. When they are soft and plastic, press them together as you gently twist them back and forth. If they are stiff, put a layer of *slip* (liquid clay) between them and press them together. To add a handle, use slip in the joint and twist and press at the same time.

Smoothing clay surfaces. Use wet fingers or a moist sponge on clay that is moist; use a barely moist sponge on clay that is dry. Too much water cracks dry clay.

254

Drying your ware. Some clays can be left to dry out in the room without cracking; others must be dried slowly. If your clay cracks, use a plastic bag to retard the drying. Ware that is fully dried in the room is *bone dry.* Ware that is half dry, moist but not plastic, is *leather hard.* Ware that is dry and ready for firing is *greenware.*

How to make a coiled pot. This is the best hand process for such pieces as pitchers, bowls, and lamp bases.

1. Wedge your clay and roll a soft plastic piece into a ball about 1½ in. in diameter. Place this at the center of a *bat* (plaster slab) on a bench whirler and press it flat with a palm to about ⅜ in. thick.

2. Cut this clay bottom to shape with a sharp pencil.

3. Take another piece of clay and roll it out into a rope on the table until it is about as thick as a fountain pen.

Fig. 7.17. Wedge your clay until no holes appear when it is cut by the wire.

FREE FORMS
ARE FUN TO MAKE

Fig. 7.18. Some suggestions for pottery, by Fred Vollman.

255

Fig. 7.19. Some coil-built pieces unglazed. This is called bisque ware.

Fig. 7.20. Some coil-built pieces glazed. This is called glost ware.

256

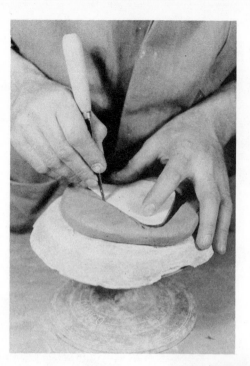

Fig. 7.21. Cutting the bottom of a pot to shape.

Fig. 7.22. Rolling out a clay rope for coil building.

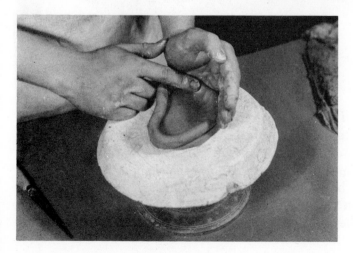

Fig. 7.23. Welding the first coil to the base.

257

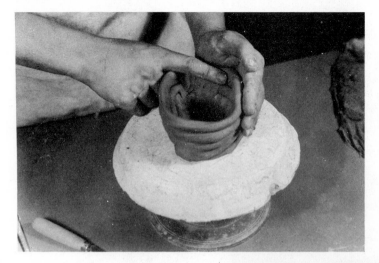

Fig. 7.24. Adding the final coil.

Fig. 7.25. When the pot is leather-hard, hollow out the underside, leaving a foot or rim for a base.

Coil this rope around, and on top of, the base and cut it off to the right length.

4. With a forefinger or modeling tool weld the rope to the base on the inside as you back it up on the outside with your other hand. Then weld the outside, backing it up from the inside.

5. Add one coil at a time, welding as you go. Vary the diameter of the coils to fit the shape of the pot. When the pot is finished, let it dry leather hard, so that you can do the smoothing.

258

Fig. 7.26. A mold of moist clay is formed to the shape of the inside of the desired bowl.

Fig. 7.27. A slab of clay is rolled to a uniform thickness between two sticks.

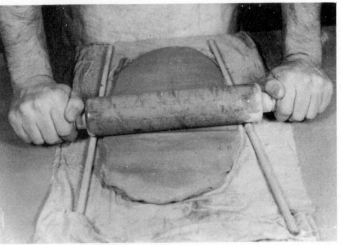

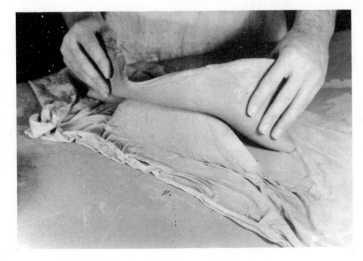

Fig. 7.28. Lay the slab over the mold which has been covered with a moist cloth, then cut it to shape.

Fig. 7.29. Smooth the dish with a moist sponge.

6. Then turn the pot upside down and with a *wire loop tool* scoop out the underside about ⅛ in. deep, leaving a foot, or ridge, around the outside. Sponge the pot smooth.

7. With a sharp pencil mark your name and the date on the underside, then set the pot aside to dry.

How to make a low dish. 1. Cut out a full-size paper pattern of the desired shape; trace it on a piece of cardboard and cut it out.

2. Shape a piece of clay on the bench to fit this outline and to fit the form of the inside of the dish. This is the mold, bottom side up. Stretch a damp cloth over it.

3. Wedge a chunk of clay so that it is soft and plastic, but not sticky. On a damp cloth press this clay out into a flat sheet, about ½ in. thick, using the heel of your hand. Lay a damp cloth over it and with a rolling pin roll it to thickness.

4. Peel the clay from the cloth and lay it over the mold. Smooth it to the shape of the mold and trim the edge.

260

5. Roll out a rope for the foot and weld it in place.

6. Let the dish dry just enough that it will hold its shape, then lift it off and smooth the edge. Add your name and date, let it dry to leather hard, and smooth it with a moist sponge.

How to model a figure. 1. Cut and roughly shape the parts.

2. Weld them together with slip.

3. Bend and shape the figure to give the expression you want. Let it stiffen until it will just hold its shape.

4. Model in the details or add them as separate pieces of clay.

5. Any part of the figure that is thicker than one inch should be hollowed out to prevent cracking in drying and firing.

How to slip-cast pottery. You can make several pieces just alike by means of slip-casting in *plaster of paris molds*. This method is used in industry to produce quantities of identical ware, for example, art pottery, tea pots, electrical insulators, and sanitary ware. Slip is liquid clay. When

TRY SOME
OF YOUR OWN!

°ANIMALS
AND BIRDS°

F. VOLLMAN

Fig. 7.30.   Some ideas for clay figures, by Fred Vollman.

Fig. 7.31. The rabbit is decorated with underglaze colors. The rough texturing was done with a sharp modeling tool.

Fig. 7.32. Sticking the parts of a figure together. When they are all welded, bend and shape the piece to get the expression you want.

Fig. 7.33. Very fine detail is possible in clay. The paper clip gives an idea of size.

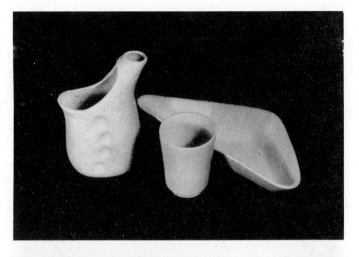

Fig. 7.34. An assortment of pieces made by slip casting.

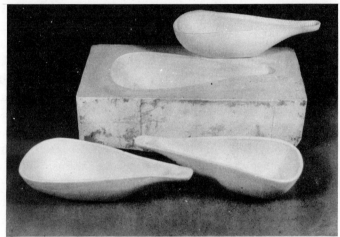

Fig. 7.35. These dishes were slip cast in this mold.

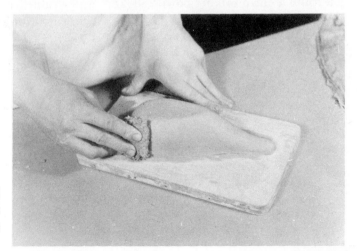

Fig. 7.36. The clay model is placed upside down on a board around which cardboard is tacked.

it is poured into the plaster mold, water is absorbed by the mold and a clay shell is formed in the cavity. After a few minutes the slip is poured out and the cast is allowed to stiffen until the mold can be taken apart.

Make the model. 1. Make the full-size model of solid clay. Build it bottom side up on a piece of board which is about one inch larger on each side than the model. Waterproof the clay side of the wood with paste wax before you add the clay.

2. Tack a strip of cardboard around the block. It should be high enough to allow about an inch of plaster above the model. Be sure there are no leaks in this box.

Determine the amount of plaster needed. One pint of water mixed with 1½ lb of pottery plaster makes 35 cu in. of plaster. Find the volume of the box, subtract the volume of the model, and divide the remainder by 35 to get the number of pints.

Mix the plaster. 1. Measure the water into a clean mixing bowl. Shake the plaster into the water and let it soak for three or four minutes. Use either the Regular grade or the No. 1 grade of pottery plaster. The latter sets slower.

2. Slip a hand into the bowl and, keeping it below the surface, stir until the plaster is ready to pour. In three to five minutes, when it is thick as a heavy malted milk, pour it quickly over the mold. Wipe the bowl clean immediately with some crumpled paper, then rinse with water. Never pour plaster down a drain. It hardens under water.

3. After about thirty minutes the box can be taken off and the clay model removed. Rinse out the cavity and set the mold aside to dry.

Make the slip. A ready-made slip is preferred. Follow the manufacturer's instructions for mixing and aging. If this is not available, soak some of your dry clay scrap in water until it can be stirred into a heavy, smooth paste. A gallon of this will make a great many casts. Mix in more water until it is like heavy cream. Sieve it through a 30-mesh screen.

Fig. 7.37. Plaster is poured over the mold.

Fig. 7.38. A kiln loaded for a bisque fire. The cone is placed where it can be seen through the spy hole in the door.

Pour the slip. 1. When the mold is dry, it is ready to use. If it feels warm it is dry; if cool, it is wet. Sieve the slip just before using.

2. Pour the cavity full, noting the time on your watch. As the level drops add slip. After five minutes scrape the edge of the cavity to see how thick the wall is. The longer the slip is left in, the thicker the wall.

3. When the wall is about $\frac{3}{16}$ in. thick, pour out the slip and let the mold drain, upside down. In about an hour the clay shell will have shrunk free. When it is stiff enough to hold its shape, remove and trim. The mold should dry again before using.

How to fire your ware. Clay becomes hard and strong with firing because some of the particles melt and fuse all of the ingredients together. It must be fired high enough to get strong but not too high because it will warp and slump. The manufacturer of your clay recommends the firing range. If, for example, it is cone 07–04, you should not fire it higher than cone 04 nor lower than 07. Cone 05

may be just right. The potter's furnace is a kiln.

The bisque fire. The *bisque fire* is the first fire and is as hot or hotter than other firings. The ware must be bone dry before firing or it may explode. In loading, do as follows:

1. Arrange the pieces to conserve space. Small pieces may be placed inside large ones. Put those of uniform height on the same shelf.

2. Place the cones where they can be seen through the spy hole and where they will be free to bend without touching the ware.

3. Close the kiln and turn on the low heat for an hour, then medium for an hour, and then high until the desired temperature is reached. At this point shut off the heat and let the kiln cool to room temperature before opening. Different kilns require somewhat different operation. Follow the manufacturer's recommendations.

The glost fire. This is the glaze fire which fuses the glaze to the ware. Loading requires much care so that pieces neither fuse together nor fuse

265

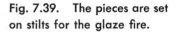

Fig. 7.39. The pieces are set on stilts for the glaze fire.

to the shelves. Each piece must be placed on a *setter*, which for your ware will be a *stilt*. Use as large stilts as possible. Place the pieces not closer than ¼ inch. Select the cones to suit the glazes, place them, and fire as for the bisque. In any one fire all the glazes should mature at the same cone.

Temperature indicators. You need some means for telling when the kiln is ready to shut off. If the kiln is equipped with an accurate *pyrometer* it is just a matter of reading the dial.

Pyrometric cones are used as temperature guides, too. A cone is a slender clay pyramid which softens and bends with heat. The correct cone

or cones is selected to match the maturing temperature of the clay or glaze. The following information is for Orton Pyrometric Cones.

Cone	Temperature Equivalent	Cone	Temperature Equivalent
020	1202	07	1814
019	1220	06	1859
018	1328	05	1904
017	1418	04	1940
016	1463	03	2039
014	1526	01	2093
012	1607	1	2120
010	1643	10	2381
08	1742	20	2786

Set the cone in a plaque of clay. If your clay matures at cone 05, use cone 05. Cone bases are cut at the correct angle for setting so that the

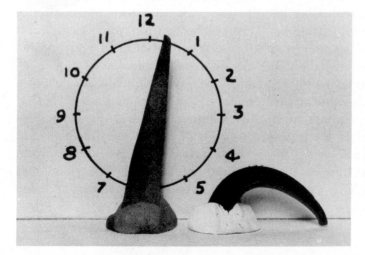

Fig. 7.40. The upright cone is set at the proper angle. The kiln should be shut off when the cone tip is at 6 o'clock, or before.

cone bends against the flat side. Cones are read by the position of the tip as at 3 o'clock, 4 o'clock, and 6 o'clock on the face of a clock. The maximum heat indication for a cone is at 6 o'clock. Added heat melts it and makes it useless. Shut off your kiln when the cone tip is at 6 o'clock.

Glazes. A glaze is a glasslike coating fused to the clay to add usefulness and beauty. It makes ware waterproof and in addition makes it easier to clean.

Selecting a glaze. The best glaze for you to use is one that flows in melting. It may be glossy or dull, transparent or opaque. It preferably should melt at a lower temperature than that to which the clay was fired. For example, if your clay fires to cone 05, then the glaze should mature at cone 06 or lower.

To find the best color for a particular pot make some tests. Take some pieces of clay about half the size of golf balls and press them into little bowls. Scratch numbers on the underside for identification, then dry, and fire them. Try your glazes first on these. Make a set of samples as follows, applying each to a different test piece.

1. Take a pair of glazes and mix together a teaspoon of each.

2. Apply a coat of one of these glazes, then lay a coat of the other on top.

3. Reverse the above order.

Try several pairs of glazes in these combinations, then add a third color and repeat the trials.

What makes the color. Ceramic colors are usually the oxides of certain metals. Rust is an oxide of iron. Browns, reds, tans, and blacks can be made from iron oxide. Copper oxide gives blues, greens, blacks, or reds; cobalt gives blue. If you have time to experiment with such oxides you are in for some surprises.

How to apply glazes. Ready-made glazes are usually sold in powder form. Add water a little at a time and stir until the mixture is like thick cream. Brush it through an 80- or 100-mesh sieve to break up lumps, then add water until it is like thin cream. Give the bisque pot a quick rinse in running water to remove dust and finger marks. With a varnish brush lay on a heavy coating, about $\frac{1}{32}$ in. thick. Do not brush it like paint. Cover the inside first. Let the glaze dry before firing. Clean the foot so it won't stick to the stilt in firing.

Glaze defects. Once in a while a glaze behaves badly. Rather than feel discouraged, try to find the cause and the cure. Here are some defects and their remedies.

1. Sandpaper surface—the roughness means that the glaze is too thin. Next time add a second coat.

2. Crazing—the glaze has a fine network of cracks. It was underfired or on too thick.

3. Crawling—the glaze pulls up in lumps leaving bare spots. This is usually due to dust or fingermarks

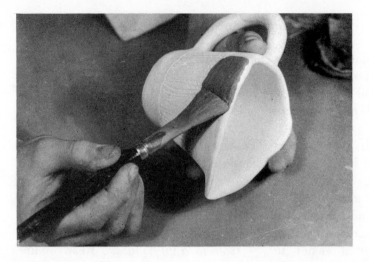

Fig. 7.41. Glaze applied with a brush should be laid on, not brushed out.

on the bisque or to the glaze being applied too heavily.

How to decorate pottery. There are so many ways to decorate pottery that we can not describe them all. The following, in addition to glazes, are recommended because they are always appropriate and they are easily done.

1. Finger marks and tool marks lend interest to handmade pottery. They tell how the piece was made and they provide textures that make unusual patterns under a glaze.

2. Incising is an ancient method for applying designs. They are scratched into the leather-hard surface. Try a sharp pencil for fine lines and a modeling tool for broad. The grooves may be filled in with a contrasting color of clay or with *engobes*, which are colored clays.

3. *Sgraffito* is a technique developed long ago in Italy. Paint on a coat of an engobe, of a color contrasting to that of the fired clay, on leather-hard clay. With a modeling tool, nail, toothpick, or other such tool

scratch through the engobe to expose the clay. After bisque firing, apply a transparent glaze.

4. Designs can be painted on leather-hard clay with engobes or *underglaze* colors. After bisque firing you should apply a transparent glaze.

5. Carving is easily done in clay. Outline the design on the leather-hard clay and then cut away the unwanted clay. Fine detail will likely be hidden by the glaze.

6. Invent some decorating methods of your own. Try them on samples first.

Good housekeeping makes good sense. The clay you use is clean even though it may look like mud, and it must be kept clean if you want good results. Listen—

1. Before rolling your clay on a bench make sure there is no dust or dried clay on it.

2. You will spoil your clay if you wedge it on a clay-crusted wedging bench.

268

Fig. 7.42. Incising (cutting in) a design on leather-hard clay.

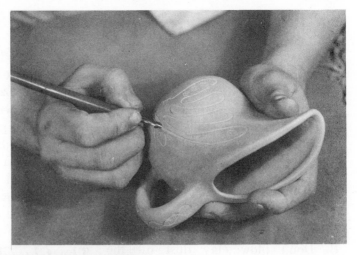

Fig. 7.43. Scratching a design through a layer of a contrasting color of clay or glaze shows the clay body underneath. This is called sgraffito.

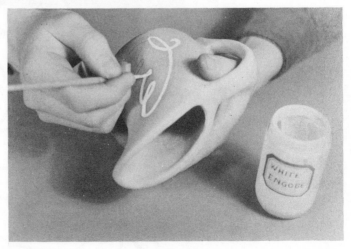

Fig. 7.44. Painting on a design with engobes (colored clays). Use them like tempera colors. Put them on greenware for best results.

3. Wash your tools before the clay hardens, to save time.
4. Rinse out bowls, pans, and sponges before using.
5. Keep dry or liquid glazes covered when not in use.
6. Take pity on the sink. Don't wash any more clay than necessary down the drain.
7. Rinse your hands frequently so that they don't get crusty.
8. Don't blow clay dust off the bench; wipe it up with a damp cloth.
9. After washing your hands at the end of the period, "excavate" beneath your fingernails.
10. If you get clay on your clothes, let it dry, then brush it off.

Safety makes sense. 1. Never open the kiln until the ware is cool enough to handle. This protects the ware, the kiln, and your fingers.

2. Watch for razor-sharp burrs on the bottoms of pieces being unloaded from a glaze fire. These can be chipped off with an old file, but watch for flying chips.
3. Such burrs can be ground smooth on a grinder. Use a face shield. Hold the pot lightly against the wheel, but do not use the tool rest.
4. Spilled slip is slippery.

The Glass Industry

Glass is as old as the earth. Nature made the first glass through the intense heat of volcanic action. Back in the Stone Age, primitive man made arrowheads, knives, mirrors, and jewelry from obsidian, a volcanic glass. If you have a collection of rocks, you probably have some samples of obsidian. It is hard, smooth, glossy, and usually black,

Fig. 7.45. A primitive Egyptian glass worker.

although it may be brown, red, or green.

The first method for making hollow ware of glass involved the dipping of a sand core packed around a metal rod into molten glass and then winding the trailing tail around the core. Several dippings were necessary.

The use of the blowpipe was discovered by Phoenician glass workers about two or three hundred years B.C. The worker dipped the end of a hollow metal tube into molten glass and gathered a ball of it. Then by blowing, turning, and swinging the glass bulb he shaped it into the desired form. This invention is considered one of the great discoveries in history since it made glass products available to all people. To this time they had been luxuries. The use of molds for blowing and pressing followed and further simplified the production of hollow ware. Rolling and drawing processes made sheet and tube glass possible.

TYPICAL GLASS PRODUCTS

Products used in buildings	Windows Block Plate glass	Wall panels Insulation— foam glass Glass fiber
Products used in the home	Lighting fixtures Mirrors Tables	Dishes Art glassware Book ends
Lighting products	Lamps Signs Television Photography	Signals Projectors Insulation
Products used by industry	Glass piping Flasks, pots Bottles, retorts Jewel bearings	Chemical apparatus Optical instruments, lenses Filters Insulation, insulators
Other products	Safety glass Bullet-proof glass	

How glass is made. Glass is a close relative of clay chemically, but in other ways it is quite different. It is not dug out of the earth and used. It is shaped while hot and soft and hardens on cooling.

Batch mixing. The raw materials, silica sand, lime, potash, soda, lead oxide, cullet (crushed glass), and metallic oxides for color as in ceramic glazes—for example, cobalt for blues, copper for greens, and gold for reds—are added in the correct proportions for the type of glass desired.

Melting. The batch is melted in a firebrick-lined furnace, usually gas fired, to temperatures from 1800 to 2800° F approximately, depending on the type of glass. It becomes soft and viscous like molasses.

Forming and shaping. Glass is shaped while in the molten state. *Blown* by mouth or machine into cast-iron molds, it produces hollow ware.

Molten glass is dropped into the cavity of a mold and a plunger *presses* it into shape.

Glass is formed into sheets by *rolling* between large steel rolls like clothes through a wringer on a washing machine.

Glass tubing is formed by *drawing*. It is pulled through a die which determines the size and shape.

Annealing and tempering. As soon as the glass has been formed it is reheated in a furnace called a *lehr,* to a temperature somewhat less than the

Fig. 7.46. In the manufacture of plate glass the batch is automatically injected into huge furnaces. A batch consists of carefully measured amounts of soda ash, salt cake, silica sand, lime, and other chemicals depending on the type of glass being made. After the glass is "cooked" at about 2800° F. the fiery mass is ejected by gravity from the other end of the furnace between huge steel water-cooled forming rolls. *(Courtesy: Pittsburgh Plate Glass Co.)*

GLASS FORMING METHODS

MAKING GLASS TUBE

MOLTEN GLASS IS POURED
ONTO A REVOLVING MANDREL.
IT SLIDES OFF AS A TUBE.

CUTTER

AIR IS BLOWN THROUGH
IT TO KEEP IT FROM COLLAPS-
ING UNTIL IT HARDENS.

BLOWING GLASS IN A MOLD

AIR

BLOW
IRON

GLASS

MOLD

HINGE

MOLTEN GLASS IS
GATHERED ON THE END
OF THE BLOW IRON.
A BUBBLE IS BLOWN
AND INSERTED IN THE
OPEN MOLD.
THE MOLD IS
CLOSED AND THE
BUBBLE IS BLOWN
TO FILL THE
MOLD.

WHEN
COOL, THE
GLASS
HOLDS ITS
SHAPE.

MAKING SHEET GLASS

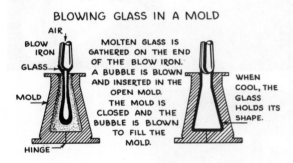

AS THE GLASS TRAVELS OVER
ROLLERS, IT COOLS
INTO A SHEET.

MOLTEN GLASS IS
DRAWN THROUGH
ROLLERS.

PRESSING GLASS

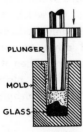

PLUNGER

MOLD

GLASS

A "GOB" OF
MOLTEN GLASS
IS PLACED IN
THE MOLD. THE
PLUNGER FORCES
THE GLASS TO
FILL THE MOLD.

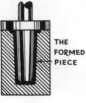

THE
FORMED
PIECE

Fig. 7.48. Cake dishes in the making. As a gob of hot glass hits the mold, it is immediately whisked away on a steaming merry-go-round mechanism called a rotary press. Here, automatic plungers stamp it into final form. *(Courtesy: Corning Glass Works.)*

Fig. 7.49. Here at the forming rolls plate glass begins to take form. As it leaves the rolls it passes through lehrs. These are ovens in long tunnels in which the glass is annealed, and cooled down to room temperature. Then it is cut into large plates. *(Courtesy: Pittsburgh Plate Glass Co.)*

274

softening point. This annealing relieves strains and prevents cracks that would otherwise result.

Annealing followed by quick chilling increases the strength of glass and is called *tempering*.

Grinding and polishing. The surfaces of sheet glass are ground and polished to make it smooth and easy to see through.

Decorating. The techniques used for decorating glass are different from

Fig. 7.50. These revolving discs, using a sand and emery abrasive, grind the plate glass to uniform thickness, and remove bumps. Polishing is the next operation. It is similarly done. The revolving discs are covered with felt and use rouge (iron oxide) to produce a high polish. (*Courtesy: Pittsburgh Plate Glass Co.*)

Fig. 7.51. Kodak camera lenses are ground and polished by machine. Notice how the lenses are arranged on the curved polishing heads.

those used for clay. Decoration is cut, ground, etched, sand blasted, painted, gilded, silvered, stained, and fired on with enamels.

How to cut sheet glass. With a little practice you can cut window glass easily and quickly. The trick is to score an unbroken line on one surface from edge to edge. The glass breaks evenly on this line. If it breaks elsewhere, it is because the line was not evenly and completely scored.

Tools and equipment. A flat level table, a piece of soft wallboard larger than the glass, a sharp glass cutter, a pair of canvas gloves, and some scrap pieces of window glass are needed for your glass cutting.

The cutting. The wallboard provides a flat surface for supporting glass. Make your practice cuts on the scrap glass.

1. Start with the cutter wheel at the far edge; press firmly, and with a smooth, uniform stroke draw the cutter toward you across the glass. You must make the score in *one* stroke. Do not retrace the score; the cutter will be dulled and made useless.

2. Practice until you can make the complete cut in one stroke, before you try it on good glass.

3. Place the glass score over the edge of the wallboard and table. Hold the one side down firmly, grasp the other and press down sharply, and the glass will snap in two.

4. Now make some practice cuts against a straight edge before you cut your glass to size.

How to smooth glass edges. *With abrasive powder.* This method is recommended for smoothing edges of flat glass as well as those of cut bottles, jugs, and the like. Sprinkle some coarse abrasive powder on a piece of plate glass or a flat cast-iron block. Add enough water to eliminate

276

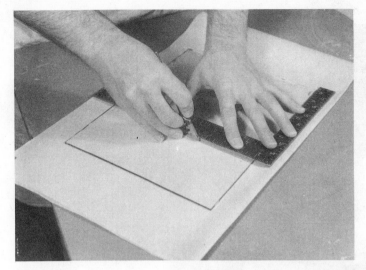

Fig. 7.52. How to cut a piece of glass. It is being scored with the cutter.

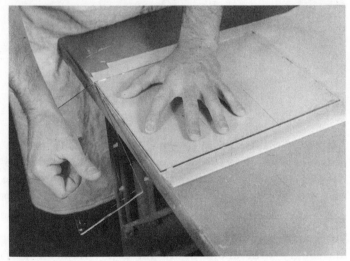

Fig. 7.53. The glass snaps in two easily when it has been evenly scored.

any dust. Holding the glass in both hands, slowly rub it back and forth edgewise over the abrasive. When the rough edges are cut away, use a finer abrasive.

With power sander. A wet sander will speed up the grinding. Be sure the belt has silicon carbide abrasive. Do not use a power sander unless water can be used with it for cooling. Hold the glass edgewise and firmly but lightly against the belt.

How to cut off a bottle. Cutting a bottle in two is not difficult with the tool described here. You can easily make it. The current should be only enough to heat the wire. An auto storage battery with a rheostat, or a toy transformer, will provide sufficient current for this purpose. It is not advisable to connect it directly to 110/15 volts.

To use the tool, clamp the resistance wire loop around the bottle, adjusting

277

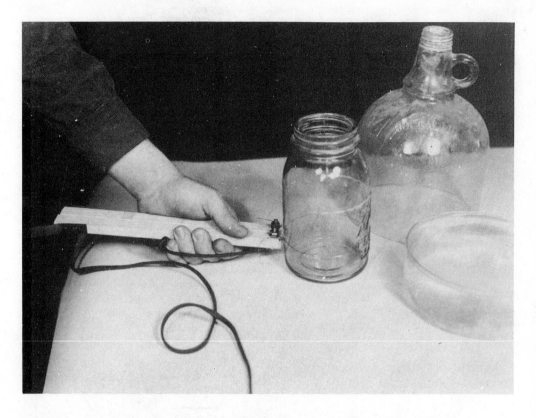

Fig. 7.54. You can easily cut glass bottles and jugs with this simple cutter. The resistance wire is drawn snugly around the bottle and is heated for a few seconds. Plunging the bottle into cold water completes the cutting. The gallon jug at the right was cut with this tool. The idea was obtained from the Corning Glass Works.

the length with the screws so that it fits snugly with about a $\frac{1}{16}$ in. gap between the terminals to prevent a short circuit.

Turn on the current for about twenty seconds, shut it off, then quickly remove the clamp and immerse the bottle in a pail of cold water. This sudden chilling should crack the bottle cleanly. If not, increase the current for the next try.

Drilling a hole through glass. Holes can be cut through glass with an abrasive but not with an ordinary drill. Use a short length of brass or

copper tubing of the same outside diameter as the desired hole. Slot one end with a hack saw about $\frac{1}{16}$ in. deep to make it easier to keep the abrasive cutting.

Insert the drill in the chuck of a drill press which is set for its slowest speed. Place a soft wallboard pad under the glass and build a dike of clay on the glass around the hole location. In this put about a half teaspoon of No. 120 silicon carbide grit and about a teaspoon of water. Use only enough pressure to keep the drill cutting. Too much pressure will crack the

278

Fig. 7.55. Glass can be drilled almost as easily as metal. A piece of aluminum tubing is being used here.

glass. Keep the abrasive fed into the drill with a small paintbrush. Along with this you will need a good supply of patience because glass cuts slowly.

Glass blowing. The glass blower that you may have seen at work at a fair or exposition is known as a *lamp worker* among glass craftsmen. From soft glass tubes and rods he fashions vases, ships, birds, horses, jewelry, and the like in sparkling colors and with amazing skill. As for most skilled craftsmen, his techniques look much simpler than they are. He heats the glass over gas burners until it is plastic but not melted. Then he can draw it out into hairlike threads, blow it into beautiful forms, and otherwise shape it.

The Porcelain Enamel Industry

Porcelain enamel is a vitreous (glasslike) coating fused to a metal base at high temperatures varying from about 1000 to 1600°F. It is not porcelain as in clay products. The industry that has developed around this process got its start in this country just before the turn of the past century. The first porcelain enameling on ferrous metals here was done on the insides of cast-iron kettles and pots. By 1900 enameled bath tubs, sinks, and lavatories were being produced in quantity. Since 1925 porcelain enameling on sheet steel has become the major part of the industry. At present, enameling on aluminum with low-

279

Fig. 7.56. Edward Winter is one of America's foremost enamelers of murals on steel. He is shown here holding the drawing used in making the huge panel of the city of Cleveland.

temperature enamel is being perfected.

The early Egyptians successfully fused vitreous enamel to bronze and copper. To decorate their armor, they made shallow hollows in the metal, filled them with the enamel, and fused it with heat.

Enameling for art purposes reached perfection long before industrial enameling in foreign countries. In the United States industrial enameling got a head start; art enameling is only now really coming into its own. The center of the movement is Cleveland, Ohio. One of the most famous American enamelists today is Edward Winter of Cleveland, whose steel panels and murals are superbly done. Other well-

known enamelists include Kenneth Bates, Cleveland; Harold Tischler, New York City; Karl Drerup, Compton, N. H.; Mitzi Otten, New York City. Look for examples or pictures of their work. After you have done some enameling, you will truly appreciate their artistry and craftsmanship.

PORCELAIN ENAMEL PRODUCTS

Products used in structural work	Prefabricated building Wall panels Theater and store fronts Outdoor signs Wall tile
Products used by industry	Chemical tanks, piping Hospital equipment Plumbing ware Scientific equipment Jet engine lining Flue linings

Products used | Kitchenware, pots and pans
in the home | Appliances, refrigerators
 | Stoves, sinks, washing machines, table tops
 | Plumbing fixtures
Decorative | Architectural murals
products | Artware
 | Jewelry

Composition of porcelain enamel. The enamel is composed of borax, silica sand, soda ash, feldspar, clay, zinc oxide, and other chemicals. They are melted together into molten glass and then plunged into cold water, a process that shatters the mass to bits. The product is *frit*, which, when finely ground, is applied to the metal.

Why metal is enameled. Porcelain enamel increases the usefulness of many metals. It has all the qualities of glass: resists acids, corrosion, weather, heat, abrasion, and stains. It is easy to keep clean and sanitary. The colors never fade and decorating is easily done. Metal enameled with porcelain is as permanent as the porcelain itself.

How porcelain enameling is done in industry. The metal pieces are formed, holes are punched or drilled, and the product is otherwise completed before the porcelain enamel is applied. Here is the typical processing:

1. *Cleaning.* All dirt, grease, and oil is cleaned from the metal. Cast iron is sand-blasted.

2. *Pickling.* Immersed in an acid bath, the metal is chemically cleaned. The surface is roughened by acid action to make a better bond with the enamel.

3. *Ground coating.* The metal is given a first coating of the enamel frit by dipping or spraying.

4. *Firing.* After the ground coat is dry, the metal is passed through an electric furnace and the enamel is fused on.

5. *Cover Coating.* If additional enamel is desired, it is sprayed on, dried, and reheated to fuse with the ground coat. This coat may be for color or decorative design.

How you can do enameling. Enameling is a very interesting process and is easily done with a minimum of equipment. You will need the following:

Heavy *sheet copper*, 24 to 32 oz.

Enamel for copper. Specify it as vitreous enamel for copper, ground finely. Many colors are available, either transparent or opaque.

Pickle. Add ½ oz nitric acid to 1 pt cold water in a glass or pottery bowl.

Adhesive. This is mixed with the enamel to make it stick to the metal until the heat takes over. Mix 1 teaspoon of powdered gum tragacanth in 2 tablespoons of alcohol. Add this to ½ cup of water and it is ready to use.

Steel wool. Grades 000 or 00 are used for cleaning and polishing the metal.

Furnace, kiln, or burner. A small electric furnace capable of 1400 to 1500°F, such as a pottery kiln, will do. If this is not available, use a large Bunsen-type gas burner. A blow torch will work for small pieces if it

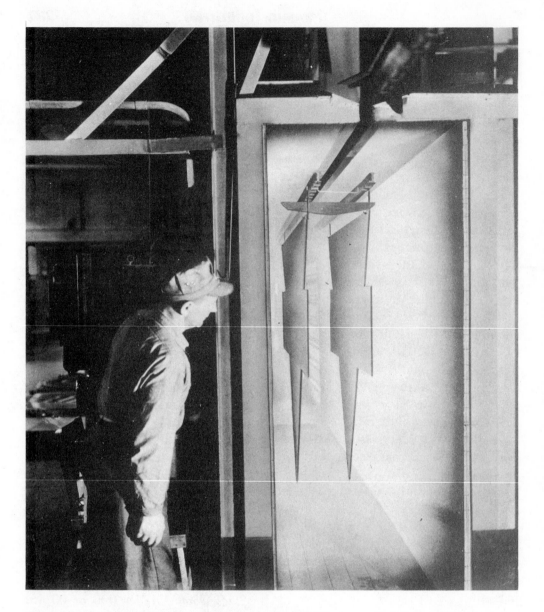

Fig. 7.57. A pair of enameled signs passing through the enameling furnace on a conveyor. (Courtesy: Porcelain Enamel Institute.)

will heat the copper to a bright cherry red.

Tongs. A pair of long-handled tongs or a fork for placing and holding the metal during the heating are needed.

Setters. Stilts used for setting glazed pottery can be used for holding the metal during heating.

Miscellaneous. You will also need some small artist's brushes, some salt shakers for sprinkling enamel powder, and some transparent stencil paper.

How to enamel copper. For the first project, let's make an identification tag or pendant with an initial or other simple design on it. Follow these steps:

1. Clean the copper well with steel wool.

2. Immerse the copper in a pickle for 10 to 15 minutes, while you are preparing the enamel. Suspend it on a wire to keep your hands out of the acid. If you do get it on them, rinse well immediately in running water.

3. Rinse the tag in clean water just before you apply the enamel. Blot it dry between paper towels, without touching it with your fingers.

4. Mix the enamel. Put ½ teaspoon of the desired color in a small glass cup and add enough water to cover it. Stir, then let it settle. Pour off the water. Add a few drops of gum solution and stir.

5. Apply the enamel ground coat. With an artist's soft brush pick up a load of the enamel and lay it on the face of the copper, patting it on evenly. Add more so that the thickness is between ⅟₃₂ and ⅟₁₆ in. Another method is to paint on a coat of gum and while it is wet sift on the ground coat.

6. Dry out the moisture by holding the tag over low heat. Do not let it get hot enough to form steam.

7. Place the tag in the hot kiln or the flame and heat until the enamel is melted. When it looks wet and smooth all over, move it to a cooler part of the kiln or flame until the enamel hardens. This might mean that you will have to shut off the kiln and let it cool.

8. When the piece is cool enough to handle, brush a thin coat of gum over the hardened enamel. Apply the colors to make the design by sifting them through a stencil with a salt shaker or by means of a brush. Dry out and refire.

If you wish to make designs with fine lines and detail, use *ceramic decorating colors*. They are applied on the fired enamel and then the piece is refired. Use them like paint, with an artist's fine brush. Follow the manufacturer's instructions for firing so that the colors come out bright and shining. The firing range is usually from cone 017 to 019. (See page 266.)

Safety makes sense. The hazards in this work to watch for are burns by acid and fire. When using nitric acid, keep your wits about you and follow these suggestions:

1. Always add the acid to the water, not water to the acid. Add it very slowly, don't dump it in.

2. Make sure the acid bottle is plainly labeled. It should have a tight-fitting glass stopper. Store it in a safe place, away from metals.

3. Keep the pickle in a strong glass bowl with a lid. Label it *Nitric Acid Pickle*. Don't put it in a closed cabinet where the fumes can attack the contents.

4. If you get the acid on yourself, rinse it off immediately, not five minutes later, with a lot of water. Call it to your teacher's attention.

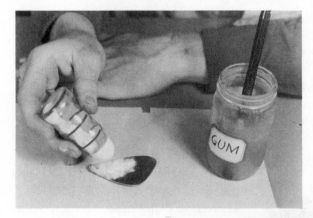

Fig. 7.58. Ground enamel is sifted onto a copper pendant.

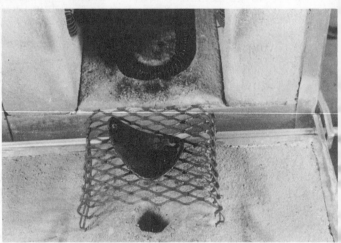

Fig. 7.59. The pendant has been fired and is covered with a glassy coating. This is the furnace described in Fig. 5.9. Metal lath makes a convenient setter.

5. You might get a spatter on your skin without knowing it until you feel it sting. Rinse well at once, and if it still burns apply some baking soda and water. If the burn is severe, get to your doctor right away. The longer you wait, the deeper the burn.

6. When using a flame, remember, it is fire. Keep your sleeves rolled up and out of the way. Use a safe source of heat. If you use a blow torch, ask your teacher how to use it safely. Always turn it off when it is not in use.

Good craftsmanship needs good housekeeping. To enamel copper

successfully you must work carefully, taking great pains to keep everything clean. Keep your fingers off the copper until it has been pickled and rinsed. Use only absolutely clean bowls for the pickle and for mixing enamel. Try to work slowly, and deliberately, and carefully as does a chemist when he is running an experiment.

The Portland Cement Industries

You may have watched concrete being poured for a sidewalk, a basement foundation, or a street. You may have

284

Some Designs for Enameling

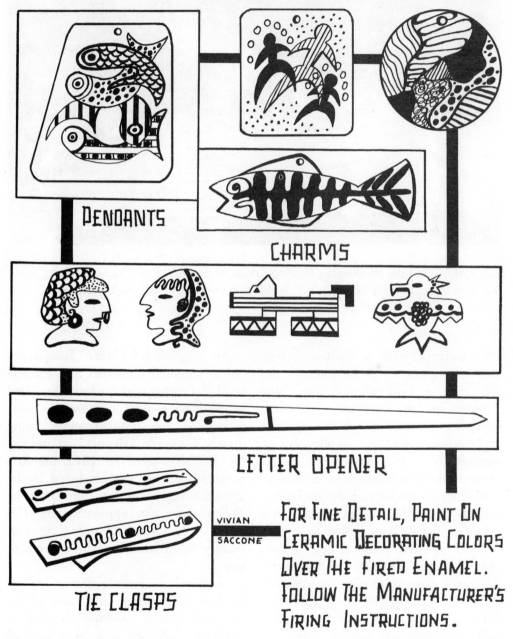

PENDANTS

CHARMS

LETTER OPENER

VIVIAN SACCONE

For Fine Detail, Paint On Ceramic Decorating Colors Over The Fired Enamel. Follow The Manufacturer's Firing Instructions.

TIE CLASPS

Fig. 7.60.   Some ideas for enamel designs, by Vivian Rich.

Fig. 7.61. The Lake Washington Floating Bridge at Seattle, Wash., is actually a 1.3 mile long "floating highway." It is the first pontoon bridge to be built of concrete. (Courtesy: Portland Cement Association.)

seen a truck with a built-on mixer churning away as it traveled to the job with a load of concrete. But whether or not you have seen these everyday occurrences, you have walked and ridden on a lot of concrete. Today concrete is an indispensable material used in the construction of highways and bridges, docks and dams, houses and skyscrapers, burial vaults and underground shelters, and so on.

Two types of cements are of concern to us here, *portland* and *gypsum*. They are close relatives, yet products made from them are very different. Both are ceramic products from which other products are made. They are called cements because, mixed with water, then harden to rocklike masses.

An English bricklayer, Joseph Aspidin, patented a cement that became hard and strong under water. He called it portland cement because its color resembled the natural stone being quarried on the Isle of Portland off the British coast. In 1872 the first portland cement was produced in the United States at Coplay, Pennsylvania. Today there are approximately 170 mills in 34 states producing approximately 900,000,000 sacks of cement per year.

Portland cement is the chief ingredient in concrete and most of the portland cement produced is used in concrete, although it is also used in mortar, stucco, masonry paints, asbestos shingles, and the like.

Fig. 7.62. The raw materials for making cement are burned together in huge rotary kilns which are often longer than a football field. They are lined with fire-brick to withstand temperatures as high as 2800° F. *(Courtesy: Portland Cement Association.)*

How portland cement is made. Portland cement is made of limestone, shale, clay, slate or blast furnace slag, shells, and chalk or marl. Gypsum is added to control the setting time of the cement. The ingredients go through the following processing:

1. *Quarrying.* The materials are dug from the earth.
2. *Crushing.* The large rocks and chunks are broken.
3. *Hammer milling.* The pieces are crushed still smaller.
4. *Ball milling.* The pieces are finely ground.
5. *Blending.* The ingredients are proportioned and mixed.
6. *Drying.* Moisture is driven off.
7. *Burning.* The ingredients are fused into masses, called *clinkers*, in a kiln at 2600 to 2800°F.
8. *Crushing.* The clinkers are crushed.
9. *Grinding.* The particles are ground into a dust.
10. *Sacking.* The cement is blown into a closed sack through a small flap. The standard weight is 94 pounds per sack.

Concrete. Portland cement concrete is composed of sand and gravel (crushed rock, slag, or other coarse material) bonded together with a paste made of cement and water. When cured or completely set it is a hard, rocklike mass, resistant to fire, water, weather, and abrasion.

The qualities of concrete are varied

287

Fig. 7.63. Forms are needed to hold concrete until it hardens. In this photo concrete is being poured into forms for a bridge pier. (Courtesy: Portland Cement Association.)

to suit the job. It can be made so heavy and hard that it weights 250 pounds per cubic foot, or so light and soft that it weighs as little as 30 pounds and can be sawed and nailed like a board.

How concrete is made. For large construction jobs, the concrete is usually made at central "ready mix" plants and is delivered by truck. For small jobs, portable mixers make the concrete right where it is used. In all cases the correct proportion of the ingredients is determined in advance so that the concrete will be as desired.

When mixing is complete, usually in two or three minutes, the batch is poured into the forms, which have been built to the desired shape. It is immediately tamped so that it settles to all parts of the form. The concrete gradually hardens or cures so that after a few days the forms can be removed. During this aging, the concrete is kept moist so that it will be as strong as possible when completely cured.

As soon as walks, drives, floors, and the like, are poured, the concrete is leveled off and allowed to set for

Fig. 7.64. On small construction projects concrete is hauled in wheelbarrows from the mixer to the forms. (Courtesy: Portland Cement Association.)

a few hours. Then it is finished, or given a surface treatment to make it smooth or rough as required.

An all-purpose concrete mix. The following mix (called 1:2½:3) makes a good concrete for general use in floors, walks, walls, driveways, fish ponds, and the like. Use clean water, washed and screened sand, and gravel. One and one-half cubic feet of the dry mix will make one cubic foot of concrete. When concrete is thoroughly mixed it is of a uniform, gray color because each grain of sand and gravel is coated with the cement paste. Mix

the water and cement thoroughly, then add to the aggregate.

Gallons of water per sack of cement	Portland cement	Aggregate	
		Sand	Gravel
5½, if sand is damp	1 sack	2½ cu ft	3 cu ft
4¾ if wet	(1 sack cement = 1 cu ft)		

Proportions for convenient measuring are:

1 measure (gallon, quart, bucket)	1¼ measure	3 measures	3¾ measures

Some things to make of concrete. To make such projects as de-

289

scribed here, these items are needed: a mixing pail, a heavy wooden mixing paddle, a finishing trowel, and a five-gallon can to hold water for rinsing cement from the tools. Do not pour this down the drain; dump it on the ash pile. You can buy the portland cement and the aggregate locally.

The mixing

1. Add the cement to the water in a mixing pail and stir until smooth.

2. Mix in one-half of the aggregate, then mix in one-half of the remainder. Add as much of what is left as is needed to make a thick, heavy, not watery concrete.

Fig. 7.65. An easy-to-make boat anchor.

A BOAT ANCHOR

The mix

¾ pt water

1 pt portland cement

3 pt dry sand

4 pt gravel, ½ to ¾ in. size

3. Pour it into the form, insert the hook, and tamp by bouncing the can a few times. The concrete should cure for a period of three days before the can is cut away.

4. Wash your tools thoroughly in the rinse can.

A BASEBALL HOME PLATE

The form

Make the form of scrap lumber and coat the inside with old crankcase oil to seal it. Be sure to use the official dimensions of the plate. Cut the bottom board to the size of the plate and nail the sides around it.

The mix

Use the $1:2\frac{1}{2}:3$ mix mentioned before, starting with $3\frac{1}{2}$ quarts of cement. Figure the amounts of sand and gravel needed. Use only enough water to wet the particles. The concrete should be very stiff, not runny. Check your answers with your teacher.

The mixing

Mix as for the boat anchor and then pour the form full and bounce it a few times. After it has set for an hour or two, smooth the top with a finishing trowel. Don't trowel too long because you will bring water to the surface. Let the plate cure under damp cloths for at least three days.

A FEEDER FOR DOGS, CATS, OR RABBITS

The form

Shape a piece of moist clay to the form of the inside of the feeder. Lay this upside down on a board which is about $1\frac{1}{2}$ inches wider than the clay on each side and end. Keep the clay moist until the cement is poured. Nail sides on this base which are just high enough to allow a $1\frac{1}{2}$ in. thickness for the bottom of the feeder. Waterproof the inside of the form with a coat of old motor oil.

The mix

$\frac{3}{4}$ to 1 qt water

$1\frac{1}{2}$ qt cement

3 qt sand

The mixing

No coarse aggregate is used because the walls are thin and the surfaces should be very smooth. Mix the water and cement into a paste. Add most of the sand and mix well. The final mixture should be thick, heavy, and plastic. Add the rest of the sand if needed. Pour the form full and bounce it a few times to settle the

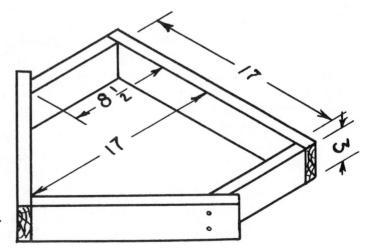

Fig. 7.66. Form for home plate.

Fig. 7.67. The form for an inexpensive animal feeder.

mix, then strike it off level with a straight stick. Let it cure for two days before removing the form, then soak the feeder in a pail of water for three days. After it is dry, coat it with a suitable color of enamel. Get a paint that can be used on cement and follow the directions on the label.

Gypsum Cement Industries

Gypsum is a soft rock which chemists know as *calcium sulphate*. In this country it is found chiefly from Texas north through Kansas into Michigan, and from California to Utah.

The early Greeks and Egyptians found that when this rock was ground up and burned, and the residue mixed with water, it hardened into a rock-like mass. They used it for wall plaster and for mortar in their buildings. The Egyptians used it in the great pyramids. The first gypsum

plaster plants were near Paris, France; thus the name "plaster of Paris."

Most of the gypsum rock mined is converted to cements and plasters. It is ground finely and then heated to drive out most of the water. This is called *calcining*. Then it is ground again and is ready for use as plaster of paris. The unusual quality of gypsum plasters is that when mixed with water they harden and become like the rock from which they are made.

COMMON USES FOR GYPSUM

In paints—for filler and pigment.
In rubber—to make it hard and strong.
In matches—to form the heads.
In concrete—to control the setting.
In tooth paste—to polish.
In movies—for stage sets and snow.
In wallboard—for the core of plaster board and rock lath.

292

Fig. 7.68. This is the interior of a gypsum mine. (Courtesy: United States Gypsum Co.)

In roofing—for light weight, insulation, and resistance to fire.

The farmer uses it for conditioning soils.

The dentist uses it for molds to cast crowns.

The jeweler uses it for molds in casting precious metals.

The doctor uses it for casts to hold broken bones.

The potter uses it for molds in mass-producing ware.

The artist uses it for sculpture.

The builder uses it for plastering walls.

The policeman uses it for making impressions of foot prints, tire tracks, and so on.

Types of gypsum cements. There are many different gypsum cements, each suited for different uses. Following are the common ones for your use. They deteriorate with age so keep only a sack or two on hand. Only clean, cold water is used for mixing.

Pottery plaster. This is very porous, to permit absorption of water from the clay, and is available in the three grades Regular, No. 1, and No. 4. Regular is fast-setting, No. 1 is medium fast, and No. 4, slow. The recommended proportions are 1 pint of water to 1½ lb of plaster. Setting begins in 3 to 5 minutes.

Casting plaster. This is the plaster for general use. It is less porous than

293

pottery plaster, becomes hard and strong, and takes paint well. Use 1½ to 2 lb to a pint of water. The less water the stronger and the less porous the plaster.

Keene's cement. Much of the marblelike wall covering in public buildings is Keene's cement. Centuries ago Italian craftsmen perfected the process for coloring gypsum plaster to resemble marble. Threads imbedded in the wet plaster, when pulled along, left the colors in streaks.

Keene's cement is a slow-setting plaster which becomes very hard and strong. After it is set, it rings like clay bisque when struck.

Plaster separator. To keep plaster from sticking to plaster or other porous material a coating of separator is necessary. Use potters' mold soap when making slip molds. For casting plaster in plaster molds, use a mixture of two parts kerosene and one part petroleum jelly. Brush the separator into the cavity before the plaster is poured in.

How to make a plaster mold. The method for making plaster molds for pottery has been described (see page 264). You may make a mold from a metal, china, or glass object by this method, too. Select an object which is not ornate and imbed it in clay up to the parting line, then follow the procedure as given. There should be not less than one inch of plaster around the object. Instead of slip being used to make the cast pieces, use plaster.

Painting plaster objects. Plaster objects take paint well if they are thoroughly dry. First seal the surface with two coats of thin shellac. When dry, this forms the base for enamel or tempera colors.

How to use Keene's cement. Keene's cement sets more slowly than do the other plasters. It remains plastic for about an hour. Use it for book ends, lamp bases, desk sets, and the like. Here is a list of the materials you will need.

Keene's cement. Buy it in 100-pound bags from a builder's supply store. Three grades, Regular, Fine, and Superfine are made. Regular is less costly and quite adequate.

Colors. Get lime-proof plaster colors, red, yellow, brown, and green.

Waterproofing wax. Mix one pint of kerosene in a pound of melted paraffin. Do not heat the kerosene. This wax is for waterproofing the insides of a mold.

Abrasives. 2-0, 4-0 and 8-0 waterproof abrasive papers are used for shaping and polishing the hardened cement.

Sealer coat. Mix four parts of boiled, refined linseed oil with one part of commercial paint thinner or turpentine.

Polishing wax. Use paste polishing wax for a final finish.

Molds for casting. A mold is needed to hold the cement while it hardens into the desired shape.

The surfaces of wooden molds that will be exposed to the cement must be sealed well with the waterproofing wax. Metal molds should be coated

Fig. 7.69. Colors are added to the Keene's cement and then are streaked through it to produce the marble-like effect.

also to prevent rust from staining the cement. Dishes and bottles, when used as molds, should be given a very thin coating.

The mixing. The first step in mixing is to calculate the volume of the mold in cubic inches, then find the number of pints of water and the pounds of cement from this proportion. One pint water and 3 lb cement makes 35 cu in. Now follow these steps:

1. Shake the powder into the water and let it slake for 3 to 4 minutes.

2. Mix with a strong spoon until it is free of lumps.

3. Shake in some of the colors, but use them sparingly, since too much weakens the casting. With the edge of the spoon cut the colors into the cement; do not stir them in. Criss-cross the cutting to distribute the colors.

4. Dump the batch into the waxed mold and bounce it several times. You can now re-streak the colors if you wish. Let the cast harden overnight before removing it from the molds.

Drying. From three days to a week are required for drying. Set the cast in a current of warm air, but not in an oven. Shaping and polishing can be done as soon as the casting is hard enough to ring when tapped, whether or not it is dry.

Shaping. When the cast is hard it can be sawed, drilled, planed, and filed as easily as wood. The cement is

295

Fig. 7.70. Pouring the cement into a form to make a flat tile.

corrosive to tools, so be sure to clean them well after using.

Polishing. Polishing is done under water. Use a dishpan in which the cast can be immersed. Start with the coarse abrasive and follow with the fine in succession.

Finishing. The cement must now be bone dry. Sand it very lightly with some worn 8-0 paper. Apply a heavy coat of the sealer and let it soak in. Rub with a clean, soft cloth and set it away to dry overnight. The next day rub the surface to a gloss and apply paste polishing wax. Several coats of the sealer can be used to give a greater gloss.

Lapidary

The cutting and polishing of gem stones is called *lapidary* and the person who does it is also called a lapi-

dary. When primitive man found that all of his time wasn't needed to provide food, clothing, and shelter he began to make ornaments of stones and shells, which he wore. These were eventually used as money, and with the development of methods for cutting and polishing, certain stones became more valuable than gold.

The first examples of cut and polished stones are claimed to be the official seals used by the governments of Egypt, Syria, and Babylonia about 5000 years ago. The early lapidary used sapphire points to cut other stones and sapphire dust for polishing. Many of the gems we see today are synthetic or manmade. Synthetic gems can be so accurately made that it is impossible for anyone but an expert to tell them from natural stones. Imitation rubies are made by melting oxides of

296

aluminum with chromic oxides for color.

Hardness of stones. Some stones are harder than others, and this quality is used in identifying them. The standard for comparing hardness is the Moh scale.

Diamond	10	Apatite	5
Cordundum		Fluor	4
(ruby, sapphire)	9	Calcite	3
Topaz	8	Gypsum	2
Quartz	7	Talc	1
Feldspar	6		

This is a rating based on the diamond, which is the hardest of stones. It does not mean that the diamond is twice as hard as apatite nor ten times as hard as talc. A file has a hardness of 6 or 7 on this scale.

How a lapidary works. The lapidary follows a step-by-step process. The stone, if large, is split along a natural line with a hammer and chisel, as one would split wood. This is called *cleaving*, the object of which is to divide the stone so that several smaller and more valuable ones can be made. These pieces are then cut to the approximate desired size on a diamond saw. This is a metal disc with diamond dust imbedded in its rim. The dust cuts the stone.

The smaller pieces are now cemented to *dop* sticks, so that they can be easily handled, and are ground to the rough shape on silicon carbide abrasive wheels. Stones that are transparent are sometimes *faceted*, or cut with many sides. Holes are drilled with a small brass tube and diamond dust. (See page 278.) Polishing is done on a revolving horizontal disc called a *lap*, which is coated with abrasive and water.

Lapidary equipment. Complete outfits for home and school use are available at reasonable cost; however, you can assemble your own to include the following:

¼ hp electric motor and a grinding head.

120 and 220 grit.

1 in. by 6 in. silicon carbide grinding wheels to fit the head.

1 in. by 8 in. hard felt buff.

Several wooden sanding discs with waterproof silicon.

Carbide abrasive paper to fit, in grits 280, 320, 360, and 400.

An assortment of polishing compounds: tripoli, rouge, and tin oxide.

Several dop sticks made of 8-in. lengths of ⅜-in. dowel rod and a stick of dop cement (stick shellac).

Since grinding is done on wet wheels, a hood over the wheel and a pan under it is necessary.

How to polish a stone. Some of the stones that you may find here or there need only be polished to bring out their beauty. Select one that has a smooth, even surface, then follow these steps:

1. If the stone is small, cement it to a dop stick. First warm the stone in hot water. Melt some cement onto an end of the stick, using a hot piece of iron. While the cement is warm, press it onto the stone.

2. Use the felt buff at a speed of 400 to 500 rpm (revolutions per

Fig. 7.71. A lapidary outfit. (Courtesy: Craftools, Inc.)

Fig. 7.72. A stone is cemented to a dop stick so that it can be easily held for the grinding. This stone is being ground on a lap, which is an iron disc. Oil and abrasive powder are used on the lap.

minute). Hold the tripoli against the face of the revolving buff and charge it with the abrasive. Hold the stone lightly against the wheel, rotating it and moving it back and forth across the face.

3. After the stone has been brought to a gloss, proceed with the rouge and finally with the tin oxide, which is your finest abrasive. Polishing is a slow process and the harder the stone, the slower it polishes. When it no longer gets smoother, it is time to stop. Pry the stone loose with a knife.

298

Fig. 7.73. The final polishing is done on a felt wheel using rouge (iron oxide) or tin oxide as the abrasive.

How to grind and polish a cabochon. A *cabochon* is a stone that has been cut and polished to smooth, rounded surfaces. It may be of any shape. Start with a stone that is not much larger than you want it to be. Make sure it is free from cracks, then

1. Cement it to a dop stick so that you can grind the bottom first.

2. Use the coarse grinding wheel and with water dripping on it hold the stone lightly against the wheel, moving it back and forth over the surface. No tool rest is used. Grind until the surface is flat.

3. Crack off the cement and reset the stone. Grind it roughly to shape on the coarse wheel and follow with the fine wheel, 220 grit.

4. Polishing is started on the sanding discs, first with the coarse, and then with the finer. Dip the stone in water frequently and do not hold it in one place on the disc. Keep it moving. The final polishing is done on the buff, as has been described.

You can make synthetic gems. From the glazes you use on pottery you can make jewels. Put a thin layer of ground flint on a piece of broken bisque, and on the flint drop some globs of glaze. When the glaze is dry, put it in the kiln and fire it. The glaze draws up into balls and when cool can be tapped loose.

Some Things to Find Out

1. How grinding wheels are made.
2. How lenses for eyeglasses are ground.
3. Why abrasives cut.
4. How pencil lead is made.
5. How the Indians made adobe brick.
6. How sandpaper is made.
7. How synthetic jewels are made.
8. What ceramic industries there are in your state.
9. How the American Indians made pottery.
10. How bullet-proof glass is made.
11. Why safety glass is safe.
12. The story of the giant mirror of Mount Palomar.
13. What outstanding contributions to the ceramic industry were made by the early Chinese and Egyptians.
14. How glass is spun into fibers.

299

15. How ceramic products contribute to a finer living for you and all Americans.

You can find answers to these questions in books, magazines, booklets, and films listed below, in encyclopedias, by visiting industries, and by watching skilled craftsmen work.

Some Group Projects

Exhibits for school and for store windows

1. How pottery is made. Show the steps from the raw clay to the finished ware. Include examples of pottery made in class.
2. How porcelain enameling is done. Set up an exhibit of porcelain enameled ware. Conduct demonstrations to which you can invite your parents and students in science and in home economics.

Production projects

1. Organize your class into a pottery industry to produce a quantity of a single item by slip casting. This might be a school souvenir.
2. Set up a production line to make copper pins or charms that could be enameled.

Service projects

1. If there is a children's home in your vicinity, three or four of you might arrange to teach the youngsters to make things of clay. Perhaps you could do this one evening per week.
2. Build a concrete fish pool for someone in the neighborhood.
3. Replace a broken section of sidewalk on the school grounds.

Assembly programs

There are traveling glass blowers and potters who put on demonstrations for schools. Perhaps your class could sponsor such a program. Write to the ceramics department of your state university for some names.

Sources of Ideas and Information

Books

1. Davis, Pearce. *The Development of the American Glass Industry.* Cambridge, Mass: Harvard University Press, 1949.
2. *Engineering Experiment Station News.* Vol. XIX, No. 4, October 1947.
3. *Engineering Experiment Station News.* Vol. XXIV, No. 4, October 1952.
4. Giese, Henry. *A Practical Course in Concrete.* Chicago, Ill.: The Portland Cement Association, 33 W. Grand Avenue, 1948.
5. Kenny, John B. *The Complete Book of Pottery Making.* New York: Greenberg: Publisher, Inc., 1949.
6. Olson, Delmar W. *Pottery: Getting Started in Ceramics.* Scranton, Pa.: International Textbook Company, 1953.
7. Phillips, C. J. *Glass: The Miracle Maker.* New York: Pittman Publishing Corporation, 1948.
8. Thompson, Thomas C. *Enameling on Copper and Other Metals.* Highland Park, Ill: The Thomas C. Thompson Company, 1205 Deerfield Road, 1950.

Booklets

1. *Abrasives for the Lapidary.* Engineering Bulletin No. 135. The Carborundum Co., Niagara Falls, N.Y. Describes cutting and polishing of stones.

2. *A Lecture Course on Coated Abrasives.* Behr-Manning, Troy, N.Y.

3. *Cement and Concrete Reference Book.* Portland Cement Association, 33 W. Grand Avenue, Chicago, Ill. An annual; be sure to ask for the latest copy.

4. *Crystal Gazing.* Fostoria Glass Company, Moundsville, W.Va. Describes the process of making glass crystal ware.

5. *Master Caster.* United States Gypsum Company, Chicago, Ill. How to mix and use gypsum plasters.

6. *Picture of a Pottery.* The Haeger Potteries, Inc., 7 Maiden Lane, Dundee, Ill.

7. *Porcelain Enamel.* Porcelain Enamel Institute, 1010 Vermont Avenue, N.W., Washington, D.C.

8. *Pottery Through the Ages.* Doulton and Company, 11-13 E. 26th St., New York, N. Y.

9. *The Art of Making Fine Glassware.* The Cambridge Glass Company, Cambridge, Ohio.

10. *The Mirror of Mt. Palomar* and *Glass is Coming of Age.* Corning Glass Works, Corning, N.Y.

Films

1. *Blowpipes.* Owens Illinois Glass Co., Film Division, Toledo, Ohio. The History of glassmaking.

2. *Crystal Clear.* Modern Talking Picture Service, Inc., 14 E. Ontario Street, Chicago, Ill. The manufacture of table glassware.

3. *Simple Slab Methods; Throwing; Pottery Decoration; Glaze Application; Stacking and Firing.* American Art Clay Company, 4717 W. Sixteenth Street, Indianapolis, Ind.

4. *The Drama of Portland Cement.* Modern Talking Picture Service, Inc., 45 Rockefeller Plaza, New York, N.Y.

5. *The Making of Fine China.* Castle Films, 1445 Park Avenue, New York, N.Y. 542 South Dearborn Street, Chicago, Ill. 7356 Melrose Avenue, Los Angeles, Cal. 287 Techwood Drive N.W., Atlanta, Ga.

Magazines

1. *Ceramic Age.* 421 Parker Street, Newark 4, N.J.

2. *Ceramic Industry.* Industrial Publications, Inc., 5 South Wabash Avenue, Chicago 3, Ill.

INDEX